BLACK AND GAY
IN THE UK

Published October 2014 by Team Angelica Publishing,
an imprint of Angelica Entertainments Ltd

Team Angelica Publishing
51 Coningham Road
London W12 8BS

TEAM
ANGELICA

www.teamangelica.com
A CIP catalogue record for this book is available from the
British Library

ISBN 978-0-9569719-6-8

Printed and bound by Lightning Source

*Cover photograph by Rikki Beadle-Blair. With thanks to
Nathan Clough and Michael Moulton.*

To
Geoff

Black and Gay in the UK

An Anthology

You have been a great strength in the past few years & many thanks for your wisdom & support of House of Rainbow

Revd Jide Macaulay
8th January 2015

TEAM
ANGELICA

Foreword

In the early 1990s two ground-breaking anthologies of black gay men's lives appeared, *In The Life* and *Brother 2 Brother*. These exciting, provocative, and in some ways problematic volumes were emblematic of a surge of black gay self-naming, self-realisation, and even cultural nationalism. This aesthetic and political uprising was, alas, rapidly curtailed by the pre-combination therapy AIDS epidemic, and few of those who contributed to it are with us today.

These were very much African-*American* works, and I remember waiting breathlessly for a black British equivalent to emerge. That the wait has been until now, with the emergence of a confident and distinctive black British voice on the world musical stage, is perhaps not wholly coincidental.

Times have changed in other ways. The essentialism and identity politics that informed those earlier anthologies perhaps speak less to this present moment, and indeed to black experience in Britain in general, which is increasingly varied, broadened as it has been by so many diasporic arrivals, most markedly in recent years, perhaps, from Nigeria and Somalia. Blackness as a category and marker of identity has become less fixed, less monolithic, more interrogated by those it names.

Understandings of sexuality too have changed. We are now gay, lesbian, bisexual, queer, questioning, trans, pan- and intersex; and even gender itself has been deconstructed.

So why this anthology, focusing on the lives and experiences of black gay men in Britain today? Not least because these categories, these markers of identity, remain real and salient for many, if not most of us. They emerged from – and through resisting and defying – the historical facts of racism and homophobia. That resistance, those assertions of selfhood, self-definition and self-reclamation, should be recorded, explored, interrogated and celebrated.

In inviting writers to contribute work to this anthology we set as few parameters as possible, stipulating only that contributors – who could themselves be of any race, sexuality or gender – should focus on some aspect of black gay men's lives; of black gay male experience. There was no political or cultural agenda beyond the desire to create a kaleidoscopic collage that reflects, celebrates and commemorates black gay lives in Britain in 2014.

– John R Gordon

I was always different. And I liked it. Yeah, it got me in into trouble sometimes, brought me occasional pain, but I never wanted to be anyone else. Why? Books. I was taught to read unusually young and words were my window into wider worlds – around me and within. My mother had books on her shelves by Angela Davis and James Baldwin. I fell on them and into them, drank in their brave faces, read their potted biographies, revelled in their defiance. Rebels with voices. Revolutionaries who could write. I devoured books about blackness, immersed myself in novels about homosexuality. Curled up in their pages. Transported. Educated. I realised that I was not mainstream, but I also knew that I was not the only one. We were out there and we were everywhere. Since I was three or four years old, despite ongoing struggles with shyness, I have felt the call to the page. There was a drive and duty to set down my affections, my observations, my passions. It was my mission to celebrate my senses. It was my given crusade to light a campfire to call all living things to the light, to celebrate all that I have, and bear witness to the visions of my brothers and sisters. To catalogue. To create. This book is our campfire. And whatever your race, sex or sexuality, it burns bright for you; to warm you. To illuminate you. To gather us together and inspire our next lovely step. Thank you to the warriors, shamen, witchdoctors, Souljahs, boy-wives and bold beauties dark and light who have so generously shared their visions in this volume. Thank you for holding this endeavour in your hands and giving it life. This collection of writings is for all the boys, girls and girlboys out there in their wide wild worlds. This anthology is a reminder that you are unique, but not alone. This book is your call to the page, to the stage, to the canvas, to the camera, the internet and the arena. I hope it inspires you to tell the world the secrets of your survival. Let them know that your strangeness is your strength. Because you are valuable. Because you are loved. Because your story is our story. And it's a story of love.

– Rikki Beadle-Blair

Contents

Four pieces by Adam Lowe

AFLAME

for Jack Tyson

I.

Diamonds may be a girl's best friend,
but leave them by her bedside. Tonight
I need something hotter, the colour of blood:
adorn me in bullet wounds, poppy fields
on my skin. Rubies are underrated. One day
I will be draped in them. Diamonds
and pearls are clean, elegant, see-through
—but tonight I want fire on my body.

II.

He wants fire on his body. Bring him
a shift of feathery flame. Bring him
aluminium oxide and chromium,
a butt of ginger wine. Together
you'll make magic in glass goblets.
Drunk on the stigmata of desire; clutched
close and glowing at his throat.

III.

See the ring of lovebites I hide
beneath these kisses. Jupiter bruises,
all of them, ringed around my neck.
Tonight I want fire on my body;
I want red coals to sear my skin. This heat
will move through me like an infection.
I will feel it rising. Let me sweat it out.
Bring me the phoenix's tail,
bind me, pull me closer, because
tonight I want fire on my body.

IV.

There's a fire in his body. You can feel it
licking at your face. It boils from
a private pussy, in that space where
boys have pussies too. He told you this
in fits of kisses, and pushed your head
to his lava neck. Embers burned there.
Rubies are such an underrated stone. One day
you will both be draped in them. You'll find
there's a fire on your bodies. Let it glow.

EASY NAMES

Down at the craft centre, after our fucking was done, we attempted to make jewellery but he said he wanted me to stay inside him. Wanted me to run beads in circuits round his balls, from the root to the tip, smooth over glans to join the bead of dewy semen cresting the head. Wanted me to thread him with my mouth. Wanted me to hold his name there.

So we pulled string through rows of little glass gems and pretended it was us still fucking. Laid out, darting through, bunching ourselves together. The segments of a bracelet.

He slid into the bracelet, showing it off like a dowry. He wore the necklace I made like my spunk around his clavicle. He made a ring of the beads too, and wore that like my sphincter, tight against his knuckles.

These were mostly unsaid things. Things for which polite society doesn't have easy names.

When we returned home we emptied and filled each other. We were the snake eating its own tail.

Afterwards, we lay around, deflated. The room stank still of our sex. We looked at the jewellery we had made. It was cheap plastic. The lustre gone. But it was pretty enough in its own way.

HER HEART

The queen wanted her heart, saw in the mirror the beauty
of her and saw she must have it, that she must have her heart.

She felt cold for the want of that white skin, like snow, she
longed
to be wrapped in. She felt black inside, an evil ebony, for the
desire

to put that hair in her mouth. She bled jealousy for the colour
of those lips; felt constricted by that tiny waist, those wide

woman's hips; wanted to bind her, comb bone teeth through
her hair—
but mostly, when she looked in the mirror, the queen wanted
her heart.

TOUGH LOOK

Well then, that's how you'll move:
with purpose; leonine strides.

You'll thatch your skin thicker
with a patchwork of diva, all Liza,

Whitney, Marilyn. You'll scare
men who fall out of Wetherspoons,

invoke platitudes from girls streaked
the colour of shoe polish. You'll

be you: a little braver, a little bigger
— but it will always sting inside.

Things We Do To Get What We Want

By Edd Muruako

I n my first year at drama school I was as camp as Christmas. I used to walk round the building in a bright blue jumper, red trousers and yellow jacket. I had come fresh from performing arts college, which during my last year there had turned into a massive, prolonged orgy session. Everyone had experimented. Everyone had kissed everyone. Boys had kissed girls, boys had kissed boys and girls had kissed girls, and like a free-spirited hippie I left college confident and sure of who I was.

Walking into drama school with an extra spring in my step perpetuated by the sounds of Sylvester James, Ronnie Dyson, Gloria Gaynor and the multiple Seventies disco compilation albums that were on constant repeat on my iPod playlist, my confidence was high. There wasn't much that could faze me, I was sure. I wanted desperately to be an actor and I was going to do it.

Looking round my year-group I was quick to notice that I was in a minority category in terms of race. There was myself and just one other black actor, and he would leave in the middle of the three-year process. However, like most drama schools the atmosphere was very gay-friendly: many of the pupils and some of the teachers were also 'that way inclined' and so there was never the need to conform to heterosexual norms. I had never considered my (perceived) sexuality to be an obstacle. My thinking had always been, 'As long as you can act the f**k out of a part when the lights are on, who cares what you do when they're off?'

I was so wrong.

I quickly became very aware of what roles were on offer to me while training, and indeed after graduation. I was forced to become very aware of myself, my image, and what I put out there, not just as an actor but also as a person. I rapidly discovered that what I put out was not what people expected –

or wanted. 'Your personality traits go against your casting,' I was often told.

I would be lying if I said this wasn't soul-destroying because it was. I was an eighteen-year-old, chubby-going-on-muscular, high-pitched camp black man who was being expected to fill castings for alpha male, intimidating, aggressive, physically-imposing heterosexual black men. 'Well, of course I can do that,' I would reiterate to myself. 'That's why they call it acting!' – only to be answered back by a sea of tutors chorusing, 'Casting begins at the door, not when they shout "Action".'

I was failing before I got the chance to read a single line of the script.

Even though I was grateful for the heads up, that hurt like f**k. Acting was all I'd ever wanted to do, and there was no way I was going to let foolish things like pride or the right to be who I was get in the way of that.

Thus, beginning the transformation of one's self:

Switching down the voice, controlling the walk, doing away with the vibrantly-coloured clothes and becoming a more stereotypical – and so more acceptable – version of an urban black man. I was in the closet. Again! I told myself, 'It's just clothes, the odd vocal adjustment and monitoring how one gesticulates. I'm still me at the end of the day.' But I wasn't, not really.

I would reminisce about that young, loud, gay and proud black boy who tore it up at G.A.Y.'s Camp Attack on Friday nights. When the DJ played Gloria Gaynor's 'I Am What I Am'. I would go crazy for that song more than any other. Mind, body and soul were one. My dancing was off the chain because of what that song meant to me. I felt the lyrics from the bottom of my gut. It had been such a long, fucking painful road to 'acceptance' that tears of joy would often brim in my eyes just at hearing Gloria's *a cappella* intro.

I look back now and it seems like I'm seeing a completely different person. My whole mentality is different today. It's hard to imagine myself being that free and wild. And I often ask myself, 'Who was that boy?' And then there's a slight feeling of guilt and sadness as part of me feels I sold myself out and will probably never feel like that again. 'But such is life'.

*

The transformation ended up being a double-edged sword in many ways. Drama schools at that time clearly were not built for ethnic minorities. All the plays I tackled during my three years there were clearly stories stemming from a middle-class to aristocratic backgrounds, with most character descriptions screaming to be played by a white actor, so I ended up playing colourblind versions of many less significant characters.

In some cases having plays chosen from such genres highlighted the importance of Received Pronunciation. Ninety-five percent of the class spoke RP as their mother tongue; I was an East Ham boy with a London-Cockney accent. So there was never a term when I wasn't thinking about vocal placement, glottal stops and dark 'L' etcetera. In my final year we had mock auditions with a few casting directors. I had learnt my pieces to perfection. I had worked hard on my Othello speech and my contemporary, and I was keen to show the industry professionals what I could do. Two casting directors from *Holby City* awaited my entrance. After a small intro, I began. Both pieces went better than I expected.

'Nice audition, Edd. That was an Othello I would actually pay to see at the National Theatre and I've seen a lot. You had the right level of intensity. Great resonant voice.' So I'm on cloud nine now until she says, 'Is that your normal speaking voice?'

'How do you mean? I replied.

'The accent, you did the whole thing in RP and you greeted us in RP. For a man of colour I'm guessing that isn't your natural accent, am I correct?' She went on to tell me that what she hated about most drama schools was that a majority of graduates came out all speaking the same because of the tendency of the schools to oversell the importance of received pronunciation to their students. 'Do not lose your natural accent, accents bring colour to television, making it vibrant and interesting. Stay true to who you are.' She was firm in making her point but also visibly irritated, giving the impression that she had done the rounds at a good many other drama schools and dished out the exact same speech.

The importance and wisdom of her observation only really hit me after graduation, when castings were flooding in. In one of my earliest castings, I was up for the part of a gangsta baron who was king of the drug underworld. The director shouted, 'Great physicality but these gangstas aren't from Eton: try and be a bit more real with it.'

Interesting comment, I thought. I wasn't trying to be posh but subconsciously I must have been coming across that way. It made me realise how much training had changed me, and apparently not in a good way. I thought, fuck it! I did it again and overplayed my urban South London roots, and this time I brought the swagger I remembered from 2Pac and Dr. Dre in the 'California Love' music video. I finished the scene. There was silence. My scene partner was looking at me, speechless. Had I offered up an appalling travesty of a black man? And then suddenly the director started clapping and soon the whole room was clapping. They offered me the role there and then, which was a first.

I was onto a winning formula for auditions, and continued to take my new persona into many of my later auditions with great success.

Truth be told it wasn't much of a stretch. I was being offered mugger after mugger, drug-dealer after drug-dealer, bouncer after bouncer, security guard after security guard, rapist after rapist, copper after copper and gangsta after gangsta. When it came to films every new audition felt like the one before: broken home, council estate life, prison life, tough guy with chip on shoulder, blah, blah, blah.

It comes to a point where your eyes stop rolling and you start to see the funny side. 'I wonder what postcode I'm living in this time,' I would joke to myself. 'It was drugs last week, must be knives this week, or is it the turn of guns?'

Then there's the waiting-room section, where every black actor who looks like you is sat in what is, most of the time, a tiny room, waiting to be seen: the competition, most of whom you've seen before at previous auditions; the ones who have learnt to laugh at the situation, and the ones who are still rolling their eyes but come with hope every time that things might be different.

The assistant comes out with a full brief of the scenario and hands everyone a scene to read. Waiting to exhale, we all read. We finish reading. Hardly anyone exhales.

Commercial and corporate auditions can be deadly too. Your agent says, 'Yes, they want a BLACK actor, now go.' Usually it's for some lads' beverage, or a sports ads which requires three white lads and a token black. I turn up to find once again that the term 'Black' in the casting director's eyes actually means 'Black and Mixed-Race', a qualifier they left out of the brief. One wonders if it's ignorance or deliberate. You sit there yet again, your eyes starting to roll, or you laugh, knowing full well the role will more than likely go to the mixed-race actor because that's the way most commercials are cast these days. Mixed-race is the new black. You suspect the reason for this, but at that moment you just wish most would be upfront about it instead of wasting your time.

I decided to take a break from acting, and for a couple of years I wrote poetry and rapped at open mic nights at bars and cafés to fill that creative void. I didn't really take it seriously until one of my closest friends asked me to feature on her debut promo CD. Miss Sahhara, a beautiful black transgender singer, was working at the London gay club Heaven at the time, singing covers of mainstream pop songs. She started to record her own material and offered me a slot on one of her up-and-coming songs, 'Growing'.

Soon after that I started writing and constructing full songs and taught myself how to make beats. I joined the UK Gay Hip Hop Collective and was rocking the stage with the likes of QBoy and Mz Fontaine, performing at Heaven, Sketch Club, Disco-theque, Bootlicious, and every other gay club in the London vicinity that had featured hip-hop nights.

It wasn't until 2008 that the mainstream media started to take notice. I had written a song called 'Someone', which dealt with a man looking for love from another man. The music video was featured on Channel AKA, (known as Channel U at the time), and for three weeks it was broadcast to millions of homes in the UK. This was the first time ever that a hip-hop song with homosexual content by a male black rapper had been featured on channel U. UK radio interviews followed with Playvybz, as well as podcast radio interviews with USA station Gspod. I performed at the annual Black Prides three years in a row, had features in *the Pink Paper* newspaper, and made the front page of *The South London Press* newspaper with a full-feature two-page article. It was overwhelming.

'Wow,' I thought. 'If only I could get this much attention for my acting efforts.'

'Well who cares now?' I thought.

'You've killed any hope of an acting career,' said my then-agent. Next year he dropped me but I really didn't care: I had moved on from acting. I had found something real. I was reconnecting with that young black boy who had danced so freely on Friday nights in Camp Gay. I realised what I had written had touched a nerve with a lot of hip-hop fans, black LGBT people, people in the UK and overseas in general. It meant a lot to so many people. What started out as an almost naïve hobby had turned into cultural statement. This was so much bigger than me. Emails of appreciation started pouring in via my Myspace from fans all over the world, recognising my talent and bravery. One unexpected piece of mail came from a UK Urban artist who over time became a good friend. In that time he made his real sexual orientation known to me and a brief sexual relationship was explored. Unfortunately to this day he has remained closeted to his family and his fans. Nonetheless, we remain friends.

Just getting mail was exciting. Sahhara would often laugh at my excitement. She had thousands of fans and took it all in her stride. I remember when she appeared on the front page of *TimeOut* magazine a couple of years earlier; even then she was as cool as cucumbers. When I walked into my local newsagent and picked up *The South London Press* and saw my face looking back at me all I could think about was running home and locking the door behind me. I didn't go back to that newsagent for two weeks.

As much as the attention was welcoming it was daunting at the same time, and in some ways that was one of the loneliest periods of my life thus far. But all the doubt and depression were soon eradicated: history was about to be made and I was about to be part of it. In 2008 London Pride did something quite spectacular: they introduced a BAME stage. This had never been done before at a Pride event. The first Black, Asian & Minority Ethnic Stage was held on Romily Street in the summer of 2008. Not only was I invited to perform at the event but I was also chosen to be the HOST of the BAME stage, making me the first man of colour to ever host a stage at a London Pride event.

It was when I stood on that outdoor stage, commanding the attentions of thousands of people for a good five and a half hours, that a feeling of euphoria came over me. I no longer felt the need to fight with myself or beat myself up about things only I deemed of mammoth importance. Everything seemed so trivial now. As I looked out at a sea of smiling, supportive and cheerful faces I realised that other people's opinions no longer mattered to me. I was God's child and only He can judge me. And He has truly blessed me with love.

It was at that exact moment I realised I had truly arrived.

Live and Let Live: Confessions of a Black Boy Lost

By Edd 'MC Chewy' Muruako

I always knew from secondary school
I was different in ways that nobody knew
But I kept my cool, my desires I withdrew
Hard to come out when there's no-one to relate to
I fucked up school, my career's in a loop
It's hard to do a hula when you can't find a hoop
Felt like a plant, on the spot did a dance
Tried to walk forward, show the others but I can't
Secret life I chose to lead, did it so easily
Till the lid on my bin popped open scattered debris
'Pick 'em up, pick 'em up.' They're glowing on the ground
Strutting their stuff to a disco sound
Like lost change found everybody gathered round
I hid the Pink from the pounds before my feet were bound
Felt my mission complete, averted hidden mystiques
Stopped my brain from spewing personality leaks

 If we live and let live, we paint a picture for the kids if we live and let live...

Must I keep pulling wool over eyes, must I lie to myself every day of my life?
Feel flighty, the world on my mind, can't express how I feel , the realness inside
Cus its pinning me, the truth killing me, suicidal thoughts steady fast overcoming me
The best days are the days when I cry cus I'm close to edge with a knife by my head

Passed through school it was college where I blew
A place of expression, learnt crucial life lessons
Still hard to be true with no hand egging you
Shutting down the voices you hear deep inside of you
Your heart's begging you, plus Misery she's killing you
She's hacking off your feet, swellings deep it be critical
You need medical, emotional not physical
Self-defeating battle like the tortoise chase the hare
As you start to wear and tear you see something in the glare
So you stand and stop and stare it's a sight to beware
While you're running round the circuit, breaking down having fits
A race-car be passing while you crying in the pits
While he's stocking up on fuel, he drives next to
Stops and takes a look and with his hand reaches out to you
It's hard to let go but in my heart I know
That he's lapped me already, plus his tyres firm and steady

If we live and let live, we paint a picture for the kids if we live and let live...

Must I keep pulling wool over eyes, must I lie to myself every day of my life?
Feel flighty, the world on my mind, can't express how I feel, the realness inside
Cus it's pinning me, the truth killing me, suicidal thoughts steady fast overcoming me
The best days are the days when I cry cus I'm close to edge with a knife by my head

Exclusively alone but I feel more at home
I now become the hare, I problem halved a problem shared
To think that I was scared to face the feelings that I bared
I'm still scared, to tell my parents if I dare
I sit on this hard, moment later I discharge

Postpone to flip the card, conceal but not discard
Lord this is large, I feel so awkward
Instead of moving forwards I'm drifting backwards
I decided to wait to cut the beef from the steak
I'm not baking up a cake or cussing my own race
But to be Black and Gay be a slap in the face
A sort of double-take some nigga's love to hate
Can't lips another man in a public place
Roar meat to a shark, straight bait, check mate
Make no mistake, there's no escape
Eradicating the hate makes the world a better place

If we live and let live, we paint a picture for the kids if we live
and let live...

Must I keep pulling wool over eyes, must I lie to myself every
day of my life?
Feel flighty, the world on my mind, can't express how I feel, the
realness inside
Cus it's pinning me, the truth killing me, suicidal thoughts
steady fast overcoming me
The best days are the days when I cry cus I'm close to edge with
a knife by my head

If we live and let live we paint a picture for the kids, if we live
and let live......
If we live and let live we paint a picture for the kids, if we live
and let live......

Golden Reaper

By Rogue Scott

I was sure that July would be as sun-filled and happy as it had been many years ago, the type of sun that made you feel as if you didn't need to book a ticket out of the country but instead have a stay-vacation with your loved ones who were also staying. Wrong. July 2002 so far was filled with humid showers, and very little summer flesh was to be seen. Saying that, the warmth still hadn't stopped many men and girls around the way from showing off what they'd been so-called 'God-given'. And events were to happen that I would have never banked on.

I was eighteen and just getting over a guy I had met two years earlier. He broke it off with me because he felt I was getting too much attention from men he didn't like. Bullshit. I wasn't totally sure what I planned to do with my life. All my friends seemed to have jobs – except for the one I spent my days drinking with whilst she smoked her spliffs, watching the final episodes of *Buffy the Vampire-Slayer* together in her grotty shared accommodation. Such was life. She went to the Jobcentre to get her jobseeker's allowance, I dipped my hand in the three-foot-high jar my mother kept filled with £1 and £2 coins. Yes, I was, what I'd say – a little light-fingered around that jar. To stop her noticing it going down slowly I used to fill it in the middle with pennies, just to keep the height up.

It was a Tuesday, and Sara and myself decided we were going to spend the only good day of the summer it seemed hanging out in Hackney Downs park with a few drinks and nibbles. After sitting there for an hour or so we both shared a sigh of boredom, deciding it was time to go. We backtracked to avoid the estate where people either 'only' get mugged or don't come out alive.

We're just passing this local supermarket a lot of winos go to, right next door to the train-station, the train-station I often used to go and meet the few gay friends I had made since hitting the scene. As we walk by the shop Sara looks in and smiles. She brazenly sparks up her outed spliff, and just then some guy shouts out, 'Yo, hol' up nah, girl.'

I remember thinking straight off he must have mistaken me for a girl, as I back then had only just started to sprout hair in the places boys should and hated it, not to mention my long curly hair running just past my shoulders.

'Who, me? Nah, sorry, swear down you can't be hailing me down like no fucking bus, blood. Come correct.' Yeah, Sara was full-on when it came to men attempting to hail her out in public. Shit, if it happened to me I would be too.

'Course me calling you. Wait nah, girl.' Partly skipping towards us, and we have now come to a stop fully-turned facing him, and I can't help but watch his golden, rippled arms, and the beads of sweat that have collectively made Orion's belt on his smooth forehead just above his very full eyebrows, full in a good way, manly.

'Sara, he's...' She flicks her hand against mine, signalling me to shut up. I'm not sure if she does it on purpose but it's the same hand she's holding her spliff in, so I feel a little heat. I keep my cool.

Sara and this golden, rippled demigod get into a whole chat about weed, who she gets it from, if she ever wants any, and I back up a little. I've seen this happen with Sara before: he's chatting her up. Why does this shit always happen when the awkward, twinky gay boy is around? I give them their space while trying my hardest to check him out without being too obvious. I mean he's from around here, Hackney. If he realised I was gay and checking him out, he'd probably kill me. The song 'Log On' by Elephant Man comes to mind, and my stomach turns. Damn, his arms are all out of his vest, shimmering. It's just a little too tight for his chest as well, the nipples are rocks. I'm sure I can see his gold member through his jeans: they're not tight but they aren't loose either. My imagination runs wild and I begin to imagine him taking me to some plush house decked out all in white with glass furniture and him fucking me by an electric fireplace. Sweet. I'm getting a hard-on, so I quickly dash into the nearby alleyway while telling Sara I need a piss. What I need to do is fix myself. I've been told I'm no small boy: I cannot let them see.

Coming back out of the alley they're both looking my way. I know Sara's face and what she's thinking but I've only just somewhat met this guy, so reading him isn't so easy.

'Boss man, you sing I hear?' he says to me with a glare that makes me uncomfortable but I nod yes. 'Yeah, um,' he continues, 'Sara was saying you sing a little. I got a place nearby if you wanna hook up and make tracks.'

So when exactly did their weed conversation swing in my favour?

Who cares? He asked for my number and of course I gave it to him. I mean, if Sara didn't then I sure wanted to see him more often than not at all. His name is Shamarai, unusual name. Shamarai the golden, muscled demigod of Hackney and he now has my number. He nods his head and cracks a corner-mouth smile at the both of us, and skips in the most sexy, manly way back to the shop from whence he came.

Back at Sara's room in the shared accommodation she straps up another spliff and I retrieve my secret stash of brandy and cigarettes from the air-vent whilst she isn't looking. I'd learned over the years how to hide things away from Sara, otherwise one minute it's there, the next minute it's in her mouth. So as she get high on her high-grade weed or however them green-heads would call it, I chug back gulps of brandy just so I can feel the same buzz she'll be feeling in those few minutes. I suggest that we re-watch the famous musical episode of *Buffy the Vampire-Slayer*, 'Once More With Feeling', and as always she humours me. I got Sara into *Buffy* a while back: she loved it so much that she began watching reruns on BBC2 so she got what was going on, as well as knowing the characters and story herself. Hell, did we have a great night watching 'Once More With Feeling'! Rewinding, repeating, pausing, re-enacting scenes. Sara was the only person I could be this silly with without having to edit some of my ways. I'm pretty sure her being high on weed also contributed to it all as well.

Days went by without me hearing a word from Shamarai. That was going to change.

It was a Wednesday night and I was getting ready to go to the club Heaven in central London. Sara couldn't make it, as usual, but Elle and Mike could. I sometimes thought Sara was a closet fag-hag. Though she never seemed to come out clubbing with me or want to be around gay guys, yet she always encouraged me to take a guy's number or follow my desire in pursuing a guy.

I was lying naked on my bed with 'Custom-made' by Lil' Kim blaring out on my stereo. It was a track my mother hated due to the sexual, squirming noises of a woman coming close to orgasm at its beginning. There was always something about listening to Lil' Kim before going out that got me so hyped and feeling sexy. Making myself feel sexy was the best way to feel good, as I had no-one around anymore to make me feel that way.

The clicking tones of my Nokia 8210 start to play Aaliyah's 'More Than a Woman' ringtone, and as always I stop what I'm doing and pause the CD so I can sing along. I miss the first call, but it rings again. On answering it the deep voice on the other end speaking: 'Yo, is that you? I was chatting to you and your bredrin the other day.'

It's Shamarai, and my heart starts beating so hard I become breathless.

'Oh, erm, hi, what's going on?' I say, then hold my breath so as not to sound like a breathless mess. Looking around my bedroom I scramble through the clothes I may possibly wear that night and find underwear to put on. Some reason it seems indecent to be utterly naked when talking to a stranger.

'Ah, it-a you, then. You know you did never say what your name was. What am I gonna call you on my phone?' He was right: I didn't tell him my name. I may have made up some fantasy where I told him it seductively, my lips brushing his ear, but the reality is I barely said a word to him that day.

'Errr, Reo.' Put on the spot, all I could think of was the acronym I would tell people was my actual name when I wasn't comfortable with them: Reo = Rogue Enjoys Oral.

'Reo? Okay, handsome name for a good-looking boy like you.' Not only did it seem like he had heard the lie in my uneasy voice, but he had just given me the green light to say things to him I would only say to a guy I found sexually attractive knowing he felt the same way about me. Yes, I have

22

been known to be a word-whore and say things to men that can be interpreted in two ways – the obvious 'come and fuck me now' way, or simply exactly what I say. I'm cryptic like that.

We arranged to meet up the next day to talk about music and stuff, but I no longer wanted to talk about music. It wasn't something I was terribly interested in; it was more of a hobby of mine I'd been told I was somewhat good at.

Going to Heaven with Mike and Elle that night was a weird one. All I could think about was the type of music I could make with Shamarai, and that wasn't the type of music you'd play on your iPod. As the music pumped and the drinks flowed not even the sight of a guy I'd had my eye on for months could stop me thinking about the golden demigod, and when those sexy tunes started to play I found I had to take a break from win'ing my little waist and sit down, as that feeling I got down below, both front and back throbbing, became unbearable. Sitting down while my behind seemed to swell with the desire of being deeply penetrated by a thick, heavy-veined, precum-seeping cock waiting to be strapped up nicely in a condom, I downed the last of my vodka and Coke and let my mind wander. Elle and Mikes were having their fun and I was having mine. If I were a girl I'm sure my panties would have probably been soaked in joy-juice right then, and getting up off the faux-leather seat would have been embarrassing. Thank Goddess I had two sets of underwear on, so the seepage wouldn't show.

Thursdays were always the worst days to wake up on, especially if I'd gone to Heaven the night before. It's not so much that I'd have a hangover – I don't really seem to get those – it's just my body aches in all the places I never knew could hurt. You'd think I would have learned my lesson by now: dancing on poles like a stripper, hanging upside-down and sliding down in swirls while drunk is dangerous. Goddess, I'm such a show-off.

Shamarai asked me to meet him at an address on the council estate that both Sara and I avoid. I was reluctant to go there after dark, so I convinced him that I should show up just before the sun was due to set. He said that would be fine so long as his housemate or family-members weren't at home. I guess I should have known that I wasn't the only one expecting music to be played with bodies instead of instruments and electronic devices.

I remember as I arrived at the blocks that night and saw him already there waiting for me I felt an overwhelming need to get out of the situation. My heart belted at my chest, my mouth grew dry as if I were scoffing my face with Jacob's Crackers, and my body became hot. I was nervous – he made me feel so nervous as he wasn't the type of guy that I normally come across.

We greeted each other, or rather he greeted me by holding a fist out in front of him for me to 'touch him one'. I wasn't used to guys doing that with me and blurted out, 'I don't do that shit.' He looked at me and smiled and gave me the look to follow him. We went into the flats. I caught up with him and we took the lift to the third floor. As we got out he grabbed my hand and told me to stay by the lift.

'So why did you come today then, Reo?' he said with a slight smile on his face and looking me dead in the eye. I had thought it was obvious why I had come to see him. Now I was thinking, maybe I've counted my eggs before they've hatched.

'Well, I thought you wanted to talk about music and...'

He interrupts me with a loud exhalation of breath that travels down the corridor. 'Well, I know boys like you,' he says in a very low and serious tone, looking down at my feet. I'm becoming more uneasy at this point. 'And I like you,' he continues. 'I like you a lot. So maybe we can do a ting, what'd ya think?'

Bingo, my gaydar does work! All my anxieties melt off of my slouched body and I begin to stand tall with Lil' Kim playing in my head.

We began to chat about me and when I first realised I was gay. He couldn't believe the fact that I said I have always known. He told me he was straight, then bi-curious, and that he didn't know where his growing feeling for men came from, but when he saw me, he knew he had to have me. What a line or two to give! – dude thinks he's slick.

He spoke in short, breathy sentences as if it was a struggle for him to get his words out, but his breathing became more stable once he put his right hand down his jeans and held onto his penis. His hand in his pants began to make me feel a little uneasy again. I mean, here we are in the corridor of the flats: if someone were to come out of the lift or one of the dusty-coloured doors we would be seen, and in my head it'd be quite obvious to anyone that this isn't just a friendly meet.

He begins to rub himself hidden under the fabric of his jeans and I'm glad again I'm not white. I was thinking, had I been, the flush in my face would have been evidence that I was not particularly comfortable with what was going on. However, accompanying those feelings of unease was the thought of him taking it out so I could see if his size truly matched what I imagined it to be growing into.

Slowly he begins to pull his hand up from his pants and the way it's configured I can tell his dick is coming up for the ride too. 'You wanna see it?' he asks me, but it's not like he wasn't planning to show me anyway. 'I've got a thick dick, you know. You think you can handle it?' He stops pulling it out of his jeans and I'm staring at his jeans' crotch-area anticipating what's to come. I see the darkened skin of the beginning of his penis and I've never understood why men have a natural tan down there, and I'm sure my pupils have contracted into cat-like slits as his crotch seems closer than it was a second ago. I was pretty much a spoilt child, so him taking his time is pissing me off at this moment. He asks a second time if I want to see it, and this time I say yes.

He continues to slowly pull his dick out, and as he's doing it I'm astounded that after what seems like a full minute he is still pulling it out. Forcefully it flicks out as if it too wanted to meet the outside air and I'm in awe: it's huge. Now, this king of a cock (and I have to say cock, because penis sounds tiny) is waiting to be crowned by my now-moistened lips.

'You see, you think this is nice? You want it? You ever had a man this big?' So many questions, Shamarai; just shut up and put it in my mouth. I answer them with nods and shakes. He invites me to his crotch and I blow him, right there, in that corridor of those flats I hated.

'Thank the Goddess he bathed beforehand,' I thought to myself as I smelt the clean scent of Dove. 'I can stay down here for a good while.' But that was all short-lived as we heard a door latch open and quickly scurried into the lift like the cockroaches I'm sure infested this council estate. Luckily it was still on our floor. Taking it down to the second floor, he thanked me for coming and giving him 'the sweetest head ever'. We say our byes and part ways. By then it was dark so I had to run through the park to get home.

It was the most daring thing I've done with a guy, almost getting caught in public. Something I hope I don't submit to again.

When I got home and checked my mobile I realised that I had a few missed calls and some text messages. My mum looked at me through the crack of her bedroom door and asked if I was okay. For some odd reason I just nodded, my mouth refusing to speak. I was probably scared she'd smell the dick on my breath and then hound me about having casual sex. It's not like I had ever had casual sex up until now, and I would barely call those stolen moments with his closed eyes and his cock filling my mouth sex either, but it was the first time I had given a guy exactly what he wanted, when he wanted it, because I too wanted to. Normally it's 'I'm not ready yet.' Yeah, my idol being Lil' Kim has not brainwashed me to follow through with her lyrics. I'm more like Charlotte in that ever-so-popular American TV show about a group of four female friends all having sex in New York City, you know the one. Sex is great and I love it, don't get me wrong, but to just lay it down on the table as if it's some TESCO 'value' ready-meal is not my style. Absence makes the heart grow fonder, apparently.

Going through my texts I found three from Shamarai asking to meet with him again, and a 'Did you get my message?' text too. I didn't reply straight away. In fact I ate my dinner, (which had been sitting in the microwave for goodness knows how long), and went to sleep. I replied in the morning.

A couple of weeks went by and I continued to see Shamarai here and there. I often went to the flat he had just started to rent, though my daydreams of him and me fucking in his plush home decked out all in white with glass furniture had evaporated the instant I was greeted by the dark green walls, a musky smell I could never put my finger on, and bedroom walls littered with newspaper cut-outs of naked Page Three girls. These didn't bother me so much as the obviously used-more-than-once straight porn magazines and DVDs. I hated going there. Shamarai had turned from a demigod to a boy in the hood. His charm was still there but his exterior did not match the interior of his home.

It soon became apparent that Shamarai didn't have any plans to take me to a studio now or ever, but that was okay, I had a man who wanted to be with me, even if he wasn't boyfriend material. Besides he was a friend now. The blowjobs were just a bonus. (I'd made it clear I was not laying down naked with him in that mess). I found it nice that he'd ask me to take him to gay bars. He was really coming out of his shell, happy to be seen in public with me in gay places and around Hackney. I felt like I was a teacher, a mentor to an older guy, (not that much older). He used to ask me random questions about gay life that, if I couldn't answer, I would converse with my friends about and report back to him on.

It was late at night and it had just rained but the air was still eerily thick when Shamarai called with his usual abrupt urgency, wanting me to come over. I wasn't doing anything and I had become pretty familiar with the estate he lived in: there was no need to be fearful of it anymore. 'Come nuh, me want to see you bad you see,' he would always say. His accent over the weeks was very sometime-ish: sometimes he spoke like he was born here, others he sounded like my mum's husband, straight off the Caribbean boat.

I always went. Not that I didn't recognise a booty – or should I say a mouthy – call, but because we'd have real good chats as well.

When I arrived he made me wait a little at his front door. I could hear whispering going on behind it, I could smell weed coming from inside, and the lights were off. I was just about to press my ear up against the door to hear better when he opened it. He asked me to go through to the living-room, pointing behind him to his right. There were no windows open, and the smell of weed made me gag – at least Sara had the decency to open hers. Looking back as I walked through, I noticed a tall guy I thought I recognised from school, but because it was so dark I couldn't really make out his face till he stepped into the light from the corridor. Then I saw it wasn't that guy, it wasn't any guy I knew. The whites of his eyes looked yellow.

I sit down on the sofa directly in front of the living-room door and look at the light coming from the kitchen. Shamarai hand-signals me to go further into the room as they continue to talk. I assume Shamarai has now got some other business apart from selling weed. The door closes and I'm thankful as people taller than me usually make me feel childlike, and the guy's yellow eyes freaked me out. I bet he was a crackhead. 'So when did you start selling crack?' I ask Shamarai as he comes through the doorway.

He looks at me and smiles and shakes his head. 'It's not crack I'm selling.' Crouching down in front of me, putting his hands on my knees.

'It's my turn first,' I thought to myself, as he only gets down like this when he wants to blow me.

'I wanna try som'ink different tonight ya see, Reo.'

Looking at him with probably the most puzzled face I ask, 'What?' and he smiles again. Such a dirty smile. He gently squeezes my thighs, making small circular motions on them with his hands, smiling. His hands slowly creep to the top of my jeans and he circles his thumb on my navel and licks his lips. My breath heavy and deep, so deep it's like someone is pushing down as I inhale, he tugs at my jeans. I move in towards him almost closing my legs. He stops my motion, keeping my legs apart by holding them with a firm grip. I can feel my heartbeat through my whole body. The light breeze coming from the kitchen behind me glides over my exposed stomach and works its way up my body to mask my face, almost stopping my breathing pattern. I let out a small gasp. His eyes darken. He tears my jeans down to my ankles and takes my underwear down also.

'Get up,' he says in a low tone, so I do. 'Go on that chair there.' – pointing to the one near the living-room entrance. I get up and shuffle my feet towards the chair. I feel a searing pain at the back of my head as if he'd thrown or hit me with something like a glass bottle or marble ball.

That was the last time I saw him alone.

I black out through no fault of my own, in a haze, the room still dark and the little light in the room is a blur. He's forced himself in me bent over on the sofa. I try to get up. 'Get off, you're hurting me,' I say, annoyed, but my hands are bound over the top of the sofa. Looking up towards him I notice that it's not Shamarai who is on top of me. Panicking, I hold my breath and try not to move as I see a blurred Shamarai's head nodding to whomever is now behind me. Condom wrapper on the floor, my waist gets pushed into the wooden frame of the sofa. Sweaty and grunting the guy finishes his business with my body. I attempt to get up but the stranger begins holding my legs in place with his and then holds my arms. It's Shamarai's turn.

I couldn't believe what was happening to me, and drifted in and out of imagining I was a butterfly fleeing a predator, but I was dragged back into the situation I desperately wanted out of when Shamarai finished, picked me up and escorted me by the hand to the bathroom.

Staring at myself in the mirror, holding my tears back as far as I can, I notice the both of them looking at me in the reflection. Smug-faced Shamarai speaks: 'Ya clean, yeah?' I have no idea what he is talking about. 'He did use two ca' one did buss tryna get it in you. Me knew you like it rough.' I answer with a nod and begin to clean myself, avoiding looking at the tissues as I flush them down the toilet.

He opens the front door and tells me he'd see me again.

I walk the corridor hoping to be seen.

Leaving the flats I didn't want to go straight home. Elle's place was only two roads away, so I headed there. Luckily enough she was in. I didn't tell her what had happened at first, as she was pumping out her music and having fun, but it just flew out my mouth: 'They raped me.' Laying back on her sofa where I had fixed myself my tears streamed, filling up my ears.

She told me to call the police.

I didn't.

What was I to say? That I was sexually assaulted by a supposedly straight guy I've been seeing on the down low for a few weeks, and that his friend, whose face I have no memory of now, joined in too. Nothing made any sense. My golden demigod was not heavenly after all. He was a golden reaper, taking that that did not belong to him.

Troubled for weeks by the memory, I learned that Shamarai had been stabbed, held in hospital, and then deported back to where he came from. Although I don't wish death upon anyone, I did for many years when it came to him. For gaining my trust, grooming me for the situation, and stealing from me not once but twice.

I guess now I treat men with caution, great caution. Female friends have dominated my circles, but that's changing. I do now have male friends to hang out with, but I don't fully trust any man as a man: it's just a defence mechanism.

But life is too short to let one disastrous mishap lead my life. The cracks are still there, but are less visible.

Fetish (Desire)

By Anu Olu

Does your desire delve deeper than the damaging side of sexual attraction?

Does it reach the psyche of the object that you so dearly desire?

Does your interest surpass the physical beauty and allure of my body, my skin or my kind?

A wise voice once said 'it's a man's prerogative to just sit and drink sometimes'

It is this man's prerogative to truly feel hurt, fully burnt by my interaction with you and your kind ('s) gestures.

I have been desired (fetishized) by many.

The amount I have fully allowed myself to is not mighty but few, far and few.

I am yet to seek solace in the arms of a man where race and prejudice is truly removed from *our* space.

Will the way of my mind and my thoughts rob me of my so-deserved salvation?

Will your kind ('s) praises and earned compliments forever lack meaning?

Will this wall I have erected force me to grow old alone?

Will the fear of being incorrectly cherished override my right to the destination of Peace?

Will your words forever mean nothing?

Will status/libidinal desire slowly weather away the purity of our love to the point of nothingness and new beginnings? Is this choice my own?

I have been desired, craved, admired, held and night-timely-lusted-after... Never *truly* loved.

Perhaps my individual understanding of desire (fetish) is the crux of this self-imploding situation.

Perhaps it is I who has never *truly* loved.

Never truly loved you (me).

You.

Me.

You.

Me.

Searching for Mangoes on Apple-trees

By Ade Adeniji

E ven though I had known for sure that I was attracted to people of my own gender since I was twelve, it was not until I was twenty-seven that I did anything about it. The long wait was due to a number of reasons. For one, spending my adolescence in Nigeria had meant that I did not know any other boys like me and, deep down, I had felt I was damaged and that there was something deeply wrong with me. I also remember coming across a passage in the Bible late one evening about 'a man lying with another man' deserving to be put to death, and reaching the conclusion that the sort of carnal desires I had were an 'abomination' and that doing anything about them meant an eternity in Hell.

I left Nigeria at nineteen to return to London, where I had been born in the late '60s. By the time I got to know other boys like me, I had come to accept that pursuing my carnal desires would be a sure way to send my mother to an early grave. I was her only child, and it was her constant prayer that I find a good woman in London and have lots of children.

So for many years I did nothing. I studied, went to work and, in between, daydreamed about the moment a man – any man – would cross my path. We'd immediately fall in love, move in together and be happy forever and ever.

Well, life has a way of turning out differently from the way our youthful selves imagine it.

The first man I had sex with – at the age of twenty-seven – told me after four weeks that he was leaving me to go back to his supposedly ex-boyfriend. I had met him through his brother, who was a friend, and had hoped for much more than was offered.

The second man – who I met two months after the first –

told me after three weeks that he found the blemishes and moles on my face unattractive and therefore did not want to take our 'relationship' any further. I had met him through the personals in the back page of *The Voice*, Britain's favourite black newspaper. He was seeking a 'younger black man' and I fitted the bill; or so I thought.

The third man – about two and a half months after the second – told me after three months that he had too much 'emotional baggage' and didn't feel ready to pursue a relationship. I had met him during London Pride – we were both volunteers during the Parade – where I had been hoping to meet other gay men for friendship and possibly more.

The fourth – who I confess overlapped with the third – said he wanted something casual and nothing more: this 'something' we pursued vigorously over a two-month period, then it faded out. Him I had met at a social group for gay men who had recently come out.

And then I met Chris – the fifth man.

I was waiting for the Central Line at Oxford Circus underground station late one Saturday evening in September. There were signal failures and the tube was running very late. Next to me stood a tall white man. He had a distinguished-professor look about him. 'Typical,' he said, 'there are always problems on the Underground.' I looked across and smiled, and we proceeded to lament the state of public transport, before moving on to other topics of conversation.

We continued talking as we boarded the tube. He introduced himself as Chris and told me he worked in higher education. As we chatted away, we discovered that we only lived one tube stop from each other. When he mentioned that he lived in Bow Quarter I heard myself say, 'I've always wanted to go there, it looks so nice and posh whenever I walk by.' Bow Quarter was a residential complex in East London which looked like an old brewery, and had been converted into houses and apartments. It is true that I had always wanted to explore the area, but on hearing myself say that out loud, I knew instantly that it came across as though I was making a move on my fellow commuter.

Chris immediately invited me back. Embarrassed, I declined, saying that it was very late and I needed some rest, but perhaps next time. As the tube neared his stop he asked for my telephone number, which I gave without hesitation. I took his and then, giving me a very wide grin, he got off the tube and I stayed on for one more stop.

Neither of us had used the word 'gay' but as we had chatted away I somehow knew that he was, and I knew that he was keen on me. I looked around the crowded carriage, wondering if any of the other passengers had understood what had gone on between us. It felt exciting to be wanted and to be desired. As I got off the tube I started to regret that I hadn't taken Chris up on his offer. I was going home to an empty flat and it was the weekend. 'Surely it would have been nicer to have someone hold me close,' I heard my inner voice lament.

Shortly after I reached my apartment, by which time it was past midnight, the phone rang. I knew immediately that it was Chris. 'Can I speak to the heartbreaker on the Central Line?' I giggled like a shy teenager. My heart was racing and I found myself lost for words. Chris said he could not stop thinking about me and wished that I had come home with him. I managed to say that I wished I had gone back with him too. He said he could get a taxi and come round to mine. Without hesitation, I said 'sure' and gave him my address.

Chris arrived just before one, with a bottle of wine. He seemed much taller than I remembered as I stood on tiptoe and our lips found each other. We settled on the sofa and took turns finding out about each other. He was forty-seven and I had just turned twenty-eight. In the heat of the night, the age-difference felt irrelevant. What mattered in that moment was that someone desired to be with me. I hadn't felt this way with any of the previous four men I had been intimate with. None of them had come to my apartment in the middle of the night simply to be with me. This was what I had always daydreamed about, I told myself as we eventually fell asleep after a long period of devouring each other.

We spent hours in bed the next morning, talking about our childhoods, careers and families. Chris had so many stories to share; he had done many things and been to so many places. It felt like I had almost at random picked up a book and was discovering a whole new world. 'This is so romantic,' I thought to myself.

We eventually left my flat in the early afternoon and went to the Columbia Road flower market for lunch, choosing a café he liked. Afterwards we headed back to his place and I finally got to visit Bow Quarter. We saw a lot of each other as the days unfolded. As his apartment was much bigger than mine I spent more time there and would often go into work from his. Chris enjoyed cooking and we'd spend a lot of time talking and laughing in the kitchen.

As the weeks went by I came to see that Chris really wanted to be in a relationship. He wanted us to be together and did not hesitate in introducing me to his friends. He told me that he had no other family and that, when he died, I would be his sole beneficiary. It was at this point that something started to change within me. This was new territory.

Up until that point in my life I had never really thought about what being in a relationship meant and involved: like a lovelorn teenager I had simply longed to be in one. And here I was in one, with someone who really wanted to be in one, and something within me felt out of place.

I didn't understand. Why could I not simply enjoy what was going on? This was what the previous four men could not or would not give me, and yet... My mind kept pondering, trying to figure out why I was not content.

At one point I thought perhaps it was the age difference. After all, there was a nineteen-year age gap between us. Chris had done so much with his life and it felt like I was just at the beginning of my own journey. There were times where I would catch the eye of someone younger when we were out, and I'd ask myself why I wasn't with someone my own age, with whom I could share my voyage of discovery on more equal terms.

Then I thought, perhaps it was his height. I had to stand on tiptoe or he had to bend down in order for us to kiss. This often made me feel self-conscious, and it was not how I had imagined kissing the partner of my daydreams.

Then I thought, perhaps it was because Chris was white. He never really understood when I talked about prejudice and discrimination. I had also come to learn that all his previous partners were black, and I became insecure that he was only going out with me because of my colour, and not because of my personality and character.

Then I thought, perhaps it was because Chris seemed keen to change me. Within a few weeks of knowing each other he had suggested that I get another job with more money. At the time I was working in administration at a university. I knew I was capable of doing more, but was passionate about the project I was working on, so the financial reward didn't matter that much to me. I said as much, but Chris wouldn't drop the subject.

Then I thought, perhaps it was because of what others might think of our relationship. Here I was, a younger black guy with little money, going out with an older white guy with money. People were bound to think I was a scrounger. I found myself becoming hyper-sensitive whenever we were out, and often insisted on paying my own way, for fear that others would misinterpret our relationship.

I never shared any of this with Chris. 'He doesn't need to know,' I concluded. My doubts were mine alone. It was during this period of reflection that Chris suggested we go to Paris for the weekend. We had known each other for about six weeks at this stage. It felt like a great idea. I had been to Paris with colleagues from work when I was twenty-one, and had fallen in love with the city. Going on an adventure with Chris felt like what our still fairly-new relationship needed. We planned to go on a Friday, returning on Monday. I insisted on paying for my own train ticket and, as a compromise and a kindness to my malnourished wallet, agreed that Chris could pay for the hotel!

During the week leading up to our departure the first man resurfaced in my life and we ended up doing the deed that same evening. A few days later one thing led to another with the third man and we also ended up doing the deed. And on the Friday I boarded the train with Chris. It wasn't the perfect start to the romantic weekend I had envisaged, but I was hopeful... or was it denial?

The journey went smoothly and we arrived at Gare du Nord

late Friday evening. Chris knew Paris well and had no problem navigating the metro to our hotel, which was in Le Marais district. Le Marais is very central, its narrow streets dating back to Medieval times, and is busy with boutiques and bars. We went for something to eat and spent the night drinking in one of the local gay bars.

The next day was spent wandering around the city, taking in the sights and exploring the side-streets. After dinner that evening we took a walk along the footpath that runs parallel to the river Seine. As we strolled Chris pointed to a few men who ambled by saying, 'He's gay'; 'He's definitely gay.'

'How do you know,' I asked. Chris explained that the foot-path was a popular cruising-ground. I had no idea what cruising meant and Chris explained that it was where gay men came to meet other gay men for casual encounters.

We continued on down the footpath. It felt exciting. Even though dusk was falling, it was still just light enough to see that the men who walked by were of different ages, races, looks and heights. When we got to the end of the footpath I took Chris's hand and asked whether we could walk back the same way. He told me that he was tired and that I should do the walk by myself: he would wait for me. And so I went down the footpath again, and into the shadows.

I could feel my heart beating so fast as I left Chris behind. I avoided eye-contact with each man initially. I did want to look, but it felt so scary. 'What do I do after we make eye-contact, what do I say,' I wondered. Halfway down, I heard a voice say something in French. I stopped. 'Sorry, je ne parle pas Français,' I responded stiltedly.

'Are you American,' he asked.

'No, British,' I replied.

In broken French and English we made attempts to com-municate. He was slightly taller than me, with short dark hair. He was about my age, perhaps younger. He lived on the outskirts of Paris, in the banlieues, and was staying in a hotel nearby. As I took in his details, wondering where this might all be leading, I heard a loud voice behind me scream, 'I DON'T BELIEVE IT! Here we are in Paris on a romantic weekend and you are picking up men!'

I turned around to face a puffed-up Chris. I couldn't see him clearly in the darkness, but it was clear that he was not amused. My new companion faded back into the shadows. I could not get any words out of my mouth and so I simply ran. I ran to the end of the footpath and up the steps away from the Seine to the boulevard above. Eventually I stopped, crouched down and tried to gather my breath.

'Are you okay,' I heard a thick French accent say behind me. It was the man from the footpath. My earlier excitement came back. 'He's keen,' I thought.

I told him I was fine and, when he asked who that man was, I found myself saying, 'Someone from my hotel. I felt sorry for him this morning and had breakfast with him, and he has since been pestering and following me around all day.' I really don't know what came over me to make me say that. But in that moment I remember so desperately wanting to be with this newly-found young Frenchman. Chris felt so old, tired and familiar. Standing on the street that night beneath the lamp-light I felt so alive. He told me that I was cute, that he really wanted to be with me, and asked whether I'd like to come back to his hotel. It was tempting, and I pondered what to do next. Once again I heard, 'I DON'T BELIEVE IT!! You're *still* talking to him!' I told the Frenchman that I was sorry but nothing was going to happen and marched over to Chris.

'I was just talking to him, nothing more,' I shouted. 'You told me it was okay to walk down the path.'

'HE WANTED SEX, NOT CONVERSATION!' Chris yelled. 'How can you be so naïve!'

Chris was right: I knew what the cute Frenchman had want-ed and, much as I hated to admit it, I also knew my own intentions and desires. Here I was, on a romantic weekend with an affectionate man who was attracted to me and doted on me, and yet I was longing to be with another. I suddenly needed to get Chris back on my side and decided that the only way to do that would be to cry.

'I really had no idea what the man wanted, you know I am new to all this,' I said in a strangulated voice, willing myself to cry. Chris snapped at me to stop pretending, saying that I was only feeling bad because I had been caught. Out of nowhere, the tears suddenly started to flow. 'You know I have never been away with a boyfriend and this is all so new to me. I feel so alone without my friends.' The more Chris urged me to stop the more I cried, until he caved in and hugged me.

We walked home in silence, our hands occasionally touching. The silence continued as we undressed and climbed into bed. I did not want to be physical with him that night; truth is I wanted to be elsewhere. 'It's just a body,' I told myself as he slowly took possession of me. 'It's just sex and does not have to mean anything.'

Things were different the next morning. Though at first we barely spoke, it felt like we both wanted to forget the drama of the night before. We agreed to spend the day apart to give us the chance to explore the city individually. The temperature was mild, so I found an outside spot at a café where I sat and read *Giovanni's Room*, by James Baldwin. The first man had given it to me when we had met earlier in the week, telling me that it was the perfect book to read in Paris, as Baldwin had lived there while writing it. It was, for I could relate all too well to a protagonist who was caught up in a world of lust, confusion and endless searching.

Later that evening, I decided to open up to Chris and let him know more about my life-journey. I had always been afraid to let people in and had worn a façade of being in control, content and happy. I told him that I had never imagined living my life openly as a gay man. I had decided when I left Nigeria that I was going to commit suicide when I hit thirty because my life was doomed to be one of rejection and loneliness. He looked bemused as I divulged all this, and told me jokingly that, as I would soon be thirty, I should make sure I wrote my will and leave all my belongings to him. I immediately put my façade back on, making light of what I had just disclosed, silently vowing never to share anything so intimate with him again.

Eventually our weekend break was over and we were back on the train heading to London. Something was different, not just with Chris, but within myself. Up until my encounter with Chris I had always believed that going into a relationship required no more than saying yes to any man who crossed my path. Sex, dating and being in a relationship – they all meant the same to me. I had literally gone to bed with the first five gay men who had given me any attention and, each time, I had automatically read more into the situation than what was being offered. This time was different from all the others: this time I was the one who wanted to walk away.

Chris and I parted at the station where we had said our first goodbye, what felt like years ago. We didn't see each other during the week but kept in telephone contact. I eventually went round to his the next weekend for dinner. As always he had made a wonderful meal, the candles were lit and his log fire was burning. We made our way through dinner as he talked about our future together. It was as if he had forgotten all about that night in Paris, as if it had never happened. Eventually he fell silent.

'I don't want to continue with this,' I quietly told him. I felt nervous. What if this is my last chance at love, I wondered. Chris looked surprised and asked me why. 'I think you have a lot of issues and need therapy,' I heard myself say. I cringe now as I remember that moment. Here I was, at twenty-eight, so confident that I was not the one who was wounded, who was damaged.

'We all have issues,' replied Chris.

'But you have more,' I said. It would take me many years to accept that I did indeed have issues – some I had known about during that conversation with Chris, and many more I would come to discover as I tried to navigate being emotionally intimate with a man.

The evening came to an end. Chris had tried to talk me out of my decision, but my mind was made up. During the weeks that followed he kept in touch. The more he tried to rekindle what we had, the more I felt he had issues that ruled a relationship with him out. Days became weeks and the phone-calls eventually stopped.

A few months afterwards I bumped into Chris in the street, something that was bound to happen as he lived so close to me. He seemed happy and told me about his new boyfriend – who was also black, and younger than me. Chris invited me back to his place. In a brief moment of nostalgia for what we once had, I accepted the invitation. I wasn't sure of my intentions, or his, and kept an open mind. Nothing happened: it appeared that we

41

had both moved on. We would, from time to time, bump into each other and use the opportunity to catch up, and then gradually we faded from each other's lives.

Prior to Chris, I had never met any other black gay men. The first five men in my life had been white. Shortly after my Parisian adventure with Chris, the third man introduced me to another black gay man of African heritage. We would become fast friends and Chris would become the funny anecdote I'd tell at parties. I'd tell them about the cruising area on the banks of the Seine, the cute Frenchman, the tears and the old distinguished Englishman.

Many years later I bumped into Chris again. I was around thirty-five, him fifty-four. My memories of us together had faded to the point where I was no longer sure what was true or false about my brief relationship with him. I had reduced our time together to the Parisian anecdote, in which I had cast him as the somewhat predatory older man who took advantage of the vulnerable younger one.

He had bought an apartment at the end of my street. In fact he had bought a couple of apartments within the vicinity. He had been investing in property and was getting ready to take early retirement. As we caught up he gave me advice on which areas were up and coming. He invited me back to one of his apartments.

Many men had come and gone, I had lost count of how many. Seeing Chris reminded me of the days when I still knew the name and number of each of the men who came into my life. A time of innocence, exploration, uncertainly and insecurity. I accepted the invitation to go back with him, partly out of duty, guilt and nostalgia, but it was awkward. We had both moved on. Even though we were both single, it felt like we were old friends who, on getting reacquainted, find they no longer have anything in common.

And then once again, Chris faded away.

I told the tale of my Parisian adventures in a staged storytelling performance in London in 2013, and I found myself once again thinking of Chris. I was now forty-five, and very different from that young man who had only recently come out and was struggling to understand what being in relationship meant and involved. I hadn't bumped into Chris for many years and wondered if he still had his apartment at the end of my street. He would have been sixty-four, and I imagined him living a life of luxurious retirement, having cashed in his property investments at the height of the last boom. I got out my laptop and typed his full name into the search engine. I then waited.

The first entry at the top of the page was an obituary. I froze: surely not. I clicked on the link and the first line that met my eyes read '...suffering from terminal cancer, [Chris] took the positive decision to commit suicide in Switzerland....'

As I read the obituary, which was dated 2007, I searched for familiar bits of information that Chris had shared with me during those first few weeks we spent together. That late-night journey on the Central Line started to resurface, our lying in bed the next morning and heading out to brunch down Columbia Road flower market, the flower-sellers hawking their fading blooms as the trading day drew to a close. Roses, peonies, petunias... By the time I got to the end of the paragraph I knew for sure that it was him. The obituary went on to say, 'Chris was only mildly embarrassed to have made a considerable amount of money from property development in London, and, having no relatives, he made a point of leaving it to people and causes whom he felt would most benefit.' Yes, that sounded like the Chris I knew.

It is now almost eighteen years since I first met Chris. Whilst I have gone on to have many significant and far longer relationships, my relationship with Chris played a huge part in my growth as a gay man. It was the first time that I came face to face with one of my self-defeating relationship patterns – a pattern that would rear its head time and time again in other relationships and encounters. Prior to Chris, I was happy to go along with being with any man even if, deep down, I was not entirely happy or satisfied. I simply went with the flow, hoping that without any direct action by me things would eventually change and I would find what I was searching for – even though I had no idea what that was.

In thinking of the young man that I was when I met Chris, it would be tempting to cast one or the other of us as the saint or sinner. But growing up has taught me that life is much more complex and never clear-cut. Reflecting on the early years of my coming out, I now recognise that, whilst I felt I was looking for a man to fall in love with, what I was really yearning for was to feel okay within myself. To know that I was not broken or damaged. I had gone into the arms of many men, including Chris's, hoping that being with them would make everything okay: their embrace would be confirmation that there was nothing wrong with me. Sadly many of those men also had their own things that they were looking for – and it often ended up with one of us getting hurt.

It has taken me years to recognise that I keep looking in the wrong places for the things for which I deeply yearn. It is a pattern, even today, many years after Chris, that I am still working to unlearn.

God's Breed

By Salawu Owujide

That I am black, God,
I have carried the burden
for centuries across the Atlantic;
I will sing you a song
of what the castle of my skin demands.
Hell! I certainly get
what you lack.
So, hear this chorus:
your air is free
your lights are real
but why are my fists held,
held against my will?
Why can't my chisel carve out my being?
For, I still sing
having crucified me,
they still hold up my image
across a street with neon lights
with a long line of alphabet
reading: empire of hate.

A Eulogy for Rotimi Fani-Kayode

By Robert Taylor

I met Rotimi at my first visit to a black gay social group in London in the mid 1980s. He had a very gentle, unassuming manner. In fact, if it hadn't been for the hushed, rather reverential tones with which a mutual acquaintance explained who he was, I might not have guessed that I was meeting such a distinguished artist.

Our first proper photographic encounter was my portrait session. I booked him more out of curiosity than real need. During the session, watching him work for the first time, and listening to the gentle, economical answers to my endless stream of questions, I felt excited, bewildered and inspired. Up to that moment photography had just been a fun hobby for me.

And he was such a fascinating man, particularly to someone like me, new to the possibility of a black gay creative role-model, or even a black gay creative network come to that. He was quite a collection of paradoxes and mysteries: very much the fashionable and conscious black man, he could do 'cosmopolitan gay' when necessary, but this did not preclude a commitment to the Yoruba culture and gods of his native Nigeria.

There was an elegance to the way his work engaged with both Western and Yoruba creative traditions, whilst still embracing his sexuality and coming up with something special of his own. One would often come across traditional West African artefacts in his images, employed in ways that some of his more traditionally-minded Yoruba forebears might have found irreverent or problematic, to put it mildly! But they would have been missing the point. Rotimi was a Yoruba, just very much on his own terms.

He employed so many different styles and techniques in his work that it would be difficult to make simple descriptions of it that don't seem sweeping or superficial. That said, I've no hesitation using words like 'elegant', 'provocative', 'prophetic' or 'profoundly beautiful' to describe various pieces of his work (even though many of them featured me).

And yes, there was lot of male nudity, and an unapologetically homoerotic atmosphere in so much of his work. I'm still amazed at some of the things he got me to do in the studio! Observing him at work, whether in the studio or the darkroom, I was impressed by his quiet industriousness. The photo sessions that I participated in ranged from what felt like riotous parties, through sometimes strangely erotic experiments, on to almost surgically precise operations. But whatever was going on around him there he was at the centre, working with a degree of concentration which quietly demanded the best from his sitters and models. Even his camera technique was striking. He handled the Hasselblad camera like a precious lover from whom he hoped to coax all sorts of sensual pleasures.

It is not widely appreciated that latterly Rotimi and the writer Alex Hirst – his life-partner – collaborated very closely to produce images and prose in an apparently seamless union, often transcending their given labels of 'writer' and 'photographer'. The results show that the two of them got round many of the problems that might have thwarted the efforts of less solid partnerships.

When dealing with other photographers Rotimi was generous with his time and skills. This was special and not too common in a profession notorious for bitchiness, mistrust and fierce competitiveness. He gave sincere encouragement and very practical help to several of us, including those like me who were potentially direct competitors for the very few opportunities and clients accessible to black gay photographers at the time. He would often give me a great boost with just a few well-chosen words about my work. A Rotimi maxim has become central to the way that I make, as well as view certain images. He believed that a successful image should always have more than one idea or valid interpretation – something that often irritates or unsettles the lazy viewer looking for the 'right' line to take – 'Too bad,' he would say.

Rotimi's last great kindness to me was an all-night printing session in his darkroom to meet the deadline for my first-ever exhibition in America. I had not learnt to print to exhibition standards at that stage. This was particularly generous of him as he had already spent a really gruelling day leading seminars and workshops at a photography festival. I got a fine set of prints, in addition to an amazing night of fascinating conversation infused with his gentle warmth and wisdom, as well as the best and most satisfying photography lesson I am ever likely to have.

It's a measure of his generosity and confidence that he spoke so freely about the exact details of his own techniques so that others could benefit. We often traded chances to use each other as models for experimental figurative work. With his striking head of beautifully-kept dreadlocks, taut, defined physique, and gentle grace, he was wonderful to photograph. He was as close as you could get to the ideal model. Responsive and uninhibited, yet never interfering. As an experienced photographer with his own very clear ideas about image-making, he must have been tempted to interfere at times when I was photographing him. On the rare occasions that he did, I only ever felt supported. I have benefited greatly from his efforts to get me thinking about what I was doing and why I was doing it. This has proved ultimately much more important than fretting about winning anyone else's approval.

Rotimi's legacy is considerable. His photographic work obviously, his role in the setting-up of AUTOGRAPH (The Association of Black Photographers) and the inspiration he gave to many artists – of all kinds and backgrounds – ensure that he will not be forgotten. After knowing Rotimi, I feel able to celebrate my own ability as photographer without apology; to look, desire and enjoy the world in my own way. Meeting him literally changed my life.

I wonder what Rotimi would be up to now if he were alive; indeed, what he'd make of all the posthumous adulation.

He is much missed.

(A version of this piece first appeared in Body Politic *magazine in the early 1990s)*

How Do I Look?

By Leo Ofori

How do I look?

Do pink lips compromise my masculinity?

Is blue skin just plain insanity?

How brave are you to step to me?

And look past the mask internally?

How do I look?

Do you think if I join an agency they'll put me in every magazine?

Then I'll become commercially,

The one that every guy wants to be?

The one that every girl wants to see?

Both gay and straight bisexually…?

How do I look?

What stereotypes can you place upon me?

Pink and blue men are really sweet.

Pink and blue men all carry disease.

Pink and blue men have a low I.Q.

Pink and blue men have very, very… VERY… LONG fingers.

How do I look?

Repulsive?

Impulsive?

Expressive?

Obsessive?

Ugly?

Creepy?

Dirty?

Girly?

Studly?

Lovely?

Big and macho, oh-so-cuddly?

How will I look when the paint comes off?

Is My House Too Gay?

By Reverend Rowland Jide Macaulay

Part I

S ummer 2011 and I was reflecting on my life at the time, the somewhat perorated part of my Christian faith, and my family.

I have always loved talking about my relationship with my dad. Over the years we have gone from rejection to acceptance, ignorance to understanding, fear to boldness. Yet for all the impact of the love between us, and my steady growth in self-worth, there is no doubt that each higher level we attain sets us new challenges to meet.

I am very grateful to my dad. It is with his love that I am able to be most of who I am. He is a pioneer and no stranger to fighting for what is right and necessary, both for the sanctity of Christian education and for the preservation of African theology, and it is he who set me on my pioneering path to fight for what is right for me and for many. And yet the relationship I am having with my father is mired in envy, jealousy and sometimes outright evil. This comes both from within and out of the external forces of life.

In my maturity and path of life I have learnt to no longer be taken by surprise by atrocities, and people who follow the stories of my many encounters with my dad will understand and value how far we have come.

As I open up now on a new issue that is both engaging and interesting, you will recognise the extent of my growth with my father as a gay son.

'Is my house too gay?' I asked myself one afternoon.

In the first quarter of 2011 my father decided to spend his summer with me in London, where I live, giving me ample warning to make myself available and to 'de-gay' my flat. However, unlike his visit in 2003, for which I took down wall-paintings, put away photographs, hid tell-tale books and brushed all my gayness under the carpet, in 2011 I was more comfortable with who I was. I had grown into such a full and robust awareness of my queerness that it no longer mattered to me to hide gay magazines, artefacts and murals as if they were shameful.

A few weeks after he arrived, my dad announced that he wanted to speak with me, and went on to tell me that my flat in London was too gay. At first he spoke about how he felt very uncomfortable here. He seemed to have forgotten that it is my space, my comfort zone: after all, 'an Englishman's home is his castle'. Oops. As a Nigerian abroad I tend to forget that there are no rules of privacy back in Africa; that our homes there are more or less community centres: everyone comes in and out of the people's homes all the time. Well, I am sorry folks, I make my home comfortable first for me, and only then will I invite you in. If I decide to open my home to the public then I might make some areas more public and some more private, perhaps like Buckingham Palace.

Now, back to the question of my father's insecurity around my home. My front room was certainly too gay, as a large art-book crammed with erotic images of men dating as far back as the 15th century took a prime spot on the coffee-table, and several gay magazines with sculpted torsos on their covers protruded eye-catchingly from the paper-rack.

In my kitchen/dinner-area a large poster hangs on the wall with a list of countries where Lesbians, Gays, Bisexuals, Trans and Intersex (LGBTI) people are persecuted, discriminated against and criminalised. It is a reminder to anyone who sees it that we live in a dangerous and awful world, and of course for me a constant reminder of my work and challenges with human rights activism, but for my father it is just too gay.

My favourite is a poster from the World Out Games that says, 'Get your Ass Over to Copenhagen' above a set of portraits of people in suggestive modes and positions, a classic metro-sexual depiction of a freer world. Down the corridor is a poster about homophobic domestic violence, then on the corridor that leads to the steps down to my garden is a poster that reads, 'Unconditional Love for Lesbian, Gay, Bisexual, Transgender and Intersex People in Africa'. How can this be in bad taste, I queried. And finally in my bedroom is a large framed photo-graph of a naked man lying on a bed, with his well-shaped backside pushed up for a good view.

In the face of my father's discomfort I asked myself, is my house too gay? For me certainly not: it is a place of pleasure. After a long hard day I need a new focus and an environment that makes me smile and feel welcome. I need my form of art and choice of decor to fill me with a sense and assurance of my purpose.

I was concerned that my father wanted me to be closeted again. 'Never again,' I assured myself: the pain of that dark dungeon is enough for a lifetime. Another thought that waded through my mind was that, had I been in a relationship with a lovely man, (as surely I will be), and we had a large portrait of the two of us hanging beautifully on the lounge wall, (as surely we would do), would he expect us to bring it down to make him feel comfortable?

Let me not go there for now: hopefully I will have a story to tell when we get to that stage.

Many of the conversations with my father – about day-to-day life, theology, people we know and people in the public eye, and television shows – entered the gay arena; for instance he watched UK soap *EastEnders* with me, which at that time depicted an Asian family who were struggling with their gay son. We also watched *Prayers for Bobby*, a true story about a Christian mother who drove her gay son to commit suicide because of her harshness and inaccurate interpretation of the Bible.

In the time we spent together in London that summer we studied together, read books, and searched online articles about the genetics of homosexuality. I must admit that this was good for both of us, and very engaging for the tireless mind of my father, who is always looking for more to convince him of any given viewpoint. I enjoyed all of these experiences as I know that many people are unable to even begin to have conversations such as these with their parents, let alone spend so much quality time together.

I learnt that whilst my home is my home, it is also a place of comfort for those who visit me, and I want my guests to feel welcome, and therefore decided I did not need to be too direct in displaying my homosexuality. Also I felt for my father, as he is caught between a traditional view of what people's homes should be and the need for a personal and private space.

I gave my dad a book called *The Children Are Free* by Jeff Miner that re-examines the evidence about same-sex relation-ships in the Bible. He read it and said to me, 'This book is for babies.' I agreed (because of the simplistic approach to the subject-matter – though I recommend this book to anyone who wants to understand the evidence on a basic level). Then I got him another book: *What the Bible really says about Homo-sexuality* by Daniel Helminiak, a professor of systematic theology. While reading this my father took notes. I believed that the dynamics of our relationship were breaking the code of the taboo around homosexuality, as his response discussing the issue the second time was to ask, 'How can the church and the Christian community respond to homosexuality?' This is a better place to discuss the issues from than the old, uncon-structive arguments about exclusion and sin, and I am deter-mined not stop until we are both fully learned, theologically, sociologically and scientifically.

During his stay in London that summer he enjoyed and preferred the comfort of my home, with its lengthy leafy garden, the serenity of the neighbourhood, and delighted in the delicacies of all the thoughtfully-chosen and carefully-prepared meals I provided for him, from Italian to Nigerian dishes, from English breakfasts to outdoor barbeques.

After nearly three months in London, I wave goodbye to my dad as he returns to Nigeria. I want to believe that he is on a journey, and I pray that he will continue to reason deeply as we come to a better understanding of humanity, including the humanity of those in same-sex relationships.

In the end I decided not to argue or debate the level of gayness in my home with my father: I did what was right for me. However, I respected his wish that I bring all the posters, books and artefacts down, for one day only, which I was content to do as I honestly and joyfully played host for his 74th birthday. Now they are back up and we are all happy.

*

Part II

Fast forward to the summer of 2013, exactly two years later. My life was in review again. Now, at the mercies of my pen, I want to share the new development – or the lack of it – that is happening.

In the past few weeks I decided to watch a few YouTube videos about coming out as gay. I have never done a video about coming out, but I have shared my stories with many media, sometimes with a good outcome and others with horrible consequences. I am now 48 years old and coming out over and over has never been so easy. I have a family which is growing, and as the younger family members become adults I have repeatedly to readdress the issues of my sexuality.

Last year, in August, my mother passed away suddenly after being hospitalised. Prior to this final visit to hospital she had lived with diagnosed trauma since September 2010, suffering unexplainable pains which resulted in loss of hair, skin disorders, arthritis and several chronic illnesses. In the moment of our family grief, myself and my siblings came together and grew closer, thanks especially to my older brother, whose wisdom and elder's mind kept us united. I was not sure of my dad's feelings towards me as he seemed unduly distant. My fear was confirmed by many of his actions around that time, and also by what he said to me the day after my mother's funeral.

Preparing for the funeral was difficult, as I was lost at my mother's death, and I was angry all over again as I reflected on the one and only person who had authentically accepted my gayness.

My younger brother had called me an abomination and announced that I was hell-bound, a belief arising from his conservative Christian teaching and convictions; my older brother in his confusion had 'protected' his daughters from me in case they might become too comfortable with my gayness; and my other siblings had intrusive questions concerning the validity of my homosexuality. It was not a comfortable place for anyone to be, particularly in the midst of bereavement. On the day of the funeral, 28th August 2013, my older brother and I were to give the eulogy, and as we all grieved our mother passing differently, my loss may have seemed more strongly-expressed than anyone else's. I had lost not only my mother's love without conditions but a friend, my confidant.

When I came out as gay she was the first to know. My gay friends immediately became her children, especially the many who had been rejected or ostracised by their own parents. She was Mother, and she opened her little home and her heart to all my gay friends. She also came to the 'gay church' with me – the Metropolitan Community Church where I trained for ministry in inclusive theology and became a 'gay pastor'. She was no doubt concerned at what seemed like an extreme death wish mission on my part when I decided to go to Nigeria to start the House Of Rainbow, the first Christian church in Nigeria to openly welcome gays and lesbians without prejudice, but nonetheless she gave the project her blessing. After I settled in Nigeria she came to visit us and attended one of our services. She enjoyed support from members of our congregation and, on a different occasion, my dad at his 70th birthday-party enjoyed the over-indulging presence of members of House Of Rainbow who had volunteered to help serve his guests. I spoke of some of these things at the funeral.

Looking back on it now, it is surprising that I was shocked when my father called me the day after the funeral to say in the harshest, most ungenerous and angry tone, that telling the world that I am gay at my mother's funeral was disrespectful and dishonourable. He said, 'Saying you are gay is like telling the world you have got cancer,' that they would be shocked, and 'the funeral was not the time and place.' I was extremely upset and it was the first time I ever spoke back to my dad.

I share this because it isn't easy. I thought in 2011 that I had won my dad over along the many years of our journey together, in the growing understanding we had come to, in the theological education and investment we had made in scholarly books that were affirming and welcoming on issues of sexuality. I was wrong.

In order for me to understand my pain, and wanting to see what the trends are with coming out for the young people today, I still find it challenging that not many Black people of

African descent either in Africa or elsewhere feel confident enough to come out as gay or lesbian and to do so by recording a video of their stories. Whilst religion is no doubt part of the reason, I find that many people who are not of African descent are coming out as gay and Christian, regardless of the family break-ups and rejections that sometimes follow on.

In January 2014 I went on a quest to challenge myself by attending the Gay Christian Network conference in Chicago. Temperatures were below freezing, but the warmth of the conference allowed me to be both broken and healed. It was no longer about me but about the millions of LGBT people around the world and especially those in Africa. It wasn't long after I arrived at the conference that I was informed of the death of a Cameroonian activist, Roger Jean-Claude Mbede, who had been starved to death by his Christian family. Three years prior to this he had been imprisoned for being gay, and while in prison had suffered the ill health which contributed to his early death. I was upset. As if that was not enough, a few days later, on the 12th January, it was confirmed in the news that the Nigeria president had signed into law a piece of serious antigay legislation purporting to be against 'gay marriage' but in reality far more wide-ranging and oppressive. My mind went to the millions of people in Nigeria – including my father – who were said to be happy and congratulating the president and his cabinet. And equally my heart sank in depression as I reflected on the lives of the many millions of people and their families who would immediately be the recipients of this draconian and selfish law.

Within hours of the announcement 'jungle justice' had descended on the gay community: there was pandemonium and a wave of panic from the north, where gay men were hurriedly arrested and taken to court, to the south, in Port Harcourt, where gay men were being publically humiliated – and the video of this was circulated via the internet. In the east of Nigeria people were fleeing arrest, and many who were not so lucky spent time in jail and had to bribe the police officers for their freedom. In the west the police and other local criminals fattened their syndicates as they descended on unsuspecting gays, beat them, looted and collected ransom for keeping their secrets. The fear was unprecedented and the helplines set up by

House Of Rainbow and other national human rights organisations were inundated with calls for help. We received hundreds
of calls, and it was sad that the majority of the callers only
wanted one thing: 'Get me out of this homophobic country
now!' Whilst this was happening an emergency meeting of
human rights defenders was convened at a secret location. The
meeting dispersed in disagreement over details, but held on to
somehow marching forward to save the LGBT community.

With all this as background to my personal story I am struggling to affirm my faith, and also to encourage people, particularly gay people, to believe in our human, religious and
spiritual rights. The religious organisations and leaders in
Nigeria must have been contented, and evidently they were,
because they openly congratulated the Nigeria president for
alienating the poor and already marginalised. This made me
wonder: what sort of people are these religious leaders? The
media in every form went berserk, the most recent attack being
the publishing of what is purported to be the confirmed
membership list of homosexual Christians in a Lagos church
called House Of Rainbow.

Amongst those who praised the president was my father.
Hearing of this, I called him to find out exactly what he had
said, and he confirmed that he believed the law was just, but
that he 'is not convinced that gay people should be sent to jail
but an institution for rehabilitation would be a better alternative.' I was appalled. He further complained that my popularity
in the Nigeria media is damaging his reputation as the first
automobile chartered rotary engineer in the country and a
leading theologian. He lamented that all Nigerians will remember of him is that he had a gay son.

I was angry at this comment. My father has joined the ranks
of inconsiderate homophobes and I do not feel I can trust him.
However, I believe always in reconciliation, no matter how
difficult this may be. I am willing to retreat and try again in the
future.

Yemi and Femi Go Da Chemist

By John R Gordon

Yemi and Femi Go Da Chemist was premiered at London's Bush Theatre on April 28th 2014, as part of Team Angelica's *Boom!* event. It was directed by Rikki Beadle-Blair.

The cast were:

Femi – Nathan Bryon
Yemi – Issac Ssebandeke
Mixtape – Urbain Hayo
Hassan – Jaz Deol
Salim – Valentine Hanson

Characters

YEMI – black (British-born of Nigerian descent) yout, 18, short, rowdy.

FEMI – black (British-born, of Nigerian descent) yout, 18, short, rowdy, Yemi's best mate. The more feminine of the two, wears a little eyeliner and mascara.

Both of them have Ginchy-gonchy'd butts on colourful display above sagged jeans.

MIXTAPE – mixed-race black British yout, 17, fey urban style, hostile expression, volatile, cute, short.

HASSAN – North African, male, 30s, tall, wears white skullcap and kalwar shameez. Has a calm, unrevealing manner and a robust build.

SALIM – handsome, North African, 30s.

Setting

South London all-night chemist's, 5 a.m. Saturday night/ Sunday morning.

Set

A green pharmacy cross is projected on the back wall, along with the time, 5 a.m. A glass door – initially locked – divides the shop (larger area) from the street (smaller area).

Behind the counter a door opens into the shop (off stage). There should be some suggestion of aisles and pharmaceutical products.

Scene 1

In the blackout gay club music plays ear-splittingly loud.

SNAP TO: the lights are on in the chemist's but it's unstaffed. Yemi and Femi are pounding impatiently on the locked door and pressing the buzzer.

FEMI
Open up! Life an' death emergency inna di place! Open up!
(*to Yemi*)
The app did say twenty-four hours, yeah?

YEMI
I think so. But you know my screen's cracked –

FEMI
(*grabbing Yemi's mobile*)
Fuck's sake, Yemi!
(*looks at it*)
Bitch, da fuck is this?

YEMI
The clap app.

FEMI

What?

YEMI

'NHS Direct STD and emergency contraceptive failure app'.
You like download it for free and it says like clinics and all-
night chemists and whatnot.

FEMI

An' dem does deffo supply da whatsit, post-exposure profile
AIDS-cure ting, yeah?

YEMI

Yeah, you just gotta blush past dat you been a slut. Pop da
pill an' bish-bash-bosh, no HIV, no worries.

FEMI

Leave it too long an' it ain't work, though, I heard dat
somewhere.

YEMI

True, dem say sooner is better. Like with abortions.

FEMI

Den why the fuck you make us stop for that kebab, bitch?

Femi starts banging on the door again.

FEMI

I ain't want no fuckin' AIDS!

*They renew banging and buzzing until the sleepy chemist
(Hassan) emerges from within, putting on his skullcap as he
comes.*

FEMI

Fuck, Yemi! A fucking Muslim!

YEMI

So?

63

FEMI
Dem don't love the queers, is it? He probably ain't stock it –
along with the morning-after pill an' rubbers.

YEMI
Dat's Catholics, Femi.

FEMI
What?

YEMI
Rubbers.

Hassan reaches the door. Femi and Yemi force smiles.

YEMI
I beg you open up, boss. We did trek all the way from Vauxhall...

FEMI
...and we got like proper urgent medical needs.

Hassan reluctantly lets them in.

FEMI
Thanks, boss.

*Hassan moves behind the counter. Yemi starts to approach
him, but a suddenly embarrassed Femi is browsing the
shelves.*

YEMI
You want me to speak with him, gyal?

FEMI
(*nodding*)
But tactful, though.

*As Yemi and Femi do their best to swagger to the counter,
Mixtape, a hostile-looking youth also in club clothes, stalks*

past the shop. Noticing them, he stops.

YEMI
(*clearing throat*)
Yeah, um, we, I mean, not 'we', we ain't like dat with each other – my matie here had like a accident –

FEMI
(nodding)
Accident –

YEMI
With the rubbers – which obviously they was using when they did it cos only a eejit ain't use rubbers, right?

FEMI
Right. Obvs. Hashtag prudent.

YEMI
Ting is, he ain't know the status of the random what was banging him out –

FEMI
Jeez, Yemi –

YEMI
In the toilets in the club an' –

FEMI
Fuck's sake! Shut up, Yemi!
(*to Hassan*)
Ting is, boss, mostly I'm a top so this was like a rarity. I mean like –
(*dirty look at Yemi*)
To the extreme. Plus I'm bi, so –

The door buzzer blares as Mixtape bounces in.

FEMI
Oh, shit!

> MIXTAPE
Why you pa'd me out so, bitch?

Mixtape aims a punch at Femi, misses, and they fall in a tussling heap. As Yemi tries to pull them apart:

> YEMI
Come stop dis hetero-level beefing!

> HASSAN
If you don't stop at once I'll have to ask you to leave.

> MIXTAPE
So I'm HIV, so what? It's only like practically half the queers in London. At least I told you!

At that Yemi gets them apart. Mixtape glares at Femi.

> FEMI
> (*off Yemi's look*)
I was hot for the brer, gyal, and den he come out with dat. Hashtag gutted.

> YEMI
Dat's why you pa'd shortie out an' den got bred by some random in the toilets?

> MIXTAPE
Sorry, da fuck?

> FEMI
Yemi! Get a dick in your mouth an' stop blurtin'!

> YEMI
Hashtag inconsistency.

> FEMI
It was cos I was, I dunno, like shook. I mean – AIDS, Yemi!

> MIXTAPE
It ain't AIDS, bitch, it's HIV.

FEMI
Dat was so big I just had to blow off the pressure, so I –

MIXTAPE
Did the most dumbest thing possible –

FEMI
How you get it, den? Being a nun?

MIXTAPE
I got it the way you look like you're gonna get it, and your matie, who knows?

YEMI
Nah, I'm clean though. Probs.

MIXTAPE
(*to Femi*)
Why you treat me like shit, still?

FEMI
Cos what I was feelin' for you, it was – suttin' real. An' den you –

MIXTAPE
What, got too real?

YEMI
And the random?

FEMI
Aw, Yemi, it was dat go-go dancer, all buff an' waxed an' hench in dat thong packaged to go. Like porn but real-life, you know? And none a dem don't play safe in porn, is it? Dem go in raw, get bred, snowball, cream-pie, the whole nine inches. Plus, true-say I was a lickle bit wavy.

MIXTAPE
An' now you come cryin' the chemist? Dem drugs is harsh, man. An' they don't always work. They didn't for me.

HASSAN
You want the post-exposure prophylaxis for HIV?

Femi nods.

HASSAN
I'm sorry, we don't stock it.

Anger at this pulls Yemi, Femi and Mixtape together.

MIXTAPE
What, cos of you're religious?

YEMI
Dis is Britain, man! We got rights! Who I fuck with, dat's between me an' God!

FEMI
You fucking hate there's a cure, I bet.

MIXTAPE
You probably think we deserve it!

HASSAN
You need to go to Accident and Emergency: no chemist stocks it.

FEMI
But the app said –

YEMI
To be fair, F-dot, it was more for the morning-after pill, though.

FEMI
I ain't pregnant, though, am I?

YEMI
I thought it was like the same ting, though, like, spunk equals troubles, right?

68

Femi kisses his teeth, blushing.

HASSAN
A and E will sort you out, inshallah.

FEMI
(*leading Yemi out*)
Come gyal, let's get back on road before you blurt more foolishness an' we get struck by lightning.
(*to Hassan*)
Sorry 'bout alla dat, boss.
(*to Mixtape*)
Come with, yeah? I stand you Nando's, yeah?

Mixtape shrugs acquiescence. As they exit:

YEMI
Nando's?

FEMI
Dey always got a Nando's at hospital. An' KFC...

As Hassan locks the door behind them a male voice calls gently from within:

SALIM
Hassan...

A handsome, sleepy-looking North African man appears in the doorway behind the counter wearing only Calvin's.

SALIM
Come back to bed, habibi.

With a smile, Hassan crosses to him. Taking each others' hands, hand-in-hand they exit.

BLACKOUT.

Three poems by Rhys Wright

'Joe'

There was you,
White, pale, translucent, trans, feminine,
A glorious sight to behold!
Blood, geisha, a boundless wave,
Blond, brunette, green, blue, grey
I love (d) you,
There was me,
An amalgamation of deformities, inequities and infamy,
Lucifer herself embracing Gabriel,
My black skin, edged and scrapped, whipped and denied
Asantehene! A line of great African Queens calls for me,
There was he,
Black, white, Arab,
Graceful, wha gwan, brethren,
Sane, same, equality, perfectly formed,
A wedding ring, silver and gold,
A union for God to behold,
There I was,
Watching, aching, arching, burning,
Chopping, gnawing, biting, crawling,
My heart bled and turned into sand,
Oh, my God what have I done?

'I am not gay'

I am not gay

Proud statue, peacock with embodied jasmine and shimmering light,

The sun god, the prince of peace.

Oh fucking ho'sanna,

Ploughing over the earth, sinking my rays deep into the ocean,

I am not gay,

Every cave, every pipe, every dam, every river bed,

I am day itself, the great omnipresent force,

Worshipped and adored by my fans of Social Media,

I am not gay,

My rays is undiminished, unrepentant and insurmountable,

A litany of euphuisms bow down like autumn leaves,

Turning red, then green, they whisper to me,

But when night falls;

I begin to change,

My rays now is moonlight,

Shimmering against trees in parks,

 Light exposes them,

The dead come to life,

Fathers, brothers, Turks and Nigerians,

Sucking, slurping, pumping, raw, nymph,

They try to run,

My rays move slowly across the ground,

They know.

'Black Disabled and Gay'

Be standing,
For you are Black,
Rich in the colour,
Endowed by the beauty of Africa,
Nkrumah's son,
The Black Star of Zion,
Ethiopian knights pay homage,
Cleopatra's Daughter,
Delicate like the humming bird,
Be Standing,
For you are Gay,
From a line of poets and philosophers,
Rich in colour,
Educated by Lawrence in the matters of love,
Forgotten by history, forgotten by nature,
Claim your inheritance,
The blood, the crucifix, the papacy, the marches,
Gentle like a hare,
Be Standing,
For you are Disabled;
An amazing illustration from Buddha,
Allah designed you,
Jehovah breathed life into you,
You are a beacon of unrivalled power,
You are a beetle,
Lord of their own destinies,
Be Standing,
For you are you,
Formed, human, undeniable

My Own Private Stevenage: Notes of a Native Gay Son

By Giles Terera

I

On the one or two occasions each year when my mother permitted herself to buy a new dress or pair of shoes she would always take me with her. I had three older sisters but she would look at me like a spy and say, 'You know what looks good Giles, come.' She was tall, elegant and really should have remarried, but when my father died she found herself with a choice to make, and like so many of our mothers she decided her children must come first. She prayed deep, went to work up at the hospital every day, and remained a handsome widow in a small town.

Stevenage was a good place to grow up in the eighties. An hour north of London with a population of 60,000 or so, its claim to fame was that it was the first new town built after the war. Everyone's grandparents had been bombed out of the East End and had subsequently made a new home for themselves in Stevenage. It had a lake. Parks. Churches. A theatre. Half a dozen or so black families, zero gays and me.

I was the kind of kid that old ladies would coo over in the street. The kind that made the class laugh. But apart from that I was pretty standard, not particularly camp, not particularly boisterous, but then who knows, if I was presented with the nine-year-old me right now perhaps I'd think... oh, *definitely*. Who knows? At any rate I wasn't picked on or bullied much. Perhaps some kid called me blackie or burnt toast every now and again but not enough to really hurt me. If I thought about them long enough those kind of names always seemed silly to me. We were the only Black children in school, but come Saturday we'd go up to church with all the other Black families and be surrounded with faces the same colour as ours. So Sister

Such-and-Such and Brother So-and-So were as much a part of our family as our many aunties and uncles and cousins down in London.

The church was where I learned to sing. Mother loved to sing. She knew a million songs. If you asked her if she'd ever wanted to be a singer she probably wouldn't have given it a second's thought, she just loved to sing. There wasn't a moment in my childhood that wasn't accompanied by song. As we'd walk back from the park on those late Sunday afternoons she'd sing 'When You Walk With The Lord', or as she'd plait my sisters' hair she'd sing 'What A Friend We Have In Jesus' or 'Blessed Assurance'. As she cooked the stew she might sing 'Softly And Tenderly' and as I helped her in the garden I'd hear here sing 'Redeemed, How I Love To Proclaim It':

> *I think of my blessed Redeemer,*
> *I think of Him all the day long:*
> *I sing, for I cannot be silent;*
> *His love is the theme of my song.*

I didn't understand them all but I loved those songs, boy, and I loved hearing my mother sing them.

Yet as unshakable as her faith was, she never forced her views on others. Her bible never left her bedside but you wouldn't hear her telling anyone, 'You need to come to the Lord.' As far as I can see she went the way Jesus most often went. That is to say, if you want to make a lasting impression on someone example can be more effective than word. She told us that it was wrong to lie, but more importantly we never knew her to lie. She told us to respect our elders but more importantly she respected her elders. Told us to always look presentable, and I must tell you she always looked amazing. To my little brown eyes, anyway. The difference between me and my sisters, though, was that I always told Mother she looked amazing. Which is perhaps how I ended up going with her to get the outfit for whichever wedding or christening was coming up. I didn't want to *wear* the dresses, mind you, in fact I didn't really like being in clothes shops for too long, never have, but I had good taste, apparently, and it made me happy to be there and share in the few fleeting moments of our family life that my mother was able to give over to herself.

This one time the two of us went up to the shops to wait for the bus into town. My mother realized she needed change, so we quickly went into the newsagent's to get some. As soon as we're inside she goes into this deep conversation with the woman who runs the place. I'm probably twelve or thirteen at this point and have endured enough years of the stop-and-chat situation to know that hours could pass this way and meanwhile we'll miss our bus. I'm pacing and looking at chocolate bars, leafing through one of the football magazines, squirming that the bus is going to come and go without us. Meanwhile those two are yak yak yakking about something which both are finding hilarious. Unable to interrupt I huff and puff, rolling my eyes knowing that disaster is literally around the corner. Finally I nudge up to my mother so that she will ask me what's up. 'Gonna miss the bus,' I mutter, but she's not listening, the two of them carry on with the great debate, and sure enough I see the bus come round the corner, pull up at the stop, let some old ladies off and drive away. Finally when we leave the shop my mother smiles at me and says, 'Let me tell you something, son, and I want you to remember this cause it's true: never ever run for a bus or a man, because there'll always be another one right behind.'

I'd like to think the chewing-gum fell out of my mouth, but in reality my eyes just fell to the pavement as I tried to work out if I'd really heard what I'd just heard. Mum chuckled as we crossed the road but I blushed in the morning sun.

II

I eventually found out I was gay by being told by others. I'd left school and gone to college to study performing arts in the next town. I was writing, playing music, acting and had started to stretch my wings in the world.

Up at the college I made friends, but in many ways was a lot shyer than I'd been at school. This is a natural phase, I suppose, but I developed the unfortunate habit of keeping my hand in front of my mouth, even when talking. Which for an aspiring actor ain't so good. I didn't like my lips. They were big and pink and I felt bad about it. To this day I still find myself licking and chewing my lips when I'm self-conscious. Ah, well. At this college there was a student union building. Occasionally my band would play gigs there. Well, every day there was this group of young Black guys who would come and just hang out at the student union. Smoking a little. They'd be there all day, and whenever I went past coming in and leaving the building they'd call out 'Batty boy!' or whatever they could think of that day. I felt bad. Some days if I saw them there I'd wait till they'd gone, some days I'd think fuck it, I'm just gonna walk tall. 'Batty Bwoi.'

This did two things. It forced me to acknowledge what my own feelings were regarding my sexuality. It also made me wonder why it was only the Black guys who had a problem with me. Nobody else seemed particularly bothered by what I was or did. My teachers were trying to make me feel better about myself and these guys were trying to make me feel worse.

There was one guy who if he saw me would nod a kind of half acknowledgement, or at any rate not call me names, but things with the others got worse. One day I walked past – perhaps I was wearing beads; I was into beads at the time – and they called out and called me over. I sure as hell wasn't going over there but this was a definite challenge: I couldn't just ignore it and pretend I hadn't heard them as I'd done every time before. I would have to actively confront them, even if it was in the form of defying them and walking away, which is exactly what I did.

I stopped, looked each of them directly in the eye, stood my ground, left the ball in their court, waited for a response, filling up with half anger and half fear, and finally walked off towards the gate. But not before being struck by a very clear thought. By this point they'd been calling me names as I passed every day for almost a year and a half. I'd gotten used to it, but that day as I looked at them I thought – I'm almost done here at college. I'm about to go and audition for drama school in London. I'm gonna find a way to get myself through the three year course, I'm gonna graduate and start working and somehow I'm gonna be an actor in London and see the world, but something tells me that I could come back here in twenty years' time and still find you standing here, sneaking cigarettes off students and picking on some gay kid who's just trying to find his feet.

I felt freed by this thought but it also made me feel sad. These young men had in that moment become ghosts. Phantoms of the student union. In a purgatory of sorts. The lack of progression, the lack of advancement stung me. I didn't ever want to be stuck anywhere. Their actions made me strong in a way, but I wished there was someone or something that made them strong too. They deserved better. What potentials did they have within them that were sitting there wasting? All I was trying to do was realize my own potential. I couldn't believe that they hadn't been called the same names in the playground as I had, or been forced to fight simply for being Black. So why play that same misery-making role for somebody else? I didn't know, but what was clear was that they saw something in me that they didn't like or accept, that they felt threatened by and, more importantly, it was something they would rather I denied, repressed or ignored. Just so long as I didn't wear it for all to see.

This struck me then as a terrifyingly dangerous idea. That I should somehow pretend that I was something I wasn't for the benefit of someone who didn't even know my name. These were ideas I felt I could neither entertain nor be shackled by.

III

Once I was in London, though, I found that I was able to use the distance as an excuse not to tell my mother I was gay. For three years I was growing as a person and at the same time I was withholding who I was becoming from her. This began to tear at me and finally, after too many years of my heart being bullied by fear and my mind becoming adept at producing a series of excuses to remain essentially closeted, finally my soul took over. There are times when neither the head nor the heart rules, when something deeper steps in, and I found myself knowing I had to tell my mother.

I knew before I came out to her that possibly she'd never be able to fully understand it. Her faith and her Christian upbringing were perhaps just too deep, too solid and too sure.

As a child in Barbados she had grown up inseparable from her grandmother, a legendary old-school Victorian matriarch who you knew better than to mess with. Everyone called her 'Ouise and she and my mother went everywhere together. The Barbados side of my family is a succession of no-nonsense, praying, cooking, smart women. My mother though, being the penultimate of eight, a somewhat frail child, and generally the apple of her father's and grandmother's eye, came up as the delicate flower of a very populated house. Nevertheless, when it came to the Lord you could just as soon move Everest as shift my mother's faith. And we all know what the Bible has to say about homosexuality.

What's more, as well as her own views on the matter, my father being dead, I knew that when I told Mum she'd find herself having to react on his behalf too. We often heard when we were growing up, 'I have to be mother *and* father to you, you know.' My father, brilliant and intellectual and African – well, even my vivid imagination would have to work overtime to dream of a situation in which he would take news of having a homosexual son with a chuckle and a pat on the back. So – like many of us – it was with a deal of trepidation that I went to my mother one Sunday during my first acting job – the National Theatre production of *The Ugly Duckling*. Title role. The journey home that day was a long and uneasy one.

Still, I knew my mother. And I knew her heart. She was the funniest person I ever met but she wasn't someone you'd describe as a gregarious, 'life and soul of the party' type. She was more the kind that, if others at a party saw someone drunk and embarrassing themselves, she might see someone who's going through a tough time in their lives. She'd been through a lot, and if you'd been through some stuff too and you sat down and talked to her about it you'd feel that she understood. She wouldn't judge you. She'd get it. And you might feel better. It struck me then as now that this is the fundamental characteristic of Christianity, I'd suggest the most admirable. It was in this sense that she appeared to me one of the most Christian people I've ever met. So I went to her.

After hearing me out, and for a long while appearing to silently look back through the years, she finally told me that though she found this difficult to understand, she loved me and she'd always love me no matter what.

I anticipated it was something she'd possibly always struggle with, so it was important to me not to be militant with her regarding my sexuality. She deserved more respect than that. I wanted to let her see that I was still the same person. I hadn't grown big pink horns. I was still her son. I knew that for a long time questions would tug at her mind in her waking hours – what if he gets into this or that situation? But I felt that she'd ultimately ask herself the same questions whether I was gay or straight, and she'd likely come to the same conclusion: if she brought me up right then I'd be okay.

As the months and years passed occasionally we'd come back to the subject. She met one of my boyfriends and I observed that her overriding feeling ultimately became – yes, I'd rather he had someone to love him than no-one at all.

Once I came out to her we were able to stitch up the tear that had appeared in our relationship so smoothly that you'd never notice the joins.

She got sick too, and this also shifted her perspective and brought us closer than we'd been before.

The most important things in her life were always her four children, and I was well aware that she would need answers, either from herself, or God, or both, as to whether this was something that she might ultimately be bound to take responsibility for. Was my sexuality a result of our circumstances? No father or father-figure, a house full of females. She loved me, yes, but was this something that could have turned out differently? Her anxieties springing from the fact it's hard enough to be Black in British society, let alone Black and gay. We didn't discuss it a great deal but I knew that I took up a lot of her praying time.

Then one day she was washing the dishes. She wasn't singing this time. Something was on her mind. She told me that she'd received a letter from my aunt in Barbados. My auntie was upset, my mother said, because I had 'been seen holding hands with a man in the street in London.' I was stunned momentarily, and my mother was troubled in a way I wasn't used to seeing. I had no idea who'd seen me or how this information got all the way to Barbados without going via my mother, but at any rate I was fairly certain whoever had seen me probably hadn't in fact seen me. Because though it's possible I might have had a boyfriend at that moment, and didn't feel the need to hide anything from anyone, I can't say that public displays of affection came easily to me then.

But either way the point was that my mother, on reading this letter from Barbados, had found herself in the position of being on the receiving end, by way of association, of a kind of indirect homophobia: she was being accused in some way. Or at least that's how it felt to her, I could tell.

This was something utterly new to her, and how she would respond would probably shape our relationship from then on. It did in fact. She was quiet there in the kitchen. Possibly her initial feeling might have been anger at me that my behaviour could in some way present to her a potentially awful situation she would now have to deal with, but as we stood there something in the tone of her voice told me otherwise; that perhaps this moment was more about her than me. I asked her if she'd responded to the letter and she said not yet. I was looking at my mother who now found herself – not for the first time in our upbringing – in uncharted waters. I observed that peaceful determination that I had seen so many times before shift in her, and I don't think I was wrong in feeling that right there in our kitchen her response to this accusation might now be –

Was Giles holding hands with a man in the street? Well so what if he was? So what?

I received an invaluable lesson from her in that moment. She had really asked herself the question. She hadn't simply reacted out of blind loyalty to her son, nor had she reacted with blind loyalty to what she'd always been conditioned to accept as the natural way of things. No, she had really examined what was in her heart and then been true to what she'd found there. I saw that and I've rarely felt more grateful or loved.

The reason I mention these things is because to me they seem to represent something of the fundamental dilemma of what could cautiously be described as the Black British Gay experience.

The British sensibility is more or less to say that what you do in private is essentially your business. The Black sensibility might generally be described as: What one does impacts on all. The conflict therefore between sexuality and community can be a great one. I have many Black gay friends. Some out and proud. Some out in London but not to their families. Some not out at all. Some, like me, were raised in the church and recognize the residue of an ongoing dialogue with our hearts, which, if we're fortunate, the unfolding drama of life gives us answers to. But the conflict of how to reconcile the truth of one's heart and nature with whatever cultural responsibilities one may find oneself left with is a conflict that can be brutal. At times tragic.

Two events occurred in Britain at that time which affected me profoundly. Landmarks of that dense handful of years between leaving school and leaving college. Both involved the death of a young Black man whose life should have been long and full.

Stephen Lawrence was murdered in 1993, disturbing and shifting our collective cultural understanding of racism, the police, the justice system and the nature of what we call British society as a whole.

Then in 1998 Justin Fashanu died.

Justin Fashanu, one of the finest British football players of his generation. The country's first million pound Black signing. The very first professional player in England to come out as gay. Which his own brother, fellow footballer John Fashanu, described in the press as:

'an affront to the black community... damaging... pathetic... and unforgivable.'

Justin Fashanu, who won awards and scored goals wherever he went despite racial abuse from the terraces, the opposition, his own team and management. And who was found hanged in a deserted lockup in East London after being accused of sexual assault by a sixteen-year-old boy he'd met whilst coaching a U.S. team. The last words of his suicide note reading, 'I hope the Jesus I love welcomes me home.'

He was thirty-seven when he wrote those words, as I am now as I write these, and I wish with all my heart that that young man hadn't felt the searing shame and desperation which left him with what he felt was only one choice. I wish his brother had been strong enough to stand by him rather than abandon him. I wish the football profession wasn't saturated with racism and homophobia – but then I wish our *society* wasn't saturated with racism and homophobia. But it is, for now, and I am grateful beyond words to Justin Fashanu, that in spite of all he faced he attempted to be true to himself. He was no angel I'm sure, as none of us are, but he didn't live hiding. His example as an athlete was stunning, his example as a human being was not to say, hide who you are, reduce who you are and therefore deny who you are, but endeavour to be true to who you are. He tried. He could have, like many others, married a beautiful woman, lived a lie, stayed at the top of his game, had relations with men on the down low and received all the honours other legends enjoy, but what kind of life would that have been? A damned fine one some people might say, but who could think that and truly have Justin Fashanu's own wellbeing and inner peace in their hearts?

No, so long as we force each other to die and hide, and re-press, while we accept to reduce ourselves with denial, while we pretend that AIDS doesn't know our address, while we teach our children that it's better to be unhappy than true, while we open our arms to the idea of preaching love whilst practicing hate so that our brothers and daughters lay butchered in their homes or are forced to flee them, so long as we think that racial bigotry and sexual bigotry come from different places, then we walk a very precarious path and may stand a long time on the threshold of our collective and personal potential.

I have observed at close quarters the damage wrought on individual lives, on good men and women and their families as a result of fear. Therefore the catastrophe wrought upon us so long as our culture remains in the closet is a terrible price to pay for something so beautiful, so simple, so indiscriminate as Love.

Because when we do love and encourage and inspire and show generosity of spirit and respect ourselves enough to teach our young people to act from a place of bravery rather than fear then we not only enrich the lives of those young people but we enrich ourselves and perhaps, most importantly, we enrich our community, our Family. I see it all around me today and I myself have benefited from such a generous worldview. Therefore how could I do anything else but try in my small way to do the same?

IV

I loved going out with my mother, whether to shop or visit a friend. What I felt for her was as sure as anything I have ever felt.

And one day it was my turn to choose something. This time a watch she was getting me for my birthday. There were three I liked. I asked her now –

'So, which one looks best?'

'Well, I like this one, but which one do you feel best wearing?'

'...This one.'

'Well then.'

When the Wrong Wall Hears

By D'relle Wickham (Khan)

Ssshhhh...
Don't tell nobody
Don't tell a soul
Let me speak a soft word
From my lips to your ear
Ssshhhh....
Don't speak too loud
I don't want the walls to hear

Ssshhh...
Have you heard the latest news?
I'm glad I ran into you today
You know that boy, the funny one?
Whose arms look limp when he runs
I heard that he was gay

Ssshhh...
There she is now
Look there's the one
She's the one I was talking about, the one with the queer son
I wonder how she sleeps at night
Or even dares hold her head high
Being gay just isn't right
She should feel so ashamed

Ssshhh...
They say, please calm down
But I can't, not now my secret's out
I made sure I didn't say it loud
I whispered softly, I didn't shout
'Cause I still want to make my family proud

Ssshhh...
There he is
Stay close to him
Don't make a noise
Don't let him see
Get close enough
Then attack! Attack!
We'll make sure that poof
Doesn't come back

Ssshhh...
He lay so peacefully
No more light in his eyes
No more words to speak
They said he'd make a recovery
And yet we buried him
And placed the wreath
The policemen said he had tried to run
That's trivial news when I'm burying my son
He was the light in my life,
But taken away
And all because my son was gay

Dear Father

By 'Danse Macabre'

Dear Father,

I am involved in the most beautiful self-loathing. In gay slang, perhaps more commonplace in the 1970s than now, those of us with my affliction are called *Snow Queens*.

Black men, it seems, still represent a rampant sexual threat: oversexed and after the white males' women. True or not, *my* libidinal interest lies in the white male. But he has no interest in me – his own narcissistic gaze transfixes him. Consider this remark by Damien Hirst in *On the Way to Work*, (Faber 2001, p39):

> ...having a relationship, I always say to myself, 'So what if you fucking walk in and there's three black guys shagging your girlfriend?' I think if I can't come to terms with that, you know, I'm not alive. I have to believe that the kind of bit where she loves me is protected from that, and no matter what kind of *physical atrocities* [my emphasis] you can perform, it doesn't affect the love of someone else for you.

Considering the length of time it has been since I last saw or spoke to you it might appear churlish to pass pleasantries here. However I hope, sincerely, that this letter finds you in good health and that you are living happily and comfortably.

I am certain your first response, after nearly eighteen years, will be to ask why your estranged son, having parted on tumultuous and bitterly acrimonious terms, has decided to write to you.

Be aware that this is an open letter.

These days when I look in the in the mirror, I see more of you than I do myself. My features are betraying me. There was a time when I despised you; wished you dead. In the place of what I saw as a maniacal disciplinarian I would have a lantern-jawed, stubble-faced American cowboy, a Marlboro Man, for a father. I would have an understanding *white* father. Now, a little wiser, I wonder how *you* felt and coped at my age. I guess that is what fathers are for: they have trod this road before – set a precedent. For the white male, as you no doubt already know, and as I will talk about later in this letter, everything hinges on this precedent, *everything* is built upon precedent.

It is likely that you will find some of what is written here and how candidly I write disturbing and even repulsive. This letter is in parts an excoriating self-examination and an account of a kind of psychic collapse initiated by constant cultural alienation. It is also an anxious and perverse attempt at rehabilitation.

Know that this is neither a plaintive cry for help nor a protracted suicide note, and that I offer no apology for the brutality of my honesty or for causing you offence. You are an educated (and now elderly) man and I am sure you can stomach most of what is discussed here. I don't believe I can have this 'conversation' with anyone else. And I wish, however awkward it might be, I could have it with you, in person.

I hope you understand.

The world is in the service of the white male. He has a more authentic existence than any other human.

In Pursuit of the Ideal

Do you remember bursting into my bedroom in the summer holidays when I was fifteen or sixteen? I was lying on my bed bored and innocently reading *Smash Hits* when, still holding the door, half-in, half-out, you leant in and blurted out, 'You're not masturbating are you?' I quickly put down the magazine and replied, a little stupefied, 'What? Of course not!' And you slunk off sheepishly.

We never spoke of that strange and painfully awkward moment. What were you thinking? What a queasy question to ask your son! Even if you were in fear of my mortal soul – you might have knocked!

For all your Catholic guilt (no doubt to do with your own

masturbation) you hadn't noticed the pages from men's fashion magazines that I had Blu-tacked to my bedroom walls. There, image by image on those walls, was my nascent, tumescent (and now lifelong) libidinous desire for the white male.

Those carefully torn out adverts with aquiline-nosed men from *GQ*, *Arena* and *The Face* may have become, in my particular circumstances, a belated Lacanian 'Mirror Stage'. In consuming those images I became psychically fixed on the white male as a physical ideal and, in so doing, constructed an image of my self in which my own physical and intellectual worth is negated.

Soon after you left home, I must have been sixteen or thereabouts, I got a part-time job working at a newsagent. I bought myself a better radio, books, CDs and, of course, more magazines. I also got one of those old-fashioned chest expanders. I was embarrassingly skinny, remember? Well, I damn near wore it out, I didn't know any better. Now I am top-heavy, oddly barrel-chested, with little matchstick legs; puny stubborn calves ending in ankles that are as slight as my girlish wrists. Legs that are out of proportion with the rest of my body, I look very odd indeed. I've noticed a lot of black men have little calf muscles. Not at all like the beautiful white men I lust after; the men with thick, hairy calves who jog round Battersea Park or the men at the gym. I can always find *something* attractive in even the most ordinary of white men but never in myself – or others like me.

I have to admit to not knowing you very much at all – not knowing much *about* you at any rate. From the very little I can recall you were a kind and gentle man, mostly happy and smiling, but prone, now I look back, to seething melancholic moods. You had a very short fuse, were sometimes (as I've just reminded you) a frightening disciplinarian and held (this is my one abiding memory of you) a deep suspicion of, and telling unease around white men. Now I know how cowed you must have been by the towering tyranny that is Western European culture and its indifference to us. I can see now how your feelings of self-loathing would have been manifested in controlling behaviour – you must have felt how I feel, utterly lost in the despair and wretched psychic trauma that is the apparently incidental existence of black men living in the West.

Another vivid memory comes to me as I write. I'm five or six and we are at a beach, somewhere hot. Other people (black people) like us surround us (me, you and mother), we are in a happy mood, completely at ease with ourselves. I see your tall frame set, in relief, against colossal waves crashing against the shore. I am astonished when you dive in and feel very anxious. But you are a nimble swimmer. Never mind that commonly held and fanciful archetype – the black man who cannot swim. You could swim, in heaping seas, as adeptly as a fish. I remember when you were drying yourself how the beads of seawater glistened in your black curly hair. I'm learning to play water polo, a sport played mainly by elite white men, to remember my strong and capable father – to rescue him, in my accursed acculturation, from the ignominy of the archetype.

But I still shave my head every two weeks because I don't like idea of having an Afro. Isn't it odd and tragic that I don't know the measure of black beauty? What does a beautiful black man or woman look like? Think really hard about that question. It's impossible not to reach a conclusion without holding European ideals of beauty in the balance! Which is a tragic summary of our social conditioning.

I suspect more and more that you were doing the best that you could to protect me from the vicissitudes, as you saw them, of living in a 'host' culture. You must have been wary of my unknowing assimilation into a society that was cruel and hostile towards you. It could not have been easy watching a child grow up in a 'Mother' country that would suck your forbearance dry with a ready and generous supply of slights and humiliations. It must have been doubly painful for your son to then reject you. After all, what did you and a shabby immigrant culture have to rival the allure of the grand vista, the titan lives, invention and achievements that are the history of the European? Plaintive ditties – the historical legacy of 'black music' – were not enough, not even close.

So all this, the rootlessness, the very real and pressing anxieties around being black and European, by different degrees, I have inherited from you, added to some physical and intellectual inadequacies along the way.

I live comfortably, protected (for the duration) from the travails of life that many of my white peers and black men my

94

age may have to endure. And so I wonder about the merit of dwelling on my difference, which can seem a trivial, arbitrary, and indulgent thing to discuss. I want, largely, for nothing (except for success in my field – painting), and might easily be characterised as cosseted or, as one unsympathetic tutor let slip in an exasperated moment, 'spoilt'.

There are times when it simply doesn't matter that I am black and male. But these are simply lucky circumstances that do not necessarily prevent my 'blackness' (being the concomitant prejudices, slights, and psychic trauma) from being returned to me with a jolt – in artefacts, hapless comments or the callousness of fear-ridden and insecure people – at any time, without warning. So perhaps this privileged position is the place to best analyse the fault-lines in my psyche.

And after thirty-four years 'out in the field', estranged from you and the rest of my family and with no real contact with other blacks, I, the culturally marooned black gay man, mean to report my observations so far, in the vain hope that you will be comforted that your prescience was warranted and that I finally *do* see our predicament, very clearly indeed.

So You're Black: So What?

I wonder how many black students at art schools in Europe and America make work, however well veiled, that is in some way related to postcolonial identity. A significant number, I would imagine. As there are often so few of us at elite art institutions such as the one I attend, our awareness of our otherness is naturally heightened. Here at the Painting Department it is the likes of Auerbach, Hockney and Kitaj, young white men, some of them my painterly heroes, who are destined to bring 'Apollonian order' to coloured mud. The seemingly inexhaustible supply of blue-gloved black agency cleaners, itinerant agency security guards and canteen staff greatly outnumber any ethnic teaching staff or students and are the black student's only mirror here. So, immediately upon our arrival we are reminded that we are different and, as is the case in wider society, we are in the minority.

I remember being asked a curious question in my interview for a place here. The questioner seemed to imply that overtly militant work, anything that questioned the authority and cultural hegemony of the institution, (essentially the White Male), is seen as outmoded and would not be countenanced. It remained unsaid, but one assumes there are wealthy and powerful sponsors and donors (whose sponsorship I am in grateful receipt of) who must be kept happy. It was an indirect warning not to bite the hand that feeds me. The questioner was, of course, correct in his advice, but bite I must – here in this writing at least.

Regardless of his or her good luck and efforts, should she or he care to forget it, inevitably a stare (a particular kind of incredulous stare) returns a black student's alterity to him/her with a jolt. Westerners, white Europeans, white people always shrug, deny this subtle slight – the look that in an instant betrays and causes a psychic collapse in both the gazer and the recipient of the stare. I contend that in that stare, in the work of a moment, there are these implicit thoughts:

- *YOU* are incongruous presence here – a threat to my carefully constructed notion of this place and of people like you and of your abilities.
- I fit here – *YOU DO NOT* – you undermine my birthright to be here, your presence here devalues its currency.
- *YOU* must be a token, a gesture of political correctness to assuage the 'equality brigade' of lefties with their 'white guilt'.

That incredulous stare is I think allied to what Camille Paglia calls the 'aggressive Western eye' (*Sexual Personae*, New Work: Vintage 1991, p104). It is a corrective gaze designed to discomfit, exclude and violently police and return the student's alterity to him or her by force of will. It is a gaze that means to somehow 'iron out' the being within its reach and bring it into 'Apollonian order'. Except until the European can morph all within his gaze at will, that look of malice will remain only psychically damaging. The student being stared at is reduced to what s/he represents – the archetypes for which one need only look up the word 'black' in the English dictionary. How do I know this? How am I able to construe so much from what might quite innocently be a look of surprise or even welcome? Many bitter years' experience, that's how.

Many years' experience of the incredulity on meeting a white male who discovers I am well-travelled, cultured, have educated and (to some) expensive and exclusive tastes, that I wear discreet, well-made, expensive clothes, that I am well-mannered (sometimes to the point of earnestness – discussed later in this letter), opinionated (but *how* is it I can have an opinion?), that I am (this is always the skewering blow, Father!) 'well spoken'.

This incredulity is more pronounced in, and more flabbergasting to, elite white males, who are, in general, because of the gilded nature of their class, rarely ever (dare I say, never?) in contact with blacks on an equal plane. They act out a performance of fake politeness, a strategy for dealing with 'the black' – always to patronise, belittle and remove themselves as quickly as possible.

The Freudian slips – parapraxes – come when an otherwise innocent comment from a middle-class male – 'that's a nice shirt' – betrays the thought: 'that it is unusual for someone like *YOU* to wear'. Or in the use of street slang – most commonly '*man*' or, worse, as typically used by Antipodeans and white South Africans I have encountered, the cringingly patronising and offensive variation, '*fella*'. Both are presumably used as an awkward feigned gesture of ingratiation, 'meeting us halfway'. But both are ways to mark us, a tacit acknowledgement that we have been identified and an archetype quickly allotted. Embedded deep in his psyche is the black *man* (or *fella*) I should be, returned regardless of how I might act to the contrary. That is how I know about the incredulous, telling, hurtful 'stare'.

Which student's experience would you say then, Father, is untrammelled and more authentic?

For six years my partner and I lived deep in the English countryside about forty miles south of London. All charming, green and very pleasant – apart that is, from the woefully ignorant and staggeringly unsophisticated country folk who, along with their wealthier retired ex-city-dwelling neighbours, all reacted on encountering me as though I were an extraterrestrial. The countryside, Father, despite its outward charms, is the home of perhaps the most deeply-entrenched racism there is in this country. It is, I think, where the English elite and aspirant middle classes escape to indulge in fantasies about what it means to be 'English', where they consolidate their Englishness. Anything (or indeed anyone) that disturbs this fantasy is dealt with with short shrift.

Very soon I realised that, outside of the metropolis, those who are so inclined can vent the full force of their hatred and prejudices with little censure or reproach. The black is an urban creature, you see, and he has no business wandering in the English countryside. And so he or she is fair game for slights and humiliation.

I once walked past an antique shop in Arundel, a small picture-postcard village near where we lived. In the window the owner had placed an oversized golliwog (the black male in toto) prominently in his display. Hundreds (perhaps thousands) of visiting tourists must have seen it. It seemed a defiant show of the most breathtaking callousness; eager to court a response – perhaps of solidarity or approval. The sheer scale of the artefact gave a glimpse of a terrible and inexplicable anger and fear. It was an act of confrontation begging to be censured.

In my first year here at the top postgraduate London art school I am attending, during term-time I had a daily hour and a half commute from West Sussex to London, by train. Very early each morning a sense of dread breached my thoughts as I waited on the platform alongside besuited upper-middle-class white businessmen. There is nothing more terrifying, no more shudder-inducing a sight – or indeed more erotic – than the gainfully-employed besuited white male, tall, handsome and cocksure; and utterly disdainful of me.

That same malicious stare, this time from more experienced eyes:

- *YOU* are an incongruous presence here.
- I work in The City, earn in an afternoon more than you will in a lifetime, and have bought a place, a position in life away from what *YOU* represent; the urban.
- At the very least I have bought a place deep in an ossi-fied Old England that has not been tarnished by 'col-

oured people' (the country dwellers' pet name for
blacks) like *YOU*.
- How could *YOU* possibly afford the ticket? How could
YOU afford to live here?

And in looking there is something else implicit – a kind of
smugness, a gleeful comfort in the white male's existence – the
assured fact he belongs is never in doubt.

So the black student's awareness of our alterity is heightened and fizzing. It is impossible to ignore, it frames us: even
before we are born it frames us in you, our psychically traumatised parents. Our acculturation soon transforms us from
human to black subject and I contend that in many ways we are
blighted, condemned to do what I am doing here – bemoan our
fate in attempts to wrangle a more authentic existence by better
understanding our predicament. Mulling in the corner,
metaphorically, when largely, everyone else is getting on with
the business of enjoying the party. Everyone else is *permitted*
to.

You and I, Father, are not and will never be the definitive.
We are not the aquiline, the blond-haired, the devastatingly
beautiful, articulate and cultured. We are not The Philosopher,
The Poet, The Surfer, The Great Men of History, The Astronaut,
The Quantum Physicist, The Time Lord, The Linguist, The
Artist, The Playwright, The Inventor, The Aristocrat, The Actor,
The Billionaire, The Visionary Director, the madly brilliant and
the brilliantly mad. He has set a precedent that enables him to
travel the world unimpeded in a way that I don't think you and
I can. We are bit part players in his epic drama. Really, when I
think about it, I exist, it seems, only to confirm his existence.

Slights

I am a confident, polite (to the point of earnestness) and affable
person, a little reserved perhaps, but always able to make eye
contact and smile on a first meeting. On almost every occasion
that my partner and I visit a smart restaurant frequented by
elites my very existence seems to be called into doubt. The
general sequence of events that follow happens so routinely I
can predict them each time with remarkable accuracy...

- Arrive at a smart restaurant (in England or in Europe), give name if a table has been booked or ask for a table for two; invariably if I walk into the restaurant first, the member of staff at the door will look OVER my shoulder and smile and confirm with my white male partner.

- The staff member shows us to our table – my partner is always given his menu first and always given the drinks/wine list.

- Wait for the order for water or drinks to be made. Invariably the really infuriating trouble starts here – when he or she arrives, the waiter or waitress will initially only turn to, look at and speak to my partner. My selection is incidental. His paramount.

- Later a further insult – he is always asked, in the non-committal manner that busy restaurant staff seem to have, if 'everything is alright with your food?' My partner's answer is the only one relevant here. The archetype in play here means he is the only one to keep satisfied.

- Bill – paid for by partner, which of course confirms the archetype – low-waged black man, along for the ride and not worthy of attention.

- Bill – paid by me – met with mild bemusement, payment invariably taken in a cursory, impolite way – I am jolly lucky to have eaten at their establishment.

You should note too that whenever I make an effort to interject or disrupt this humiliating series of slights the waiter/waitress/manager will address me as though I were a nuisance, making little or no eye contact. And even then I suspect that I only get a response at all because this member of staff does not wish to appear ungracious towards my, of course superior, white male companion.

It is a beautifully subtle slight akin to a magician's sleight of hand that my partner notes and acknowledges time and again. What can either of us do in our archetypal roles? Wealthy, elite white men *do* frequent smart restaurants more than blacks. I *am* an incongruous presence there. But knowing doesn't stop me feeling lousy and angry. Especially when I consider how other blacks, for instance a group of black friends treating themselves to a fine culinary binge, or a black family, would fare.

I don't mean to suggest that his existence is any more *fulfilled* than mine, but it appears yet again that in doing something as workaday as visiting a restaurant my experience varies dramatically from the white male's. And in my particular circumstances, yet again, it's my partner who gives me credence to be there – he is my licence to good service, my passkey to being treated politely.

Needless to say, I have learnt to be a very good cook.

Oh, what other ignominies have I suffered that you already haven't?

- Change and a receipt placed on the counter rather than in your opened hand (yes that still happens!).
- A person you have addressed talking *over* you and making eye contact solely with your white companion – notably in my experience this includes people who deal mainly with the elite: high-end estate agents, antique dealers, even a private surgeon who operated on me. These are a class of people, largely motivated by money and social status, who regard the black as generally without any meaningful financial clout or intellect and therefore unworthy of their time or consideration. In England these people are vociferous guardians of class, 'gatekeepers' who do not appear to be able to fathom the fact that a black person could ever share the same cultural background as themselves. In his book '*Who Are We – and should it matter in the Twenty-First Century?*' (Viking, 2010), the black journalist Gary Younge defines gatekeepers in this way:

> It is the gatekeeper's task to make sense
> of this chaos; to deny the complexity,

ignore the variety, suppress the unruli-
ness and enforce the archetype – to im-
pose the standard by which all ways of
being may be measured. The fact that
an archetype, by its very nature, exists
only as a composite character in the
imagination of its creator is less important to the gatekeeper than the notion
that it should exist. (p 109-110)

Sadly, nearly sixty years on there are echoes of Fanon
here...

I am not exaggerating: a white man addressing a Negro behaves exactly like a
child and starts smirking, whispering,
patronising, cozening. It is not one
white man I have watched, but hundreds; if I may claim an essentially ob-
jective position, I have made a point of
observing such behaviour in physicians,
policemen, employers. (*Black Skin
White Masks*, London Pluto Press
2008, p19)

- A person you have exchanged friendly emails with and
  spoken to professionally becoming flustered and no-
  ticeably bemused when you meet them in person.

Gary Younge suggests that in these moments of glaring
alterity I am an 'agent of change'. I am the pioneer, actively
changing perceptions. The frontiersman, challenging and
reforming the psychic archetype. Fat use that is though – when
one has to be an 'agent of change' such a dizzying number of
times:

I want to sail a boat – I find I am an agent of change
Visit the theatre – agent of change
Go to the opera – agent of change

Row or scull – agent of change
Visit a remote part of what is apparently *my* country for a
walk – agent of change
I want to learn to play water-polo – agent of change
Wear certain clothes – agent of change

I should cut my ambitions to the cloth that is my skin (if
that doesn't sound too clumsy or gruesome). All this stuff is
very dull and I don't mean to rant. It's just that I don't wish to
be an agent of anything; just me, as I am: I would like my
humanity returned to me.

Two Artists with the same Skin Colour and I...

1) I think Kara Walker may have anger issues

I'm in the college library, researching. I am stuck and searching, desperately, for an artist ally. On a whim, I type a name
into the library search engine. I get this...

```
Dear you hypocritical fucking Twerp,

        I'djust like to thank you for tak-
ing hold of the last four years of my
life and raising my hopes for the future.
I'd like to thank you for giving me
clothes when I needed them and food when
I needed it and for fucking my brains out
when my brains needed fucking. I hope
that the time we spent in the Quarters
with my family sleeping nearby quietly
ignoring what you proceeded to do to me –
what, rather I proceeded to do to you –
ws worthwhile for you, that you got the
stimulation you so needed, Because now
that Im Free of that poison you call
Life, that stringy, sour, white strand
you called sacred and me savior that pe-
culiar institution we engaged in because
there was no other foreseeable alterna-
```

```
tive, I am LOST.
        Before, when there was a before,
an upon a time I was a blank space de-
fined in contrast to your POSITIVE., con-
crete avowal.
        Now, a blank space in the void and
I have to thank you for forgetting to
stick your neck out for me after I crane
my neck so often in your arms.
        Dear you duplicitious idiot worm,
Now that you've forgotten how you like
your coffee and why you raised your pious
fist to the sky, and the reason for your
stunning African Art collection, and the
war we fought together and the promises
you made and the laws we rewrote, I am
left here alone to recreate My WHOLE
HISTORY without benefit of you,
        my complement,
        my enemy,
        my oppressor,
        my
        Love.[sic]
```

This text, embossed on the cover of a monograph on Kara Walker, (*Kara Walker: My Complement, My Enemy, My Oppressor, My Love*. Germany: Hatje Cantz Verla 2007, text taken from *Letter from a Black Girl*, 1998), greets me as I pull the book off the library shelf; its sentiment is raw, direct and enraged, energised in its immediacy by a chthonian anger (defined by Camille Paglia as 'the blind grinding of subterranean force... the dehumanising brutality of biology and geology, the Darwinian waste and bloodshed, the squalor and rot we must block from consciousness to retain our Apollonian integrity as persons' – *Sexual Personae* p5-6) – a chthonian anger, as I say, but one that is somewhat quelled at the end of the piece, like a passing storm. A wry comment perhaps, on the roles that we blacks are expected to inhabit – by 'gatekeepers' in either camp. And it could be argued that I'm filling one role here – that of the bewildered and angry black man.

So, is Kara Walker an ally who I can call upon to explore my opening assertion? Here is a black American woman who is given licence to express her views in artworks by a rich and troubled history: the slavery and emancipation of blacks and latterly the civil rights movement. I too am enraged when I read Fanon and when I consider the humiliations, physical atrocities and psychic abuses that he, you my parents and innumerable blacks have had to endure – worse, that our humanity has been removed from us in perpetuity and in its place our existence is framed by the most insidious, maw-like word in *his* language –

BLACK

But what do Walker and I have in common besides the colour of our skin and our embitterment? I don't believe I can relate to her more direct experience of African American history, the artefacts and imagery of slavery and the civil rights movement. Generations of American blacks that follow, like Walker, can identify with the civil rights struggle. They are gifted (in a rather perverse way) a sense of belonging and cohesion that we blacks here in Britain are not. Any link I make is a tenuous one.

What I share with Walker is empathy for the hundreds of thousands of human beings who have suffered (and still suffer) because of the colour of their skin. But even this referral to 'our' troubled history is another return to the colour of our skin.

2) Delacroix is me!

Ostensibly *Bamboozled* (Spike Lee, 2000) is a film about a television writer's attempt to sabotage his own career. Tired of being expected to write hackneyed roles for black characters, Pierre Delacroix concocts a ruse to infuriate his superiors and guarantee he is fired and a given a fat redundancy cheque.

The film's theme appears to revolve around the thwarted ambitions of black men and the way in which their success, or lack of it, is beholden to white men. In one scene Lee's black male protagonist pitches his breakthrough idea: *MANTAN, The*

New Millennium Minstrel Show. Delacroix imagines that a minstrel show featuring black actors in blackface will enrage viewers. In fact the show becomes a runaway success. Lee (who wrote the film) literally has a character dance, mid-pitch, on TV producer Dewitter's desk, an echo of a blackface artefact (the coon jigger) that is presented later in the film.

Lee's film jars, for all the wrong reasons. From what I can gather his intention is to remind us that a form of blackface intended to curry favour with and entertain whites still exists. However his intentions are too repetitively explicit, too insistent, ill-judged and unsubtle to win the sympathy of any intelligent and sophisticated audience. In fact, one wonders to what extent the film amounts to the ravings of an 'old man' out of sync with a new generation of black person.

Like Walker's artefact the film's importance lies in the way in which it confronts a diabolical period of human history littered with artefacts intended to psychically bolster white superiority while denigrating and dehumanising blacks. But perhaps its howling quality (again not dissimilar to Walker's 'Letter') might be a symptom of Lee's generation's closeness to the artefacts used in the film – coon moneyboxes, mammy figurines and the extensively-researched and reported blackface phenomenon itself.

I wonder if Lee (like any artist) is actually making a film about himself, a black American male, one of the first generation of blacks to benefit from the civil rights movement, embittered, like Kara Walker, by the legacy of his country's recent past.

It is surprising that Lee does not employ a more subtle approach in examining his characters' motivations. For example, in a parody of late twentieth century hip-hop music videos within the film, Lee produces an advert for a (I'm guessing alcoholic) drink called *DA Bomb*. The manufacturers of *DA Bomb* sponsor *MANTAN, the New Millennium Minstrel Show*. The production values and writing, in my opinion, are regrettably bad – altogether the video does not make me recollect the slick sophistication, inventiveness and high production values of ads like the one he is lampooning. Here Lee makes the rather laboured point – *DA Bomb* is an exploitative *soma*. Sadly, he doesn't ask *why* the viewers might need a soma – which, perhaps, would be too close to the bone.

There is a second parody, this time of television adverts for Tommy Hilfiger clothing. Lee cleverly re-names the brand Tommy Hillnigger and we see its designer-in-chief (the only white male in the room) dressed preppily in a green oxford shirt, tee-shirt and khaki trousers in contrast to the urban hooded 'street' black and mixed-race young men and women he is surrounded by. In several scenes Lee's incarnation of Tommy is seen head-bobbing to a bass-heavy hip-hop soundtrack with his 'homies'. But, all this is a pretence, see – Tommy doesn't even wear his own products. He is yet another white male cleverly appropriating 'black culture' to his own monetary ends. This is when Lee's pontificating in *Bamboozled* is at its most nauseating. Why doesn't he ask *how* the white male is able to appropriate black culture in this way? Why do blacks not do the same thing? What are the structures that prevent or impede blacks from exploiting street culture in the same way?

All of which makes *Bamboozled* a depressing film to watch. However its saving grace, and a pretty immense saving grace at that, is the protagonist, Pierre Delacroix. Of all the film's characters Delacroix is the most successfully drawn. I have never seen a character like him in the cinema. He is an honest depiction of the Western black man overwhelmed by a seething self-loathing, whose constant internal howl (as I see it) is, 'Why am I not the ideal?'

We are presented with an outward picture of Delacroix as tall and handsome, articulate and well-educated. But he is Lee's hate figure – an Uncle Tom, an approximate white male – note his name: Delacroix – fanciful, effete, traces, immediate traces of ownership, a slave name. The actor who plays him does so with an effete, high-pitched voice – just shy enough of outrageous camp to be taken seriously. This is a Spike Lee film after all, where masculinity, black masculinity, is always narrowly delineated.

It is apparent from his material trappings (tailored suits, sharp millinery, a stunning, large apartment) that Pierre is very successful in his career. But Lee does not qualify his success by giving the viewer a glimpse of Delacroix's 'star quality'. Pierre's discomfort in his own skin is played out beautifully in his cloyingly earnest and formal speech.

His speech is clipped, formal, tight, knowing, effortful, needy; as keen to impress and as self-conscious as this letter, Father. He, like me (and how many others?), is always alert to the looming stereotype of the inarticulate moron, the idiotic, surly, angry black man. And so he compensates *earnestly* for the archetype; and every fibre of his being is employed in an effort to be *always better than the white male expects him to be,* which is a psychic yoke that renders his existence a cruel, stumbling and tragic performance.

I hate Picasso. I love Picasso. I hate Picasso. I... (repeat ad infinitum)

In the summer of 2010 there was a game-changing exhibition of works from Picasso's Mediterranean period at a commercial gallery, the Gagosian, in London. The curator and presumably gallery-owner presented the work in the idiom of the museum, spotlighting paintings, sculptures and ephemera in vitrines as though they were artefacts from an entire civilisation. All around there is what seems like a phalanx of sharp-suited security guards.

It's a Saturday afternoon and the gallery, usually a temple-like space where I have seen shows of work by artists whose work intrigues me, Cecily Brown, Glenn Brown, Hirst and Bacon, is teeming with mostly middle-aged people. There are cooing beardies poring and slobbering over lascivious drawings of Picassos's current muse or ingénue while their wives fawn in adulation over clumsy-looking pottery that I don't quite see the merits of.

Picasso's work sails, some of it astonishingly playful, utterly effortless; the product of a busy and fecund mind. And I find him, and all of it, the cooing, dribbly, adoring middle-aged, middle-class audience, utterly infuriating. Here is an artist, bearing in mind his most well-known works are not here, whose name alone conjures what it is to be A GREAT ARTIST – what it is to be a Great White Male. Picasso's renown, his ingenuity, innovation, and his surging talent – all those elements are in play without a single received 'great' Picasso being in the gallery.

It seems to me Picasso, certainly at this stage in his career, was feted, indulged, given licence to play, and he soared. And so I detest Picasso because I envy him, I envy him because he could play, comfortable in his own skin and in the ferment of his own culture.

But I revere the work of Francis Bacon – his ability to transpose in paint the howl of nature, its excrescence, fecundity, the beautiful and silent horror of the finiteness of our existence – nature's indomitable process of renewal. And *his* great influence, among many father figures, was Picasso. In a sense Picasso's work is Father to Bacon's and Picasso's influences Father to his own.

I think the notion of the role model – the FATHER – is an extremely powerful one. Returning to what I say about becoming psychically fixated on the white male, I wonder if my reverence of a white male artist like Bacon may also be psychically damaging. Might it compound what I contend is the detrimental effect of social conditioning in the imagery that surrounds us in western culture? Is it too absurd a suggestion? And do I, and others like me, really have any choice, if the role models I would rather have, who may be better for me psychically, simply aren't there?

A new area of study related to identification and the power of images to socially condition us is emerging that may well qualify my Lacanian suspicions.

In 2005 teenager Kiri Davis made a film, *A Girl Like Me*, that discusses her growing awareness of how she, her friends and other teenage black girls are socially conditioned by imagery that surrounds them. Davis took it upon herself to replicate an experiment giving black toddlers a Caucasian doll and a black doll and asked a series of questions: 'Can you show me the doll that you like best or that you like to play with?'; '...can you show me the doll that is the nice doll?' A majority of children associated positive traits with the Caucasian doll. One wonders what intriguing results the same test would yield if it were conducted with white children of the same age and more specifically white male children.

In a 2010 programme broadcast on Radio 4 in *All in the Mind* an experiment of a similar tone was conducted to discover whether students' test scores would be affected by changing the gender of images of scientists in textbooks. The results were surprising – with girls performing significantly better when the images were of female scientists.

Clearly we must be alert to the kind of social conditioning in imagery that surrounds us, and the immeasurable damage that is subtly done to how we see ourselves and how others perceive us.

How I love the Hairy Mesomorph!

Do you know what the slang term for 'a white gay man attracted to black homosexuals' was? *Dinge Queen*!

Now, I can tell what you're thinking – 'serves him right' – because it would be understatement of a staggering order to say you don't approve of my homosexuality. In fact I think it disgusts you. Which is why, as I say, I am a culturally marooned man, estranged from you and the rest of our family.

If I were to invoke Freud in a layman-like and perhaps clichéd way (and I am unsure how prudent it is to mention this) I have always been attracted to men *like* my father, with the small detail already mentioned that my sexual preference is *exclusively* for white men; usually men who are heavily-built, with hirsute, mesomorph body-types.

However, my libidinal desire is tempered by an unsettling psychodrama: in some ways I despise my love-object because he is the ideal, and loathe my own being because that ideal is an unreachable one.

The ghost-ridden character of sex is implicit in Freud's brilliant theory of 'family romance'. We each have an incestuous constellation of sexual personae that we carry from childhood to the grave and that determines whom and how we love or hate. Every encounter with friend or foe, every clash with or submission to authority bears the perverse traces of family romance... We still know next to nothing of the mystery of cathexis, the investment of libido in certain people or things. The element of free will in sex and emotion is slight. As poets know, falling in love is irrational. (Paglia, Camille, *Sexual Personae*, New York: Vintage 1991, p4)

110

An oddity to do with being in an 'inter-racial' relationship is that there are sometimes occasions when a kind of parapraxis occurs; where our acculturation overrides our feelings for each other resulting in a slight. For example, when my partner (in a private moment) teases me whenever a monkey or gorilla appears on television. He says, 'Look, D., it's one of your cousins.' This (in the first instance disturbing) rather anxious private 'joke' bears the all-too-familiar hallmarks of the base humour of a public schoolboy that is peculiarly English. I remind my partner that my hair is tightly coiled, that he is more hirsute and his hair finer and therefore, logically, physically closer in resemblance to the simian than I will ever be – which shuts him up successfully. But I am absurdly anxious of the implication whenever I buy, handle or eat a banana.

It is unusual that my partner is attracted to me at all; by and large (in my experience) white homosexual men are not attracted to black men. Similarly, I find a lot of my straight white male friends aren't attracted to black women either. As a rule black men are a curiosity, known more for their (self-loathing) homophobia and apparently prodigious sex-drive and sex organs than as a physically attractive or valid socio-economic choice as a partner. Now I think about it, as a young man it was always the men furthest from the ideal who were interested in me sexually – older men. I guess the same acculturation at work in me applies to the gay white male too – we are after the same ideal, within the parameters of his culture.

Although having said that, do you know who holds the greatest sway in the hierarchy of gay subculture? The heterosexual white male! It appears that they too seek a psychosexual relationship with their Father! There is a strong impulse (it appears) in some corners of gay culture to conquer and claim that final normative masculinity – to corrupt the heterosexual white male's sexuality.

But the white male homosexual's perfectible muscular body – a machine trained and pummelled to accumulate as many sexual encounters as possible – along with other tropes of the masculine that many homosexual white males adopt, are no match in my view for the aloofness, the lack of self-consciousness, the sense of entitlement, the boorish confidence intellectually and physically that I observe in the ordinary heterosexual white male – he is, on the surface at least, MAN innately at ease in his own skin.

In a further twist, the white heterosexual male can profit by *appearing* to be conquered, apparently cynically yielding his sexuality for immense financial gain in the phenomenon known as gay-for-pay pornography.

I will admit, gay-for-pay pornography is an odd site in which to investigate the authenticity of the white male, but I believe something takes place in the white male's desire for himself that is very interesting. Is it narcissism? Heterosexual couples are not able to compare themselves physically – cannot mirror one another in the same way. So white male homosexuality, for argument's sake, could be seen as the white male narcissistically devouring himself. Is this a (perhaps vengeful) homosexual claiming of the heterosexual's normative sexuality; Paglia's 'chthonian' nature *correcting* the Apollonian ideal? By which I mean, the ideal is such a beautiful totality that it must perversely be despoiled or destroyed. And in that destruction lies a sexual thrill that returns the otherwise maligned white homosexual male's authenticity.

Incidentally, my partner of fourteen years, a cheery man of Scottish and English descent, is very much like you and is one of the elite white males that I spoke about, the ones who gave me the shivers on the station platform. I was until quite recently only interested in men older than me – father figures; he is eleven years older than me. He works in an elite upper-middle-class profession for which he is much admired, and is 'comfortably successful' in the way that privileged and bright people who don't need to try particularly hard tend to be. Although I have worked in the past, he is able to keep us both comfortably and is here bankrolling my (belated) higher education.

So you see, Father, I have a complex relationship with the white male. He is your proxy. I want him physically and need him emotionally *and* I am beholden to him (as Simone de Beauvoir argues in terms of women) in a parasitic way, for his ability to cut, thrust and parry and survive (which he does consummately) within the heterosexual patriarchal/patrilineal structures of his own culture.

112

In *The Second Sex* de Beauvoir acknowledges a still all-too-familiar landscape in the relationship between the white male and everyone else:

> The privileged place held by men in economic life, their social usefulness, the prestige of marriage, the value of masculine backing, all this makes women wish ardently to please men. It follows that woman see herself and makes her choices not in accordance with her true nature in itself, but as man defines her. (*The Second Sex*, London: Vintage, Random House 1953, p169)

One wonders then, where is the better place to survive psychically; which psychic location will enable me (and other Pierre Delacroix) to thrive? Among a 'black culture' that I find alienating and, (it appears to me) deeply averse to self-criticism? A culture that, like you, regards my sexuality as abhorrent. Or within a homosexual culture that is indifferent to me. Or within the fringes of an elite culture where homosexuality is incidental, but where to be black is to fall outside of a rigid social structure and where being associated with the black is to become a social pariah.

In Search of an Ally

Who has been consort? Who has been talked over and ignored? Whose voice, whose influence, whose existence is also apparently incidental, an adjunct? Who, even at the beginning of a new century, can still be unashamedly depicted as servile? Clearly, in many ways, I share my predicament with the lot of (white European) women. And so I try to rouse the feminist in a few female friends. How do they feel about the existence of a continuing hegemony that may or may not operate in our culture? What I discover surprises me.

I am alarmed when they tell me that any discussion today of 'white male hegemony' is folly – a foolish and wasteful enterprise. Women's fight for equality, as they see it, is won. Women, my friends insist, now have real choices and neither need nor want complete parity with men in all fields. In their view it is an unnecessary task, especially if one considers the ground that women have gained in material, marital, voting and employment rights and the position of 'workaholic automatons', as one put it, that men occupy today. If a male hegemony still exists, it is neutered, (not too unlike the presence of a gay black man at a table of white women). Ruth suggests I read Camille Paglia, take a deep breath and get on with the business of living; of course acknowledging the 'so-called' hegemony and dealing with the inevitable consequences of it as they arise. Another, Margaret, asked what more I (and other blacks) could expect when we are living in a society that is predominantly white? I wonder if the slights against women in our culture are now so subtle and so engrained that they can go unacknowledged, even unnoticed by my friends.

However, in spite of the fact that my own notions of gender, sex, femininity are formed by the very acculturation I am attempting to understand here, the trouble is that each of us round the dinner-table is partner to an elite white male. Each of us leads even by western standards a very comfortable, (some would argue lavish), existence; all bankrolled by the efforts of the cutting, thrusting, parrying white male. We are afforded the indulgence of being comfortable bourgeois artists because we are 'kept'. And we are indebted to the white male.

I think that women, particularly women of the class that my friends are, are involved in an unconscious collusion with the white male. They have a vested interest in the hegemony being upheld – the welfare of their sons, brothers, fathers, uncles, grandfathers.

The End of History

I was at first doubtful about objectifying the white male and white female in this letter; it seemed vulgar and distasteful. These are people who are my friends, men I admire, have deep affection for and wish no injury. How would I feel if black men (as could so easily and perhaps more scathingly be done) fell victim to the same scrutiny – the black man treated as though he were a pack animal rather than an autonomous being? The fact is, black men *are* discussed in this homogenous way, only in indirect, veiled and general terms when violence, homophobia and misogyny in hip-hop is discussed, or immigration or knife crime or low academic achievement.

I believe that profound damage is done by the absence of the Father in black men's lives. In the 4000-year-old patrilineal culture of the European we are utterly hamstrung by this loss and our achievements limited by it. In white European familial structures the example, achievements and narrative of The Father and Ancestor are a powerful psychic scaffolding *and* driving force in the white male's sense of himself and his achievement. In the white male's father's absence I believe he has the achievements of his maternal male antecedents to inspire him. Or, failing that, there is the larger, grand picture of white male achievement that will influence him in the same way the images in something as trivial as a textbook can influence female students.

Reflecting on my own experience I am at least grateful that you stuck it out for sixteen years. I always remember that you and mother became doctors at a time when it would have been a near-impossible achievement. Now your achievements guide and temper my own ambitions. And of course I would choose, in a further slight to you, the most ridiculously improbable way of life there may be for a black man in western culture – to be an artist!

I am interested, I think, in an anthropological interrogation of the human experience: in how the minutiae of our lives, those almost unnoticeable interactions, the small threads of common contact form and influence our sense of ourselves. And I have tried to convey here how I meet the world and how it rejects or accepts me in my many identities, as a man, an artist, a son, a black person, a (mercifully brief) country dweller, a homosexual, a student at an elite institution, a human being.

For those of us who are marooned and incapable of reaching the ideal, I think we construct our self-image in some ways by observing other blacks. And so in your absence I look for copies of myself, and whom do I find?

The street hawker
Those minstrels the musicians and singers – the soundtrack to our narrative!

The endlessly imprisoned black man
The drug-dealer
The swaggering black male teenager, to whom education or intellectual improvement is to accede his mind to the white male, and whose default ambition is to succeed as a sports-man or (surprise!) a musician
The legion of blue-gloved agency cleaners
The traffic warden
The bus driver
There, another blue-gloved cleaner at my gym!
The taxi driver
The latest street-talking rapper or hip-hop star
The genocidal murderer
The child soldier
The refugee
The security guard
The African dictator
The wretched, starving, emaciated, dispossessed, homeless AIDS sufferer (African)
History's slave – to Arabs, then to the White male for 800 years
The underachiever
The perpetually un- or ill-educated black man
The endless artefacts that are an attack on my already-tortured psyche.

I will choose to have no history and no psychic identity. I will forget History and settle on no archetype and I must reject – throw off violently – any that are foisted upon me. We humans are in an orgy of feasting on our 'History' – for me History holds nothing more than endless slights and a gnawing and perpetual victimhood. I intend to fashion a new being and a new landscape to inhabit and seas in which to swim.

Your Loving Son,

D.

Stretched and Pushed and a Bit Scared

An interview with Jimmy Akingbola
by Rikki Beadle-Blair

Between 2011 and 2014 Jimmy Akingbola played the character of Antoine Malick, an out black gay man latterly in a relationship with another black gay man, in the long-running BBC hospital drama series *Holby City*. Here he and out black gay film- and theatre-maker Rikki discuss issues of race, sexuality and representation.

Rikki: First, basic questions: how long were you acting before you got the part of Malick in *Holby City*?

Jimmy: I had been acting for I would say ten years. Funnily enough a friend of mine said it takes ten years to build a career, and when I got *Holby* it was probably the biggest job I'd had at that point and I just thought: great timing, all the work that I'd been putting in, now I've finally –

R: – got that job where you're finally 'really' an actor, where when people say, 'What have I seen?' you can finally say something –

J: Yeah, yeah, exactly.

R: – and they'll know what it is.

J: Exactly. I'm doing this play but, 'Have you done *East Enders*?' and it's like oh, guys, guys. But yeah, it had been ten years. I'd been doing five episodes of *Doctors* and I got sent the script and –

R: Did they see you because you were in *Doctors*?

J: No, actually in March I did an episode of *Holby* with Sharon Brewster and I played her husband, a boxer, and I was doing the show, and I shouldn't have had my phone on and the Blackberri went off and vibrated and it's my agent and he emailed me: '*Holby* have just been on the phone, would you be interested in being a regular maybe sometime, audition as a regular? So I was like, okay, yeah, thinking there's no dates, he might not come back, but yeah, I'd be interested. And then put the phone away thinking you never know who's watching.

R: So they brought you back even though you'd just been a guest?

J: Yeah, normally there's a two-year rule so I was quite surprised but –

R: They were loving you –

J: Yeah, I hope they were [*laughs*] – I think they were specifically looking for a black actor, so six months down the line, on *Doctors*, the Friday, I get an email from the agent, the *Holby* audition for a regular is next week, Tuesday or something, character's Malick, he's from the army, he didn't get on with his dad, he's a maverick, he's very stubborn, quick-tempered der-de-der-der, last line at the bottom, 'and he's gay'. I was like oh, okay, cool, d'you know what I mean? Started learning the monologue, written by Justin Young, who's done a lot of theatre and stuff, a great writer, and I was just like, 'This is brilliant.' You know when you learn something and it's just rolling off the tongue – I've got it on my showreel, and it's just a thing like, look, he bursts into the CO's office, he's like, 'Look, don't sack me, I know I just punched my consultant but I'm the best doctor there is, I'm the best there ever will be, no-one's on it like me.'

R: So kind of in that American mould of the maverick doctor –

J: This is it –

R: *House* kind of thing.

J: Yes, yeah, and actually him and Mike Craig, who both left ITV afterwards, when I sat down with them after I got the job, they both talked about American shows – *ER* and *Gray's Anatomy* – and that really excited me because we've got the same palates, and I said I know exactly how I'm going to play this. For me, Rikki, it was about – I was like nicking ingredients of Omar from *the Wire*, Mekhi Pfeiffer from *ER*, they talked about [Peter] Benton [played by Eriq La Salle] – I watched *ER* from the middle to the end, so I missed Benton's stuff at the beginning, you know?

R: Right.

J: So I thought about that, you know, and I was just like okay, you know, what's the woman in – do you ever watch *Gray's Anatomy*? Short black woman...

R: I know who you mean, she's a friend of – she's incredible.

J: She's amazing. And she was always quite militant in the early ones, dictating to the young students, so I just had all these little qualities, and I was like okay, this is what I'm going to bring to Malick, and I remember auditioning and I was down to the final three. I remember before, though, a lot of actors – you know, I don't want to name names but they were all, 'Do you remember going up for that, why the character got to be gay, man, I'm not doing that...' I'm like okay, I am. 'What!? You're gonna go up for it?' 'Yeah.' 'You're crazy. You know what they're gonna do?' I'm like, 'Listen, man, from what I've seen, when I saw the breakdown, the character sounds amazing.' I could see, right, this character's not going to be a little porter, he's like a registrar, says he wants to be a consultant – I already made up my back-story before I auditioned! I could see where this could go, and there was no guarantee, they could have just locked me down, just made him a – I feel like – a stereotypical gay guy, but they weren't going for that, and Rikki, in the rooms I was a bit like, 'He can't be like that.' Because before I started filming I met up with, you know, lots of my friends, I met up with – I can't believe I didn't get to hook up with you but – Topher Campbell, another couple of actors, I can't remember their names, but guys who – 'Guys, this is embarrassing, but I've got a part – how do I 'be gay'?' – how do I ask this question? I was having drinks and coffee with two black guys, a couple of white guys and I was like, 'Look, can you just talk to me. Let's just talk. What about this, what about that: relationships, when did you come out, where do you hang out?' And I got a sense of, quite a few of them were a bit like, I'm tired of seeing the camp thing all the time – it's cool, but we're not all like that, we're not all the same, and it was interesting, it was almost like when you get black actors saying, 'Why've they always got to play street all the time?' and stuff like that. So I really related to that and I was like, okay, in that case, let me go in a bit of a different direction – almost in that alpha male, but still gay –

R: Gay guys are big on that, don't worry –

J: What's the black gay club down in Vauxhall? I've not been there yet – I was gonna try and go but the show came out and I don't know if I can go now – Bootilicious?

R: That's something else.

J: And then my agent – he's gay and him – they're both gay who run the agency – the casting directors love him and a lot of them don't even know Malick's gay and I just like this thing of, what is people's perception of gay? So when I spoke to the other actors I just decided, okay, you know, I didn't want him to be ashamed about it, I just wanted him to be confident and at the same time, like me, don't always chat about his business. Not that he's hiding from you – I don't tell you about my business, you know what I mean, unless you get that close to me. Then you will know. And so for me I just wanted to create a character that was alpha male, gay, focused on his career as his primary thing, and actually had commitment issues because his career was his partner – stuff like that, you know? And that was the basis of Malick for me.

R: So being gay's one of his flavours as opposed to his character.

J: Yeah, yeah – his sexuality and his race didn't completely define him. He was more than that, it wasn't everything. What was great was that every storyline didn't have to be about that, and I think that's what – and it could, but it didn't need to: I felt that would be more of a stereotypical thing, and I feel that – what happened was, some people didn't catch the bits that *were* about his sexuality, so sometimes I'd meet people in the street and they'd be like, 'Yeah, when are you going to get with that nurse, that blonde one, I think she's talking to you...' I'm like, 'You watch the show, yeah?' And this is even *after* the big kiss has happened! And I'm like, you've watched it all? 'Yeah, yeah.' And I never used to say anything, I'm just like, 'You'll have to keep watching.' Now is it like you just happened to miss that episode or –

R: – or are you blanking it out?

J: Rikki, you're on the money. And some people I think they just blank it out. And I remember, I go to a Hackney Empire show, and a couple of people, they go, 'Malick, Malick, can I have a picture?' Then, 'You're not gay in real life, are you?' I'm like, no. 'Okay, let's take a picture!' [*laughs*]

R: That's deep.

J: I'm like, did you *really*...? It's like coming from love, but at the same time: 'You're not? Cool, cool.' I was like, that's really interesting. And then obviously sometimes you get messages on line. There were some really nice ones: 'Love what you're doing. Thank you for what you're doing, thank you for representing this character.' And it's really humbling, but I didn't write it. I'm backing it, I'm all for it, but –

R: Do you get any hate mail?

J: You know what, believe it or not, I didn't. I didn't. Even for the first year and a bit. I stayed in East London – you know, I'm from Plaistow – and you know in East London if people are gonna say something, they'll say it. So I'm walking around on the Barking Road, doing my thing, and I didn't get anything.

Even my Nigerian barber's, you're thinking, are they going to be able to handle it? Nothing. I was quite surprised – I was almost looking for it, but no, they were just, 'He's acting, it's a great character.' What they were focusing on was that you've got a black character that's, you know, up there, and he's the leading role, and he's the boss-man and he's very rude to his bosses, and he tells people – they were like putting that on a pedestal and they were even laughing about him kissing a guy... It didn't get to that place of, 'What are you doing?'

R: There was no negativity on the street? That's amazing!

J: I'm not lying, I'm not lying.

R: That's great, because I think people underestimate people's capacity for – people really support you. You know I did a very out gay role, what was it, twelve years ago [in *Metrosexuality*] – and people still come up to me and say, 'You did that show, I love that show.' I don't think I had any negative response. And my character was very flamboyant.

J: I remember.

R: I mean, you get a negative response in life, but I never felt portraying that character brought bad attention to me.

J: Same here. I had – I went to Barbados in my first year and this big, hench black guy with his white wife was there, and he was chatting: 'You that guy from *Holby*?' 'Yeah.' 'Well done, well done. But enough of that kissing stuff!' [*laughs*] It was really – I felt that – I think a lot of the people that normally maybe would've turned over thought –

R: 'That's a brother so I'm going to see this through.'

J: They really did.

R: So was it the first gay role you'd ever played?

J: Yes, yeah. I'd never done anything in theatre, it was the first.

And you know what, everyone was like did you not go 'aagh!'? But I didn't blink, you know –

R: With the kiss, you mean?

J: To do the role at all. First, the way a lot of people pitched the role: 'wicked, wicked, wicked – and he's gay. Oh, man.' And *The Bill* had done it. Ofo [Uhiara] was in *The Bill* [as PC Lance Powell] – I went up for that part, but he got it. And he didn't have a great time. The writing – and he got a lot of abuse at the gym. Which I think was partly down to, they didn't get the character right, and as an actor you try and do your thing, you know what I mean? And then there's Marcel McCalla who did [campy drama series] *Footballer's Wives* [and whose 'controversial' gay sex-scene from that show was plastered over the front page of *the Sun* newspaper].

R: Did he get a bad response?

J: I think so, yeah. So a lot of people were, 'I don't know if I could go there. Are you sure?' But I didn't blink. And also I did think, 'It is *Holby*,' and even though I didn't used to watch it that much – on and off, when I had friends in it – I was like, it is *Holby*. And I love a challenge. I love to be stretched and pushed and a bit scared. I wasn't scared because I had to 'do gay' but 1) I've got to be convincing as a doctor and 2) one that is gay, do you know what I mean? It was all of it, and so I was like, 'Yeah, let's bring it on.'

R: So how was filming the first kiss?

J: The first kiss? The big one in the locker room... Ah, Rikki, it was bizarre. Me and the guy, Adam Astill, who played Danny, we got on really well, just talking, and we didn't talk about it at all. And we got to the end of the day and realised, 'We're doing this, aren't we?' And he'd done it before, on stage and whatnot, and for me it was only – we worked on the fight before, and so it was the last thing to get to, and I put it to the back of my mind, and it's like, 'the fight, the dialogue...' And then we got to the kiss and it was just like, oh yeah, we've got to do this. And we went for it in the rehearsal and [*laughs*] I did find it tough. Adam was quite – he jumped in and 'let's do this' in the rehearsal and I remember doing it and going, 'Okay, this is bizarre, I've never done this before in my life.' I could feel his beard on my cheek. I'm like, this is so weird, like: this is my work, do you know what I mean? I was having all these thoughts running through my mind, and then thinking, 'That was just the rehearsal!' [*laughs*] And then they did the first few takes, and honestly I was so out of it, thinking, 'Oh man, what am I doing?' I was so Jimmy, so 'this is weird' that I didn't know what to do. And then I thought, 'Jim, stop it: just breathe and get into the character and be Malick. Do as Malick would do.' I know it sounds a simple thing, but it was all so new, it was like there was no rehearsal we'd done before, we hadn't talked about it, we just started kissing. And my brain went [*lightbulb pop*] and I thought, what would I do as Malick? What would you do as Jimmy? If this was a woman, what would you do? And suddenly the next take I was just *there*, do you know what I mean? I was there in a physical way, so it wasn't just 'cut me off from my neck and my head' and just kiss-kiss. It was: how would I hold him? What are the attributes I like in a woman, do you know what I mean? What would I do after as well – and then we did a few takes and then I was in the zone, we could try it different ways –

R: You started to respect and honour the character –

J: Yeah, totally, in terms of things like trying to get his top off and hold his face, and also there was the tension of the fighting, how that engaged with the passion. And also Malick was a confident guy, he's used to this – so there was a shock when the camera pulled away and I'm just against the locker and I'm doing the LL Cool J thing, biting my lip, mm... Cos the whole thing is, they've had an argument: the guy's punched him, and the next minute the guy's kissed him. And no-one really understood that. Everyone's 'Why you kiss him?' There was a fight. The guy hit me. The guy didn't know whether Malick was gay or straight –

R: He just detected what was going on.

J: He kissed me. And I'm like, I'm a dude, if I'm gonna have an argument with a girl and she's quite hot and she kisses me then I'm gonna let her kiss me, I'm gonna get off with her. And it was really good to go: that's Malick, and get a free little thrill. And actually, you know, I've seen those men before, where they don't know, and maybe I can help him find the right path and stuff like that. So it took a while to get that movement. We did more than five, six takes, but there was a point where I was doing like, err, 'face scrunched up' acting, and the director could have had to come and said something to me about it, but luckily I caught myself and thought, 'Come on, man, do this. It's going out to millions.' The whole point for me is to find the truth – and then once I'd made that adjustment it really kicked in and –

R: Really honouring yourself as an actor and just doing the best job –

J: Yeah, yeah, and I was like, 'Do that.' And Adam was completely in it as well and the crew were really great, and we just loved the scene as well. We'd built up to the point where there was that level of tension where they're either going to kill themselves or get off with each other, and it was nice how it came about. And afterwards we just shook hands and said, 'Well done, mate,' and he's going home to his four kids and family, and it was raining and I remember walking from Elstree getting pissed on and thinking, 'That was just surreal,' you know what I mean? And I remember thinking, how do I feel? I don't know... and I was a bit dazed, and I ended up watching *the Actor's Studio*, and it was the Dustin Hoffman one, and he talked about all his films, but obviously he talked about Tootsie, stuff like that. And it was that thing of –

R: Just commit –

J: Okay, yeah, cool, man, this is what we do.

R: What was your family's response when the kiss aired?

J: I did tell them before. Because you know people –

R: Because your family's Nigerian –

J: My family's Nigerian, and also I've got a white foster-family as well. Let me let them be in a position where they know what could be said to them by people who are ignorant. And they were all fine, they were all, 'Cool, man, don't worry about it. Thanks for telling me, but you didn't have to,' d'you know what I mean? But I was like, 'Just in case things come.' Even my older brothers were great. They're not homophobic but I thought they might rib me and that, but they were all, 'Cool, man.' That was great. So once my friends and my family knew, and they were all, 'Cool, cool,' the rest didn't really matter to me. But when it came out – because I didn't say *when* it was happening – I got hundreds of texts saying, 'Lord Jesus, Jimmy, you owe me money! I've just dropped my dinner down my shirt!'

R: [*laughs*]

J: Phone blowing up, people leaving messages saying, 'Aaah!' My sister fell down the stairs and almost broke her neck because her daughter was screaming 'Uncle Jimmy's kissing a man!' [*laughs*] – so she had to have that explained: it's cool, that's the story. So people literally lost their minds.

R: What was the press response?

J: Basically watchers really couldn't handle it. Watchers were like, 'Dear BBC, how dare you put that on and not tell us? That was disgusting.' You can email the BBC complaints office and they got tons, they got tons of complaints. 'It was violent, it was grotesque, you need to warn us.' What do you mean, 'warn us'? We're trying to take you on a journey –

R: It's a drama where people die, have things amputated –

J: Exactly, exactly. It's alright about that stuff, but just because two men jump in and kiss – 'Honestly, I'm not homophobic but I think that's disgusting having men do that stuff...' They got hundreds of complaints. And because a few weeks earlier

EastEnders had done something with Sayeed –

R: 'The whole BBC's going gay'.

J: 'What is going on?' – and I think it was quite edgy for *Holby*, because they have a loyal core of followers and they just couldn't handle it, and it was so out of the blue that some people – even though it was out he was gay – some people just shut it out that he was gay and the violence, at two minutes to nine, it just got them, and I found it quite funny. And I respect the BBC and *Holby*. They said, 'We're trying to do drama. We're trying to tell real-life stories, we're trying to honour that.' And I was like, 'Great.'

R: It's not going out at six o'clock in the evening.

J: Exactly. And it was in some of the papers. But I don't –

R: Were people asking to speak to you, to get quotes about it?

J: No, not really. Just a big picture of us, 'Gay brawl', something like that. But I remember doing a couple of television interviews and they did ask, and I said, 'I stand by it. If it was two straight guys having a fight no-one would have an issue with it.'

R: As a black artist I'm sure you get a lot of invitations to be a competition judge or patron of things – as I do, every day –

J: Come and be a guest speaker, host this, be on a panel, celebrity appearance, stuff like that? I do.

R: Did it shift? Did you get a lot of gay-related things once your character became known as an out gay character?

J: You know what was quite funny, they didn't really connect with me. Cos I even had a friend that was doing a bit of PR (off the record, cos you can't on *Holby*), handling that side of things. What's the gay magazine? *Attitude*. They didn't even come at me. On Twitter everyone's like adding them in. I was quite surprised –

R: So they didn't ask you to – the big thing is they do the naked issue – they didn't ask you to do it?

J: No, no. And the number of times *Holby* got me to get my top off –

R: Because you've got a great body –

J: I couldn't eat burgers for three years and –

R: That's really interesting: it just wasn't on their radar.

J: No. It's so bizarre I was quite surprised by that. Even like going on shows, doing interviews, I didn't really – and at first I was like –

R: Because my first thought asking you to do this interview was, 'He must have done so many of these.'

J: No, seriously.

R: Because I do, but maybe because I'm actually gay and people know, and so I get asked to represent in that way.

J: I think it's something that – *Holby*'s great but it's not got the profile something like *EastEnders* gets, it's different. It's got its core followers, but it's not got that exposure on the scale of *EastEnders*, and sometimes my business head can see them thinking, 'our readers', how many people watch that show, he's not gay anyway, it's not such a big sell.

R: Who do you think is *Holby*'s demographic?

J: A lot of Middle Britain. Mums, dads – a lot of young people as well. Definitely the rate of diversity in the audience grew from having characters like myself come in – people who never used to watch it before, and only did because of Malick and his storylines and stuff like that that you can identify with.

R: That's true: I watched it a lot more often because you were on it.

J: Look at *EastEnders*: someone's got killed recently, you see posters up on the Tube, you see trailers for it. *Holby* don't get that. One, we don't have as much money. We tried to ask for it for my storyline – I'm trying to keep the ego down but man, let's get some momentum here. But there's all this politics about space to be able to do that stuff and it's doing fine as what it is.

R: Would you play a gay character again?

J: I would. I would play a gay character again. I would like to have a bit of air between – I feel like Malick's still in people's minds – which is beautiful: people stop me in the street and say, 'Why did you leave? It's not the same. I loved him.' But I like to do different characters all the time. Of course different characters doesn't mean it's the same thing [if they're also gay]. But I'd like to have a gap. It's like Lennie James is doing another doctor series on Sky, and I'm like, that's great, but I'd like to have some air between me and that like I would with a gay character. But I would. Totally, totally. It's all about the character. If the character's great then I'm yeah, I'm all over it.

R: What did you learn from playing a gay character, if anything?

J: I learned about how strong and brave you do have to be to come out to family and to be publicly out, and what that requires in terms of the family dynamics. Going through the character and speaking to people, you know, they told me the responses from their parents, and you know, some were okay, some weren't, but just that uncertainty. The change. And some that knew what that response would be, so they decided not to, so they're still going home and everybody knows but it's unsaid. You're choosing to suffocate yourself. You're choosing to nullify yourself and be a certain way because you don't want to rock the boat for the family. I was just like, 'Wow, that's tough.' Not to say that person's weak, but those who say, 'You've got to love

129

me for who I am, if not then that's your loss.' That strength, you know? That taught me a lot in terms of what you have to go through – the laws that are being done, there are so many hurdles –

R: Because you came up in a foster-family –

J: Yeah.

R: And you never had to tell them you were black. But imagine if you had to, thinking they might throw you out. If they were blind and you saw them ticking the BNP box –

J: [*laughs*]

R: Do you think they should have had a gay actor play it?

J: [*laughs*] That means I wouldn't have got to play it!

R: Obviously I think you should have played this part, but – do you think you were essentially 'blacking up'?

J: Wow, that's a good question. I don't know how many – there are some actors I know they should've seen that are gay that, they would do Malick so well. Completely different, but – I don't think... Part of me goes, you shouldn't *have* to give it to an actor who's gay, but then part of me thinks they should definitely – I don't know how they would do it – see –

R: Out gay actors?

J: Yeah.

R: Do you think there are gay actors who wouldn't have done it because they were gay and didn't want to –

J: I definitely think there are some who aren't out and they wouldn't want to have done it because that would put too much focus on them. But I do think there are those that are out that didn't get seen and they would love to have done that, and

130

some of them that I spoke to, because they've already 'got it', it would have added a whole different layer to Malick, and actually they did get a gay guy – a white guy called David Ames – when Malick had a storyline where he went to court and they kissed – he's gay, he's out gay. There's a few producers at the Beeb who are. When I came in it was different, but now there's a few producers at the top who are gay and a bit more on it.

R: Representing a bit more.

J: Yeah, yeah.

R: I think that playing a gay character, whether you're gay or not, but particularly if you're a straight actor – has really been a big help in people's careers, because so much of the industry is gay – like about 80% of agents – managers, agents, casting directors, there's a very high percentage of gay people in those jobs. And playing a gay character can be helpful because they'll come and see that show or tune into that programme because they have that personal interest. Do you feel it helped you in the way it helped, say, Jude Law playing a gay character – or Andrew [*Spiderman*] Garfield?

J: I think it did help me. It's the double thing, isn't it? Gay black doctor on prime-time TV, it stood out completely. It was almost like a topical discussion: like, *really*? So I think it put me on the radar of a lot of people. And I think some people didn't see that in me and were surprised: they didn't think I could or would do it.

R: Do you think it harmed your career in any way?

J: No, no way. It totally helped.

R: The big fear that it'll harm you – that's gone, I think.

J: Yeah, it totally helped me. And I don't know whether I was naïve, but I didn't think about it harming me. I felt there's a possibility that if the writing's not on point it could harm me, but –

R: My brother [Gary Beadle, who played Paul Trueman] felt that way about *EastEnders*: that if the writing's not going to be on point, the black representation that he was bringing could all go wrong.

J: Yeah, yeah.

R: He liked that his character had edge and was interesting and not the bland 'forgive me for being black so I'm not going to be interesting' kind of character.

J: They were quite good with me, because the way I work – I'm not an actor who just does my job. I think about things, I've got ideas. I was very vocal about – we need to get this right. I mean, thank you for the job, but I did make it clear: we don't get this right, you'll be putting me in a really dangerous position. Seriously. I mean on a level in the black community, the gay community, there's a lot of pressure on getting this right and so – I could tell they're not getting it. I mean, this is a big thing. I've not seen a character like Malick ever on TV, and you're putting it up there, a leading character, which is fantastic, but even more so you've got to get this right, and I think they kept looking at me and going, 'Okay, okay,' and the majority of writing was on point, and I'm, 'This is brilliant, brilliant.'

R: So they did get it right.

J: They did get it right. And there was a point early on when people were like, 'Ah, they're just avoiding the issue' and it wasn't. I was like, 'Let's just slow-drip it.' There were little one-liners like, 'Is he gay?' or – you know what I mean? And I liked that it took four or five months to build up to the big kiss, you know? And I wanted it to go even longer. And it wasn't to hold back from it. I just love how the Americans do that: stretch something out. But when it came to the relationship I was like cool, kiss, but after the kiss the next guy he kisses or gets with – cos the Danny thing was just a fling thing, he wasn't really interested in him, just he's coming to him, he's gonna take his things, right? But the next – the relationship, he has to be a black guy.

R: Why did you say that?

J: I said that because I didn't want – we've already shown he'll do things with a white guy. If you came again with another white guy it has that edge of, 'He only does things with white gay guys.' And Malick's not that: he's open. It's like I'm like that with my women. I'm not one of them who's like, 'I don't do white women,' I like you, I like you. [*laughs*] And so they're the bits I'm trying to put in myself, I want him to be universal: a fine man is a fine man. I mean, he could be white, black, Asian, Brazilian, he's like, he's gonna go there. And I said –

R: So that race is not an issue for Malick?

J: Yeah. And I think that came out – I don't know what your thoughts are: some people I spoke to were like, well, yeah, but some gays – there can be more of that white club scene and then the black scene, and some do cross over but some of them don't, do you know what I mean?

R: But he's a maverick, so he's not falling into any of the –

J: There you go.

R: He's not in any clubs, he's in his own club.

J: He's a Lone Ranger. But I was also conscious of – for me it's a bit to do with imagery. Sometimes I get it when black actors and their partners – it's not that you *can't* have a white wife and mixed-race family, but I'm just surprised by the lack of just normal black families, do you know what I mean? Why is that not there? And so I really did want – cos I felt it would come across like that – I wanted it to be clear that –

R: That that's a reality, that two black men can be together.

J: Yeah. And I thought that's a positive message as well, and I felt –

R: There's a big thing online right now about where are the high-profile black gay couples. In real life there's been the big controversy about Michael Sam, the NFL player who just got picked – he came out first – everyone comes out when they're leaving, but he came out before and while he was in college – and he got chosen and it was all on CNN, the cameras were there, and he kissed his boyfriend, who was white. And people were asking, 'Why are there no high-profile black gay celebrity couples?' There was a whole thing about that there are some, but not enough: people are hungry to see two same-sex, same-race people together, and that led to some people saying, why are there no black-on-black gay characters, and I had to point out, well, I actually did that myself, in a TV show on Channel 4 [*Metrosexuality*], which is mainstream, twelve years ago. And we also mentioned, 'Jimmy's just done it in *Holby*,' and there are all these different characters. Because people are always looking to be wounded instead of celebrating what we've got.

J: And I loved it. And what I liked about it is it's about true love as well: this whole thing about Malick being able to let go and open his heart, and I felt it's like –

R: And now he's in a complex relationship where he's not sure whether he can be that vulnerable.

J: Totally, totally. And I really felt they got that right. The other guy, Paul, [Kobna Holdbrook-Smith] was a lawyer, but you could see where Malick was just like – Paul said he loved him, Malick just got up and left and you go, 'I sort of understand that' – Malick can't handle that; he needs to work on that side of things. So I was really glad they listened to me on that.

R: It was really nice, because when he crushes his hand doesn't the boyfriend appear and –

J: - try and support him and stuff like that –

R: And so we see it's the real thing.

J: Yeah, yeah. I was really glad. And then when he had another fling, cheated on him, it was with another white guy, so he was just – complicated. But there's no limitations to it: I like that. He's just a human being. He's got flaws, he makes mistakes. But I was glad they listened. Also I put in the thing about the son, because I –

R: Was that your idea?

J: Yeah, yeah, cos I've met –

R: The issue of gay fathers and sons is very interesting.

J: Yeah, and it's around me – some people in the industry, they've got the family and they've got the other life, and it's like, okay, you've got sons, kids... I'm not judging, it's like that can happen. But people were like, 'How can he have a son?' and I'm like, 'Come on, why not?' Why not. And I think it helped Malick grow a bit and you get into father-son territory.

R: And also it makes you see he has grown, because you see he had this other life before and he's been on this journey and now he's having to put the pieces together and face up to his choices.

J: Yeah, yeah, yeah.

R: So that all came from you? That's amazing. Well, I want to thank you for a fantastic performance, and also – I hope you realise, but you probably don't realise how big that is, and how over the next – this is happening to me – over the next ten years, over the rest of your life really, you're going to have people coming up to you when you least expect it – you're going to be auditioning for people who'll say to you, 'I was in school, I was in college, now I'm running – now I'm the casting director at – '

J: Seen, seen.

R: 'I'm a producer at the BBC. But at a crucial point in my life I saw you play that character and it changed the way I thought,' or it helped me get through something or understand something. Or helped me connect with somebody. You're gonna see that as a black artist, and you're going to see that as somebody who's represented diversity, and as a talented one, because that's the other thing: we need good people to represent us as well as willing ones.

J: [*laughs*] Thank you.

R: So it's huge, and I thank you.

J: I'm really proud of him. When people say, 'What's your favourite role?' I always say Malick. I do, I just –

R: Well, I hope one of your favourite roles will be one I write for you.

J: Yes, man! We're still working on that.

R: I'm on it, I'm on it.

Being Served

By 'Merlin'

I was invited to a friend's home for supper recently. On the face of it, nothing that remarkable: I was going to share a meal and a relaxed evening's conversation with a close friend. However...

Normally if my friend QV invites me round for supper I just let myself in, but this time he was very particular about me ringing the doorbell and waiting to be admitted. The door was opened by a bulky, quietly-spoken man, probably in his late forties, who welcomed me into the hallway in the manner of a butler at a grand house. I say 'butler', but the heavily-studded leather dog-collar he wore around his neck atop otherwise fairly conventional corduroy trousers and an M&S-style jumper had me wondering just what exactly he'd be contributing to the evening beyond this rather quaint personal service.

I was quickly reassured. Over the next few minutes he made me feel – in a very gentle, unimposing way – that his mission was to meet any domestic need I might express. I settled for a glass of red wine, and tried not to be too distracted by his studded dog-collar and its possible implications. As I sat down on the sofa in the main room, the first unusual thing I noticed was the state of the dining-table. It's normally littered with paperwork and assorted domestic items. The spectacle of it all beautifully laid out for a four-course meal for two suggested that my host was taking this evening's proceedings very seriously indeed. The heavenly smells wafting over from the kitchen heightened the sense of anticipation. He's provided lots of hearty and very enjoyable meals for me there over the years, but this was the smell of real grown-up sophisticated cooking of a kind I'd never expected from his kitchen. I fought the urge to giggle. What might the butler think?

QV eventually appeared, dressed as if ready to go out some-where fancy. I was relieved that I'd taken the precaution of making a bit of an effort too. We hugged in greeting. I just couldn't stop grinning.

At first I wasn't sure what to make of the way QV and the butler communicated with each other. Even though QV wasn't being remotely haughty, aggressive or rude – quite the contrary in fact – I got the impression from the way the butler responded that there'd be hell to pay if anything he did or said was less than absolutely perfect. Every time I thought I was really getting used to it all, the sight of the dog collar or some other manifestation of the butler's subservience reminded me what a bizarre situation we were in. It was just the same if I risked asking the butler for anything directly.

QV excused himself to make a couple of phone calls. I settled back on the sofa, happy to pass the time nibbling at the delicious fishy canapés the butler offered and anticipating the treats to come.

Phone calls completed, my host and I chatted a little more. After a set of subtle nods and gestures between QV and the butler we took our places at the table and the butler served the first course. He had a very assured and correct way of doing things. I was struck by the silent crispness of his responses to the merest gesture from QV. The atmosphere could almost have been intimidating but for my QV's totally relaxed demeanour in his role as master.

We were in an ordinary domestic environment – albeit being served by an exquisitely well-mannered domestic slave – but the experience rather reminded me of dining at a very exclusive restaurant. In some ways it was even nicer. No matter how well-trained the waiters are at posh restaurants they could not have begun to offer the kind of devoted attention that we were receiving. All this and no horrendous bill at the end!

As we ate and drank I found it an effort trying to talk to my friend about the kind of things that we normally enjoy exploring in conversation. As soon as the butler was out of the room I'd drag the conversation back to a whispered commentary on the evening itself and questions about what was going to happen next. QV was obviously enjoying watching my reactions to the goings-on. He seemed especially amused at toying with me, hinting at what was to come next but refusing to go into any detail. All he would concede was that there was going to be 'someone else' coming at a particular time later on; that it was 'all organised', and that I should just wait and see. We'd had several conversations over several weeks about the possible content of a 'special evening', but the not knowing in any detail about how *this* one might go, combined with the by-now utterly wicked grin fixed on my friend's face, was getting me more and more curious.

Just as we were completing the third course the doorbell rang. Making it pretty obvious that we had to move swiftly, QV asked me to leave the table and make my way down the hall to another room. The room was all but empty of furniture, apart from a chair I was told to sit on, and a large shallow mattress on the floor covered with an Indian-looking cloth. QV put on a CD and left me sitting alone in the room with strict instructions not to make a sound. Over the sound of the music I could just about hear shuffling and doors opening and closing. Then suddenly lots of metal clunking sounds followed by the swishing of what sounded like very heavy fabric. Just as suddenly all was quiet again, apart from the odd bit of unspecified shuffling. I was sure the door would swing open at any moment revealing... who knew what?

I don't know how long I sat there waiting: it seemed an age. After all that had been said and hinted at over the preceding weeks – and knowing QV – it was pretty likely that the encounter with the stranger was going to be at least vaguely sexual. So far so fabulous. But an encounter with a complete stranger chosen by a friend who enjoys occasionally 'broadening my horizons' was suddenly more threatening than exciting.

Suppose it was the sort of man he thought I *ought* to like, or that I'd normally have prejudices about? Suppose we just didn't click? What if he'd set up some very specific activity that was a complete turn-off? What if it was a great anticlimax? What if I knew the person/persons? My friend had obviously gone to so much trouble. How would I decline and not spoil the fun and flow of what had been such a great evening so far?

The door swung open and there stood QV, clasping the forearm of a rather pleasingly-proportioned young man who was so heavily blindfolded that I couldn't make out much of his face. Whilst QV was still dressed normally, his companion was making much more of a statement: leather chaps, a black

139

jockstrap and a leather body harness. Although I wasn't into the 'scene' that this rather clichéd get-up represented, this dramatic arrival was still a very sexual moment. QV gently led the man into the centre of the room. He shot me a quick look and put his index finger up to his lips as a reminder to remain still and silent.

QV told the young man to perform a reconstruction of his most recent sexual adventure in the service of another sexual master. He answered swiftly, 'Yes master,' in a gentle tone, as if obeying a loved but slightly feared father. The performance was fascinating, entertaining and surprisingly erotic. A strangely modest but nonetheless accomplished evocation of an intense encounter. He offered just enough spoken detail to reveal that he liked being dominated sexually, and that he was very focussed and serious about it all. He seemed to be getting quite aroused too. Just as he was getting to the next level of arousal QV stopped him and got him to kneel. QV then got him to confirm that he'd do whatever he was told to whilst in that room. The young man agreed. QV turned and left the room, shooting me an odd little smile as he closed the door.

Suddenly I was alone with the young man. As I got up and moved towards him he flinched slightly in my direction, confirming that up until then he had not been aware of my presence. I said hello, trying to put as much reassurance and sensuality into that single word of greeting as I could. I don't know how it landed with him, but I was starting to feel a little ridiculous and somewhat out of my depth.

This scene should have been a definition of gay heaven, but for a second or two I wondered what on earth I was supposed to do next. It dawned on me that there was no 'supposed'. I could make it all up as I went along, and concentrate on pleasing and amusing myself. The young man was there to do whatever I told him to. His needs – other than getting the chance to be a good slave – were not the issue here.

This was a rather different scenario to most of my recreational sexual encounters; I usually find myself striving – with varying degrees of sincerity – to identify and satisfy my sexual partner's needs, whilst hoping to get my personal needs satisfied along the way. Added to this was the unusual – for me – experience of having a sexual 'partner' who could not see me.

I was suddenly very conscious of what a huge part vanity, visual attraction, selection and performance normally play in my sexual encounters. In the absence of the usual buzz of being chosen, watched, visually appraised, I generated the next best thing by instructing the young man to undress me and explore me – gently –with his hands and mouth. He was very sensitive and thorough. By the time he had got down to my boxer shorts and their contents I was fully aroused. He seemed very pleased to find that I was responding and took the welcome liberty of breaking his silence to tell me he appreciated what he was encountering. The feeling was mutual I can tell you!

I liked the way he expressed himself. The fact that he was obviously intelligent and sensitive heightened the pleasure. Initially he did most of the work, following my instructions with spine-tingling panache. However, old habits die hard, and I couldn't resist leaving my 'pedestal' every now and again to explore and pleasure him before reverting to master mode.

My pleasure was even more heightened by the realisation that he looked and sounded very much like a very beautiful man I had always lusted after from afar in the 1990s. Here I was with a gorgeous 21st-century version of him at my sexual beck and call. A fantasy exceeded!

Although this gorgeous creature was supposed to be there to do most of the 'work', the more we reciprocated the better it seemed to get. I found a quite different level of arousal and satisfaction once I'd relaxed into the role of sexual slave-master a bit. It was fun finding out what turned him on, and very satisfying getting such lively responses from him. When I needed a rest I just reverted to making requests. He seemed happy however we played it.

There was a funny little episode when he slipped out of slave mode very briefly to ask if I knew much about how the evening had been set up. I sidestepped the question by calmly asserting that I trusted QV completely, and had been happy to go along with things without any clear idea of exactly what was going to happen. I'm not sure he was satisfied, but he quickly remembered himself and slipped back into his role. He just seemed to get better and better at exploring and meeting my needs.

I could happily have carried on for hours, but it suddenly occurred to me that there had been no discussion with QV about how long this 'feast' was meant to go on. I confided my concerns to the young man and we proceeded on what was understood to be the last phase of our rather delicious encounter. We then paid each other lavish compliments, I dressed, and went off to find QV, leaving the young man in the room.

On my return to QV I realised that I had a particularly silly grin on my face that I just couldn't shift. I had so enjoyed myself and couldn't hide it. QV grinned back at me. He was plainly delighted that the experiment seemed to have worked. He asked me if I was ready for dessert. I think at this point I may have burst out laughing – it seemed as if we were slipping into a very bad pink update of a *Carry On* film.

QV left the room for a short while, I presume to check on the state of repair of the young man after his extended lease labouring in the service of my needs. QV returned looking pleased with himself and asked me if I'd enjoy having the young man come through to serve us dessert. I had somehow not expected to encounter him again that evening but found myself pleased at the prospect – I was assuming he'd have to remove the blindfold. Which was good in that I'd get to see his face properly. Not so good in that he'd get to see (and judge!) me. The seven-year-old narcissist in me wanted to say, 'So, was this what you were expecting to see?' but I restrained myself. In the event my anxiety was eased by QV's warning that the young man would not be allowed to make eye-contact with either of us.

There was a quaint little scene when the butler gave the young man instructions on serving dessert. Odd seeing him being even a little bit authoritative after all the subservience. I enjoyed getting a proper look at the young man as he fussed over the arrangements. He was handsome in a boyish kind of way, with very thick dark hair in a style that made me think of a Seventies porn-star. It felt strange being with him in shared company.

Once the dessert – a lovely melt-in-the-mouth sort of cake creation with lots of cream and pungent fruit sauce – was on the table the young man went and sat on the floor at my friend's feet, almost like an obedient puppy, which in a way was exactly what he was. I just kept grinning at my friend. I was aching to talk to him about my impressions of the evening, and

142

ask him lots of questions, but this was not the time.

I'd just about calmed down enough to concentrate on eating dessert when QV asked me if I'd like my feet massaged. My eyes bulged out of my face in pleased surprise as I heard myself saying 'Yes' as if it were the most normal enquiry from one's dinner-host. The young man slid under the table and set straight to work with as much skill and tenderness as he'd displayed when we were alone. If there is such a thing as joyful sensory overload this was pretty close: my feet being expertly massaged under the table, the still lingering glow in my loins of a wonderful sexual climax only minutes before, a mouthful of the most gorgeous dessert melting on my tongue, and my friend's pleasure at having caused it all, written large across his beaming face. Heaven!

It was soon time for the butler to leave. He came and knelt at my friend's side. Only when QV was ready did he break off from our conversation to perform a little ritual of acknowledgement with the butler. He then removed the butler's collar. The butler got to his feet and floated away silently. Not long afterwards there was a similar though more sensual ritual with the young man.

At last I was alone with QV. I'd expected to have lots to say, but in fact there was very little else that needed to be said other than to thank him.

I realised that I did not know him quite as well as I thought I had, and was quite pleased with the knowledge I'd gained of these fascinating additional facets to his character. He seemed very at ease being in complete control of someone else, and had an endearingly gentle and paternal way of getting what he wanted from his slaves. I was also settling to the idea that I had rather a taste for this kind of thing myself.

The other notable thing about the evening was just how quickly time had passed by. I knew that I'd have to write about the experience to extend and savour the pleasure it had given me.

As my friend was showing me out I noticed two leather collars hanging in the hallway. He explained that if his slaves left their collars there as they departed, it was a clear signal they wanted to return for more.

I wondered what I should leave on the bench to ensure a

repeat performance...

Are You Friends With Peter Tatchell?
– a coming out tale –

By Geoffrey Williams

'So are you friends with Peter Tatchell?'
I wasn't sure who they were talking about. I had been putting this day off for the last ten or maybe eighteen years depending on how you looked at the situation; as I knew I was gay from when I was seven years old.

I remember already at that age pondering when I grew up which one of the girls in my class I would marry. My uncle Stephen would ask me which of the many girls I hung out with was my girlfriend. He always seemed so proud that I had a female cast of many in my life. As a British-born black man of Caribbean descent I needed to make sure I enjoyed my freedom before I settled with a girl. I was seven, what did I know about boys and girls and settling down? Moreover the thought of myself with a girl just never sat right in my mind. I remember having a huge crush on John Barnes, the footballer. Every time he came on the television in his red Liverpool outfit with the white shorts that just clung to his stocky footballer's thighs it was like magic. I didn't know why I was so interested in his shorts and what happened within, but I was definitely a fan and even knew all the words of his rap in the World Cup anthem of 1990, 'World in Motion'.

I had just come out to my parents as a gay man. After twenty-five years of never really having a real girlfriend I thought they knew already. Alas it would seem not, since they seemed to be struggling to get their heads around the news.

My mother reiterated the question with an icy tone that made her delicate facial features harden and her hazel eyes narrow into slits. 'So are you?'

I had no choice but to ask her in return, 'Who is he Mummy?'

My mother looked at me with disdain and hissed, 'He is the man that got slapped by Robert Mugabe for trying to make a

145

citizen's arrest on him.'

I had heard about that, I chuckled. I finally remembered who he was as well as the bitch-slap Mugabe gave to him. But no, he wasn't a friend of mine. I think I had seen him once in Bump, the Sunday night club in Leicester Square where I would go to with my friends to dance away our worries.

'No, mummy, I'm not friends with Peter Tatchell! As a matter of fact I'm not sure I really know what he does. I really can't understand what this man has to do with our discussion. We were talking about me and who I am, and really and truly who I may or may not know is not relevant. So yes, I am gay, and honestly I'm surprised that you're so shocked. I haven't ever introduced you to any girl as my girlfriend. Even you, when Tafrai and I were arguing, made reference to our relationship being one like lovers. I took that to mean you knew.'

I met Tafrai one cold and wintery night. I had gone out with my friends to Heaven, a gay club near Charing Cross station. I had gone out not looking for anyone or anything, just wanting to hear the R 'n' B and Bashment music that they played on this Wednesday night, when young black gay London would make its way into town for the midweek rave, and boogie the night away. I'm not sure who saw who first, but Tafrai came up to me looking like milk chocolate in human form. Every visible inch of his six-foot-two-inch frame was smooth and shining with a cocoa-buttered sheen that needed to be licked. He leaned in and said, 'Your smile has brighten this club.' I laughed as I thought this was stupid but also rather charming.

We had been sitting for almost an hour on the leather sofa in the living room in my parent's house where I had grown up. Although the carpet was different and the walls were now painted instead of wallpapered, the room hadn't changed much from when I was a ten year old, the picture depicting The Last Supper still taking pride of place above the dining-table. The sofa was sticking to my legs as my body was generating a supernatural amount of heat. I was shit-scared to be doing this. There was no going back anymore. I couldn't be one of those 'straight' guys who pretend to hook up with men only for sexual relief in their quest for the love of 'the right lady'. I had slept

146

with women and I had slept with men, but it was the man-on-man action that definitely made me swoon. Men were the ones that made my groin swell, that's true, but most importantly they were the ones I fell in love with.

I needed to speak the truth so I could live my life free from questions about settling down with a good girl. So that I could always be authentic in my interactions with my family and friends.

My usually relaxed and easy-going father then decided to join in: 'This is some western disease you picked up. All this talk about ancient Greek history. Or all the debates on the news trying to convince everyone that there is a link between this gay malarkey and human rights or even to our struggle to have equality. I do not believe this debate and can't condone this tomfoolery.'

Fifty years of Catholicism and a deeply religious Caribbean upbringing had made its mark on my father. He seemed confused and unable to comprehend what I had said.

I could feel that I was losing control of the discussion. However I decided to try once again to defend my position. 'Daddy, ever since I was little I just knew. I never felt like I belonged and I didn't quite understand why. As I got older and started to understand who I was and what I wanted I could clearly see that I liked men.'

'Ohhh my god, you're the girl!' my mother interrupted me. 'Do you let these people, these so-called men trouble you in your back area?' she squawked, bordering on hysteria.

I wanted to shout at my mother that it wasn't any of her business, nor was it her right to ask me such feisty questions. However, I couldn't disrespect my parents like that, so internally I counted to ten and then answered her question as calmly as I possibly could considering my emotional state.

'Mummy, I don't think that what I do at that level is any of your business. All I am saying is that I am a man who likes men. That doesn't change anything to the fact that I am still your child, I love you and I want you to accept me for who I am, your son.'

Her face was so disfigured with anger that I could barely recognise my mum. 'No son of mine can live such an immoral lifestyle and think that they can come and tell me such fuckries and I will be okay with it. I have prayed for you and maybe I did something wrong along the way but I didn't raise a buller.'

'Son, I think you need to reconsider you choice. You need to step away from this lifestyle and embrace the role that a proper man have in society,' my father added.

In all my years I had never heard either of my parents say anything homophobic. This was the first time and it pierced my heart. I was regretting my choice to take this honest approach. Maybe I had been reckless in telling them.

My father had always said that out of all of his sons I was the most easily led. Also searching for acceptance outside of the true path I should be walking. I always thought that was rich coming from him, considering he was the one who had followed his dream of being a computer analyst when his parents had wanted him to have a 'real' profession such as doctor or lawyer. However he knew what career he wanted and decided to go for it no matter what. The future gave him reason to gloat as he had become successful in this path.

'You're trying to tell me that you love other men and that you think it is okay for you to bring that mess into our house. Who else knows this foolishness about you?' my mother asked, her eyes squinting, her sandy-coloured skin glowing a red hue as her anger continued to rise.

'No-one!' I lied. I had told my brothers when I was twenty-one, and they had advised me never to utter a word of it to my parents as they were old school. My oldest brother Tony said that he had to battle my parents to marry his wife Rosemary, who was African not Caribbean, because even though they liked her they wanted him to marry a nice Caribbean girl.

My brother Michael, the golden boy, married Janet Hubert from our church. He also felt that this honesty wouldn't play out in my favour. However they were both supportive and even acknowledged the true status of my relationship with Tafrai.

'I am telling you as I feel that you're the only people I need to be honest with. You need to know who your son is honestly.'

'Let's keep it that way,' my mother curtly said, giving me the most hateful looking down. I knew she knew I was lying.

'Son, I think we need time to try to digest this. The future will tell us if we can manage to take in what you are saying,' my father – ever the diplomat – responded. My parents were childhood sweethearts who'd met and married in the Caribbean. My father was only fifty-nine but the conversation seemed to be aging him by the minute. 'We need to understand what this thing you are telling us is. It doesn't sit right with me and my faith. It is hard out there for us as black men and you're adding this other dimension into the mix. As your father I tried to give you the best start in life, and I have to say that I feel like you're throwing this back in our faces.'

The conversation I had with my parents was the most difficult discussion I ever had. I had always viewed my relationship with them as one of unconditional love. That day I realised I needed to find the strength from within to define who I am and what I stand for as a black gay man in the UK. My parent's lack of acceptance or willingness to grasp that black people could be gay made me understand I truly needed to live in my truth and fulfil my destiny.

Twelve years on, they are still digesting what I said to them. They continue to try to introduce me to young women who can change me. My relationship with Tafrai has continued, and we are thinking that maybe now we are able to get married, we should. However I am not 100% sure I could go through with such a big day without my parents in attendance.

I am still not friends with Peter Tatchell. However, like him I am ready for my voice to be heard in the fight for equality. I have endured my own slaps along the way and have gotten back up.

Seven Days Underwater

By Daniel Fry

D avid had forgotten about the pictures, but there they were, just as he'd left them: the black and mixed-race men and their admirers; the out-and-proud queens, the brooding DLs, the players and the played.

He skimmed past the usual suspects: mixed-race boys with blond hair, black men with blue eyes, twinks, thugs, Nubian bears, African emos, the scores of self-professed sluts openly seeking sexual destruction, and the odd romantic searching dreamily for love. The young ones came topless of course, posing with gun fingers and New Era hats, their faces alight with the same menacing expressions. *Real thugs don't pluck their eyebrows*, David thought, *or have names like Tingy Lingy*. But here they were, brothers in arms: the lost and lonely, the cruel and self-deprecating; singers, bankers, students and stylists. The try-too-hards and don't-give-a-fucks, all treading the line between lust and rejection.

And there he was, amidst this strange and lonely cosmos. David, reduced to his dick-size (eight inches) and sexual position (top/versatile), as he posed, almost successfully, with his eyes squinted and head tilted slightly to the side. He was twenty-seven now.

Black Gay Talk was a sex-site where only the most necessary details were exchanged. The message David received that morning therefore seemed odd. It was friendly, polite even, but stranger still the messenger had referred to him by name:

LONE_STAR: Hi David seems rude to see you and not say hello. Hope your enjoying these last days of summer. Keep smiling, Peace.

David reread the message and responded carefully. *Thanks,* he wrote, *but I don't know who you are.*

Seconds later a small J-peg appeared. David recognised him

151

instantly: the green eyes, the cornrows, the chiselled, mixed-race features. It was an older man he'd spoken to whilst working for the BMIA project. Black Men in Action was a sexual health charity that provided free condoms to gay clubs in Vauxhall, the kind of ghettoized dives where your feet stuck to the floor and glory holes were carved depressingly into every cubicle. But there amongst the usual crowd of scene queens and hip-hop heads, neatly-dressed Thomas in his shirt and jeans had stood out.

David liked Thomas at once. He liked the way the corners of the older man's eyes creased when he laughed and the gentle way his big, strong hands played nervously with the small crucifix around his neck. He'd sat patiently by the sexual health stall and over the course of an hour revealed himself to be an anxious individual going through a hard time. Thomas was forty-seven and had recently been diagnosed with HIV.

'I left the charity a while back,' David explained now. 'I'm training to be an English teacher at the moment. In fact I'm just heading to the coffee shop to do some revision. It's calm in there, plus they have WiFi.'

Thomas was familiar with the coffee shop, which was on Elms Road. In fact, as the app revealed, he and David lived less than two miles apart.

'How comes I've never seen you?' David asked.

'Like I mentioned last time we met,' Thomas said, 'I'm quite a shy guy – a bit of a hermit actually. But I'm just down the road if you ever wanna chat. I have coffee here too, and WiFi.'

David took the winding side-streets towards White Hart Lane. The halogen lights of the Shell garage flickered on as he reached the main road. He passed the leisure centre and his old school, (now refurbished beyond recognition), before taking the shortcut through the deserted allotment. Some boys liked this strange nomadic life, he thought as he watched the moonlight play off the roofs of the greenhouses. They liked meeting strangers at night, the thrill of meeting someone new. He had too once, but of course he was older now.

Thomas' house sat discreetly on a quiet street corner, its tall wooden fence shrouded by a groove of low-hanging oak trees. David had passed it twice before Thomas came out to meet him.

'We're pretty hidden away here,' the older man said, clenching a roll-up between his teeth as he lifted the latch. 'It's a bugger tryna get anything delivered.'

The bungalow was large and open-planned. White walls complemented bare wood floors while each room was decorated sparingly with vases and ornamental Buddhas. Thomas's cat, a ginger tabby called Arthur, played by David's feet as he stood quietly by the bookshelf in the living-room.

'Do you smoke?' the older man called from the kitchen.

David had forgotten about his voice, its warm huskiness.

'You mean cigarettes?' he asked, scrolling down the titles.

'Anything else?'

'You mean weed?'

'I didn't want to assume or ask or make you feel uncomfortable or pressured or – '

'Yes,' David said. 'I smoke.'

The older man appeared relieved: through the kitchen's pass-through window David watched his strong shoulders relax. Thomas must have been a bit of a player back in the day, he thought, but something had clearly knocked his confidence.

'Good,' he said. 'Cos I smoke a *lot*. That's the second thing you should know about me.'

David's finger settled on the spine of a James Baldwin novel.

'And the first?'

'Sorry?'

'You said that's the second thing I should know about you.

'Oh, I meant first.'

David thought for a moment. The slip had intrigued him. 'And if there *was* a second thing I should know?' he asked playfully.

The older man smiled to himself. In the dim light he waited for the water to boil, made a mental note that David took three sugars and, handing him what would be the first of many coffees, accepted the young man's challenge.

'Just know this,' he said. 'I don't know why you're here, not exactly, but I'd like very much for us to be friends. Good friends.'

*

The boy had a squareness to his forehead, Thomas observed, and a Caribbean roundness to his nose and cheeks that made him appear both masculine and childlike. His eyes were dark and penetrating, just as he'd remembered, but tonight the young man appeared tired. Only a quip or wordplay – of which they made many – could momentarily switch on those dark eyes, or tease out that too-big sexy smile.

'That night when I saw you and your volunteers – I'd watched you for two hours. *Two hours!*' he said, 'I'd never told a complete stranger about me before, my status I mean. Just the word HIV scared me. But you have a wonderful way with people – do you know that? I don't think you do. I could tell you cared about everyone you spoke to. You made time for *everyone*. And people loved you, they – '

'Don't.'

Thomas paused.

'Don't what?'

The boy's voice dropped to a sudden whisper. 'Put me on a pedestal. I'm not a saint. I've done things... things I'm not proud of.'

Thomas was lost for words. He glanced down at David's wrists. To his surprise he glimpsed a ladder of fine, pale scars. The boy pulled at his sleeves quickly. 'Sorry,' he said, 'I'm not very good at taking compliments.'

The cat rubbed against their ankles. Thomas scooped him up and began ruffling his fur. 'His name's Arthur but I call him Arthur Ginger,' he said proudly. 'Cats deserve last names, don't you think? They're just as good as people, if not better. You should have seen when I rescued him from the shelter. He was just skin and bone, now look at him.'

Arthur purred contently.

'He's a little lion,' the boy admitted, but he appeared distracted. He turned and lit a cigarette. 'Do you know they hired me because I was young? The charity, I mean. I found out later I beat better-qualified applicants because I was *younger*. Isn't that funny?'

'Tell me,' Thomas said, 'would you like to get away for a bit?'

The boy looked at him. 'You mean stay here?'

'Why not?'

'Do you make a habit of rescuing strays?'

Thomas was hurt. 'No,' he said, 'but I can see a lot has happened since we last spoke.'

'Yes,' the boy replied, taking a long pull from his cigarette. 'It's been a strange summer.'

The spare room had a sparse, bohemian feel: in one corner a light-bulb hung limply from an empty easel, whilst in another a dozen picture-frames rested against the wall. David stood by the freshly-made bed.

Before he left David, the older man had given him two gifts. A red polo made of cashmere and a book entitled *The Last Rider*, by A.G. Thompson.

David had always felt uncomfortable accepting gifts. The book he took gratefully: books you could enjoy and return. But an item of clothing seemed to him a very intimate gesture. After all, the last time he had seen his ex, he had been wearing someone else's jacket.

So is this what it's like to be the younger man, he thought as he climbed into bed. *To be looked after and given gifts?* He knew the older man's proposal was a bad idea, but David being David, he knew also that he would probably do it anyway.

David woke to the sound of furniture being moved.

From the hallway he could see that the sofa had been pushed back and two purple yoga mats had been spread out across the floor.

'I want to help you heal,' the older man said, 'if I can.'

'But I've got nothing to wear.'

Thomas gestured to the settee. A pair of red long johns rested over the arm of the sofa. David reached out and stroked the smooth, skin-like polyester. The tiny fibres tickling his skin.

'Is this getting weird?' he asked.

'*Getting* weird? When wasn't it?'

'When I wasn't thinking about it.'

'Then let's not think about it,' the older man said, smiling.

With that David turned around and slowly began to undress. 'Okay,' he said, lifting his shirt to reveal the small of his back, the long elegant path of his spine and the broad slopes of his shoulder-blades. He smiled. Just as he'd predicted the older man had left the room by the time he'd unbuckled his jeans.

155

The older man took the sessions very seriously and David was surprised by the smoothness of his movements. He watched as Thomas transitioned effortlessly from sun salutation to bridge, stretching with perfect poise, his toned arms barely wavering with each movement, while David's own shook uncontrollably under the strain.

'Breathe!' Occasionally Thomas would turn to hiss out of the side of his mouth, 'Breathe!'

Strange David hadn't noticed how much pain he was in before. As they rested in child pose he could finally feel how tense his body had become. He tried to concentrate but his jaw throbbed, his limbs ached and his whole being felt locked with knots and tension.

Thomas instructed him to feel the body's sensations without clinging or aversion, with an attitude of complete equanimity. But David hadn't slept properly for months and every time he tried to clear his mind he felt shooting pains behind his eyelids.

Before the session ended David had felt the briefest moment of calm. But it was a momentary wave of emptiness that only frustrated him when it passed. And immediately those painful memories of the summer just passed began rushing back in, filling him up with a familiar panic and dread. 'I want to see you heal,' Thomas had said, but it was no use. For David silencing his mind was like trying to hold onto a rope that kept slipping out of reach.

The next morning Thomas dragged the weight-bench into the hallway. The boy lay flat across the back-pad and began to lift the weights as instructed. Thomas watched as beads of sweat formed on the young man's forearms. He became distracted by his body, its warm animal smell. It was a smell that brought back memories of camping trips, summer holidays and school changing-rooms.

He felt the boy's body radiate with heat as he steadied his shaking elbows, reminding him to strengthen his core and be mindful of his posture.

He watched David's ribcage accentuate with each lift, every muscle in his forearms growing firm and taut. *What a body,* he thought, *what a gift. But the boy hates himself. He smokes, he drinks. But god,* he thought, *to have a body like that...*

But then Thomas' trail of thought arrived at the memory that yes, he too used to have a body like that, once. In fact, with his swimmer's build and dark, knowing eyes, David could have been a younger version of himself.

He touches the boy's forearms more carefully now. He pulls himself back to the task at hand. Respectfully he takes the weight of the dumbbells and lowers them to the floor. The boy looks up at him, out of breath. His brow is damp, his abdomen shaking. Thomas tries to collect himself but he is still a man. And even as he turns away he knows it is a memory he will return to stubbornly in those sad solitary hours, like a prisoner remembering freedom or an exile, home.

The man had told David to straighten his arms. And David had obeyed demurely. He wanted to impress him. He wanted to impress him very much.

To achieve this David thought consciously about each lift, constantly pulling his thoughts back from the past (thinking too much was his problem, Thomas had told him) to the act of straightening his forearms and consciously using his whole body (legs, shoulders, core) to propel his strength upwards and outwards. After days of practice he had begun to master the art of breathing in time with each movement, moving in time with each breath, until both had become fluidic and whole.

His acceptance of the older man's methods was not one of blind submission but of discrimination and understanding. He worked thoroughly, diligently, sensing that with each ache and sickly strain the older man was preparing him for some as-yet unknown war.

The boy sat cross-legged on the yoga mat making notes of the exercises they had done. He was still bare-chested and in those red long johns that had become tradition when Thomas, like a doctor prescribing medicine, handed him a protein shake and a spliff.

'You feel safe here don't you?' he asked finally.

'I feel very comfortable here now,' David replied, looking up briefly.

Thomas watched him as he passed back the joint. The boy leant back and rested his outstretched arm on the side-table, the joint resting between the fingers of his upturned hand, each muscle in his perfectly-formed arm accentuated, his torso stretched languidly. *He's becoming more confident,* Thomas thought, *he's becoming his body.*

'Do you still speak to that boy? Cameron?'

'My ex?'

'I saw you together once. Last Pride, I think it was. The young guy with the piercings. He had his arm around you.'

'You know him?'

'Everyone knows him.'

David laughed. 'Last Pride he had his arm around me. This Pride he acted like he didn't know me. You know, he told his friends he felt nothing when he fucked me. He said he actually felt sorry for the next person who dated me.'

Thomas felt like hugging the boy but instead he rolled another joint. Pride, he realised, had only been the following week.

'Is that why you started cutting yourself?' he asked.

'No,' David said not looking up. '*That* is a much longer and more fucked up story...'

'I have time.'

David put his notebook down.

'Shall we go for a run later?'

'No,' Thomas said uneasily. 'We have plenty to do here.'

'I know,' David said watching him carefully, 'but I saw this beautiful track down by the allotment – '

Thomas got up quickly. 'Maybe tomorrow,' he said. But as he rose he caught the look in David's eyes. It was the unmistakable squint of someone who had discovered a loose thread. It was the cunning smile of a sniper whose bullet had hit the mark.

David had grown quieter over the last couple of days. Whilst Thomas thought of new exercises for them to do, David found himself retreating more and more into the company of his books.

From what he could tell, *The Last Rider* by A.G. Thompson was about a young man who was engaged to a violent alcoholic. Following a drunken argument the protagonist, Raymond, is locked out of the house and forced to roam the streets. He wanders all night before coming across a deserted bar. At the bar he meets and falls in love with the bartender. But just as the hero builds up the courage to confront his homosexual feelings his fiancée reveals that she's three months pregnant. The book then jumps to four years later when, on Christmas Day, he steals a car and leaves the city. David read intently as the book described the protagonist's journey along the open highway. Rain beating on the windshield, a song on rewind, each mile take him further and further away from home and towards that delicious, terrifying feeling of being *free*. David put the book down, stunned. Finally it had clicked.

'You never leave the house,' he said suddenly.

They had been watching TV when he turned to Thomas and confronted him.

'What do you mean?'

'You never leave the house,' he repeated. 'You get your shopping delivered, you barely go out into the garden. In all the time I've been here... you've never left the house.'

Thomas fidgeted. He took a deep breath and turned the volume down.

'It's true,' he said finally. 'You might as well know.'

'How long?'

'What?'

'How long have you lived like this?'

'It's been a long time,' he said quietly. 'I've lived like this for a long time.'

After that David began to see a weariness in the older man's eyes. He began to glimpse a heaviness he hadn't seen before, a sad sort of lethargy in the way he moved and spoke. Had he been too quick to trust the gentle tenor of his voice? How, he wondered, could he have been so naïve to think that Thomas could actually help him?

'You know, it's strange,' the older man said the next morning, 'how people deal with grief.' He had been in the kitchen unpacking groceries when the boy came in to help him. They hadn't spoken since the previous night.

'When I was diagnosed with HIV, for example, I walked around for hours in a daze. Then I came to a bookshop. Do you know what book I bought?'

David didn't answer.

'HMV's Top Fifty music videos of all time. Strange,' he said, 'I never had any interest in those countdowns, those silly encyclopaedias. But after I was diagnosed I became obsessed with the bloody things. Top hundred films ever made, fifty best actors all time, hundred best songs, albums, artists, cities, buildings – '

'You were preparing to die,' David said before he could stop himself.

'Yes.' To David's surprise Thomas laughed. 'I suppose I was.'

David was reaching for a carton of milk. 'Do you think it's really possible to heal?' he asked. 'Completely, I mean.'

Thomas thought for a while. 'I think sometimes to heal you just have to stand still. Sometimes the hardest thing to do is just stop. But if you can be still and allow yourself to accept your vulnerability, then it's a start.'

They packed away the last of the shopping together in silence.

'I should get back to my book,' David said, 'but we can exercise later, if you want.'

He wondered how long the older man had lived like this. He watched from the hallway as Thomas fed the cat. Gradually something in David softened. The older man, he realized, had been healing too.

That night David had the greenhouse dream again.

Every time he closed his eyes now he would find himself alone at the allotment on White Hart Lane. The particular greenhouse he dreamt of was a haphazard and ineffectual thing. It was a nightmarish version of the one he had passed on the way to Thomas's house. Its broken frame pierced the sky, its windows glowed a toxic green. And always, when David tried to leave, it would resist. The vines that grew stealthily inside its walls would reach out gently and pull him back, their paraffin-scented limbs curling seductively like snakes around his wrists.

He woke with a start. Remembering the older man's story he wondered how Thomas had endured living alone for so long, a gentle giant hiding from the outside world. How easy it would be now to walk out into the hallway and cross the dark space between them, he thought. How easy it would be to climb into Thomas' bed and perhaps offer up the only thing he could.

David had almost come to the end of the book. The protagonist, now twenty-nine, after travelling for years as a drifter, had begun work on an isolated grain chute in the furthest reaches of South Dakota. 'To be free from people is to be free from pain,' the writer claimed. But even the snowy town with its endless winters and harsh terrain proves not isolation enough for the protagonist. One day he decides to take a final trip. This time there is no music, no Hollywood escape. Carrying a .22-calibre rifle and a field guide to the region's edible plants the last rider gathers his things, and with a profound feeling of emptiness hitchhikes deeper and deeper into the snow trail.

David felt something of that desolation. Living at the older man's house was sometimes like living at the bottom of the ocean. He wasn't sure now how many days had passed; nowadays it was as though he and the older man moved in a gelatinous time zone. They ate when they were hungry, slept when they were tired, and only the cat, Arthur, with his watery eyes and feline routines, appeared guided by any vague sense of time.

'Gay stories are often painful but a lot can be learnt about strength,' Thomas said one night. He crouched by the television cabinet and began to take out a series of novels. One by one he handed the well-worn volumes over for David to inspect: James Baldwin, James Earl Hardy, Langston Hughes.

'Have you ever tried writing?'

'I used to write, I used to write a *lot*,' Thomas said. 'I used to sing too. But these things seem less important as you get older.'

David looked at the mounting pile of books.

David,' he said as if reading his mind. 'You know you can stay here as long as you want.'

The boy paused. 'I think I've been very cruel by being here,' he said.

'Why?'

'I think... I think you've been teasing yourself with the idea of me. And I think me being here is maybe harder for you than

161

you let on.'

Thomas looked offended, but slowly his expression changed.

'I suppose you being here has made me realise how lonely I've been,' he admitted. 'But David, I'm a grown man.'

But grown men could get hurt too, Thomas knew. And as the days went on the boy had grown stronger. He was no longer the defeated child who had shown up at his door. Thomas had watched anxiously as David grew leaner, his body firmer, his muscles more defined. His shape had grown hard and masculine. He strolled about the house now in those tight fitting long johns with a newfound elegance and Thomas began to worry. He worried that he would run out of things to teach him. And soon the powerful shape of the boy's shoulders alone was enough to produce in him a sudden squeeze of fear.

Then one evening the boy said something that filled him with dread. He'd said it so quietly that Thomas almost didn't hear him.

'I think I'll go for a walk tomorrow,' he said.

It seemed like a lifetime since he'd been outside the house. Walking along the perimeter of the field, David looked out across the empty allotment, with its untidy procession of greenhouses, its rows of dug-up soil and neatly-tended herbs, and was filled with a profound sense of loneliness.

He gazed at the orderly rows of carrots and hibiscus and wondered if that's how it worked when you got older. You traded big, unstable love affairs for the safe and uncomplicated love of plants and abandoned animals. His thoughts turned to his ex and he wondered if really it was such a bad trade in the end.

The end of summer, as he had once confided to Cameron, had always felt to him like a different season altogether. On days like this, when the evenings were neither long nor short and the weather was neither hot nor cold, the world always felt unnaturally still, like a sudden lull in conversation.

This non-season would pass quickly, he knew. But for now it was almost like living underwater, with all your senses cocooned and hushed inwards. He sensed this more keenly at dusk, when even the eyes could be confused by the subtle change from light to dark: that for a few days of the year, inside that seasonal vacuum, time, for a while at least, could be gently suspended.

As he walked back to the house, he carried with him the dim hope that one day perhaps he too could learn to stop and be still.

Thomas was drinking in the dark when David returned.

'When you left today, I didn't think you'd come back.'

'There's something I need to tell you,' David said, sitting beside him. Thomas offered to fetch David a glass but the boy declined. 'I didn't leave the charity,' he said. 'I was asked to go. That day at work, after my ex left me, we'd just been given the clearance to carry out rapid HIV testing. Do you know those twenty-minute kits? Where you take a small sample of blood from the patient's finger and test for antibodies?'

'I know the test,' Thomas said uncertainly.

'Well, they needed volunteers to practice on. So I volunteered, except I kept on volunteering. I volunteered for *everyone* to practice on me... there must have been thirty people in that room but I just kept on putting my hand up... at first they thought it was funny but then...'

'What do you mean?'

David eyed Thomas carefully but found himself reliving the memory. 'I got angry,' he said. 'I demanded them to. I wanted them to carry on. To carry on pricking me, cutting me... and when they refused I got on my knees and I *begged*.'

'You wanted to be hurt.'

'It's weird,' David said, staring at his fingers. 'But I can still feel the points where the needles pierced my skin. Prick after prick.' David glanced up at Thomas. 'After prick.'

Thomas got up and began pacing the room. But David sat with his hands on his lap and continued to offer up his confession the same way that Thomas had the first time they met. He began tell him what happened that strange summer.

Two weeks after that David had been dismissed from the charity. His ex had disowned him. His world had been turned upside-down. And so David sought refuge in all the wrong places. Within days he had lost count of the men he had slept with. Young, old, even elderly; all his sexual encounters seemed to mesh into the same grisly act. Before long he found himself hauled and groped in every club basement, public toilet, cruising ground and darkroom he'd ever tried to avoid.

That summer he'd offered himself indiscriminately. *Prick after prick after prick.*

Acts he'd never known existed he complied with, things that would have once repelled him he did willingly; each time submitting with that same sense of dead-eyed passivity.

'Sexual self-harm,' David said. He could barely believe it himself. 'I'd treated men for it at the charity but – but I couldn't see it in myself – and if I did, I didn't care anymore.'

By the third month he had gone from being admired and respected in the community to being one of *those* boys; those tragic, lowly figures who linger at the end of each night, posturing hungrily long after the lights come up and the last song's been played.

The community of black men and boys he had tried so hard to help soon turned its back on him, his former profession only serving to fan the flames of gossip, and before long everyone knew about David and his fall from grace.

'Well, almost everyone.'

Thomas was speechless.

'Sexual health coordinators,' David said, 'must look pretty different without their badges.'

Thomas felt the room capsize. It was as if all his nightmares were coming true at once. David reached out for him but he pulled away.

'You chose me because I was positive didn't you?' he said, his voice shaking. 'You wanted to... you wanted me to... *hurt you*?'

'I'm sorry...'

'Sorry?'

'I needed help.'

'*Help?* From a forty-five-year old man?' Thomas spat. 'From a forty-five-year old man who could have ruined your career. Who could have *ruined* you!'

Thomas thought about the night they met and could no longer look at the boy. The idea that David had sought to use him as a final instrument of self-harm broke his heart. But still, as the boy got up, he managed to find his words:

'It's not your fault,' he said, 'what happened with that boy. For god's sake, David, forgive yourself. *Please.*'

That night David couldn't sleep. It seemed like a long time before Thomas went to bed. He listened as he had done a dozen times to the sound of the older man brushing his teeth. He watched as the reassuring shape of Thomas's shadow drifted past and waited for the familiar click of his bedside lamp. Then hours later David got up. He put on his tee-shirt and did something he'd never done before. He crossed the hallway, crept towards Thomas's room and, like a child scared of the dark, pulled back the covers and climbed into his bed.

It had been years since Thomas felt the bed sigh under the weight of another. It was a strange and merciful sound.

He held his breath for a long time and when he finally opened his eyes he saw David; David, with his loosely balled fists, David curled up like a question mark, a seahorse's tail, an echo of every man he'd ever loved. David, complicated, intelligent, fucked-up and fragile. *How could this happen?* he asked himself.

He didn't touch the boy, he daren't. He imagined it would be like touching a boy made of thorns. So he lay there, drowning in the room's blue light, afraid to move and feeling like the luckiest man in the world.

David didn't leave a note. In the end he was sure that the older man knew he was leaving even before he himself did.

But when he'd closed the gate that final morning he'd felt terribly alone. There were no shortcuts, he realised then, to resolving this terrible grief. But he was leaving at least feeling renewed by the old man's lessons. As he pulled up his collar and stepped out into the cold sunshine he was faintly aware of having been given a strange hope.

On a cold and windy beach in Ribadeo, Spain, the view of the Atlantic from the top of the rocks where he sat made David feel light-headed and dizzy.

The last couple of months had been so exhilarating, overwhelming and terrifying that he'd almost forgotten about that end of summer lull he had always sensed so keenly around this time of year.

The seasons here were slightly askew but he didn't need to look at the calendar; he knew it had almost been a year since he left the old man's house. Oddly enough he had felt it on his skin.

Today, after his students had left, something inside him had shifted. And for the first time in months he'd found himself standing in the classroom alone and completely still.

Perhaps it was the time of year that had made him revisit the old man's book. When he reached the top of the black slate cliff, it was with a heavy heart that he returned to the final chapters.

For years the protagonist had been trekking alone in the wilderness. Now in his forties, he has learned to adjust to the harsh terrain by hunting wild game and living off plants. The days turn into months and soon it's years since he's seen another human face.

Over this period he emerges as a primordial hermit, a skilled hunter and a spiritual nomad attuned to the ways of the forest. He is in his seventies when the book ends, and dies at peace, 'long since ridding his mind of the attachments of youth and false promise.'

David reread the final line:

He dies alone but not lonely; as long as he has the mountains and the air he can lay all else to rest.

David felt a chill rush through him. He reread it a third and fourth time. He turned the book over and over in his hands. Thomas he thought. *The Last Rider*. Written by A.G. Thompson. Arthur – Ginger – Thomas.

There was no mistake. Those were Thomas's words. It had been Thomas's deep voice echoing through every line just as it had been Thomas' wise and gentle words that had been with him during every exam and every stress and struggle since.

He hoped the older man had been encouraged to meet new people after he left. He hoped he had continued his recovery. He wasn't sure if speaking to Thomas again would be seeking atonement or scratching at old wounds, so he simply held the old man close in his heart and remembered him just as he had asked; he was the friend, albeit one he had never properly thanked. As David took the path back to the main road he wondered if it was really harder to bounce back as you got older. He hoped not. But he knew it was never too late to start again.

Meditations on Home

By Keith Jarrett

'Satan is a liard and him middle name is sin!
Where we a go put him? Inna de Biffa bin!'

(from 'Hip-hop Salvation')

Easter, 1997

Home is a place I like to call the Far East; a clutter of tea-coloured terrace houses where London meets Essex. Home is a place where Jesus lives and where we call each other 'saints' in greeting. Home is a place where printed 2Pac lyrics are smuggled in schoolbags and hidden under mattresses, or in between Kirk Franklin albums. It is Saturday night and I am on my way home, squeezed between three sets of legs in the back of a stuttering Ford Fiesta.

At thirteen years old, I am the smallest passenger bound for home; I must sit furthest forward and fill as little space as possible. In that space I breathe in my mother's perspiration and perfume, the olive oil on my sister's forehead, my two brothers and the sweat of their sticky palms that have been knocking tambourines all evening.

We have just left an Easter convention at a church twinned with ours. I am drawn to the window but don't want to be seen paying too much attention to the world outside. Tonight's recorded sermon is being replayed on the cassette deck at full volume. Brixton, in its wildness, is trying to out-scream Pastor Mackenzie – and, even if the volume were not cranked up, he has enough voice in him to be heard from halfway down the street where the church is located. His voice has earned complaints from neighbours, much to the pride of the congregation. *I said death where is thy sting-uh? Grave-uh! I said* Grave-uh! *Where is thy victory? Can I get an amen?* Amen. Bass is booming outside from other cars. I recognise the b-line for Notorious B.I.G.'s new song 'Hypnotize'. Sirens are whirring from all directions. Pastor Mackenzie is being disco-remixed.

I am counting down the seconds before I can turn my head again and look out of the side window. If I time this perfectly (*and be ye perfect, even as God is perfect*), I will have missed the queue at Caesars Nightclub, which always gets a sharp intake of breath from Auntie G at the front. I know there will be girls in batty riders the colour of opal fruits, platinum blonde hair piled high above their heads, finger waves snaking down forehead to temple; I know there will be men dressed head to toe in black or white, gold-chained and gold-toothed with arms wrapped around female buttocks or leaning on lampposts, or reaching for lighters; men in string vests with backward-facing baseball caps and bandanas, with wide strides and wider biceps.

I am jealous that my friends down here get to live out in the wild, in what I think of as the gun-riddled ghetto of South London. But, more than anything, I am jealous that they get to be close to what is coming. I feel my heart beat fast so fast, till it hurts my ribs, and the recognition I still feel from the last time we passed this venue is passing over into nausea. *Turn. Look.*

They call this place The Fridge.

Before my sister pushes my head away, in that two-second space before I hear my oldest brother mutter something about Sodom and Gomorrah, I feel the chill of The Fridge lift goose-pimples through the skin of my arms. A man, naked apart from what seems to be a short leather skirt; another, topless, in cut-off denim shorts; two men kissing; men holding hands; a whole bunch of men a blur as we drive past, in tight shirts and jeans, *even so come, Lord, amen.* The thought of their buttocks perching in those jeans, and the proud bare chests mocking me while Pastor Mackenzie shouts *Praise the Lord* and my Auntie is hissing *sin* makes me shiver. I want to scream. A hand covers my eyes. *That nastiness isn't for you.*

During the blackout, as my eyelids flicker against my sister's hand, I know there is something so wrong, so wrong with what I am feeling.

When I get home and close my eyes, I know the brief images of what I saw will replay in my head and I won't be able to switch them off. They will battle with the sermon playing in the car, and the unanimous expressions of disgust from my family, and my own disgust for being drawn to these men who are nothing like me. They are nothing. The Book of Romans is clear: they are what happens when a people that knew God but, in their own vanity, failed to glorify him, give themselves over to vile affections. I have heard the sermons warning about these abominations. I cannot be like them. But neither can I feel comfortable at home, when my body, my cursed body is telling me the opposite.

Back in the car, I shuffle as much as I can, squeezing my knees together and placing my bible over my crotch. I am sweating. Despite my terror, I find excitement. Despite my shame, I feel arousal. I have never before felt lonelier or more conflicted.

Blacker than thou, 2003

Home is in my rucksack, in the fabric softener smell of my UCL hoodie, which goes with me on the bus to university, stays over at my parents' house, my friends' flats, my shared dormitory room and, sometimes, the homes of strangers.

I am wearing the hoodie now, sitting on a chair by the window in a building near Gower Street. I am trying not to explain further to the university's counsellor why my same-sex attraction is unbiblical and, furthermore, not 'black'. I have not come here for my feelings to be validated, no; I have come here to be listened to, in the completeness of my experience.

In my head, I draw a type of Venn diagram. In the middle of an Afro-centric halo the word 'black' sits proudly; two circles overlapping on either side are 'Christian' and 'gay' – they cannot touch each other. I redraw the circle – they can touch each other but not if they overlap with 'black'. White people get to call themselves Christian and gay – but *real* Christians, black Christians, Christians who have grown up with Pentecostal fire, with tambourine wrists, with rolling down the aisle prophecies and tarrying nights – they would never dare to call themselves by this abomination of a word and live to tell the tale.

Our time is nearly up and I haven't spoken for the last ten minutes. The counsellor is pushing the cube of tissues my way, across the square pine table between us.

'Would you like to share what's on your mind now?'

I need to restart this Venn diagram. I need to create a new category – *'black'* –and place it in the middle of the 'black' circle. There is a subtlety in this definition, which only *black* people like me get. And that explains why I cannot be *black* and gay.

'How does that make you feel?'

The African Caribbean Society at UCL is the only place I get to mix with more than just a couple of black students, and this is where I developed my theory. 'Black' students wear their piercings and jewellery with ease: Christie in her arse-hugging jeans and gold teeth; talkative, dashiki-wearing Terry, who swears at just the right moments – and quickly became the society's president, with his easy but controlling manner; argumentative Ade who always speaks of pan-African solidarity, who has big words and big theories, which he delivers even as the meeting's discussion turns to catering at our talent show.

By contrast, us *black* students are awkward in our bodies and we move with a heaviness only visible to each other. When Kofi curses we all look at him – because it does not sound right in his mouth – and when he peppers every fucking sentence with a shitting swearword to highlight how bollocks everything all is, we feel his parents' disapproval. Kayla is a rare species at this university: like me, her parents are West Indian; like me, she hails from East London; like me, she will soon become more immersed in the Christian Union, her true home. What we have in common is the *old school* – strict Christian or Muslim parents who came to this country poor, with little or no education, working hard so that their children could better themselves and make them proud. The towns and villages of our parents' birth have changed beyond recognition; the only things they have left from these homes are the values they have accumulated and strengthened through (religious) community. And we are trying to live up to these values.

In contrast, my other black peers are international students and one or two third-generation Brits; they have grown up fully rooted in their home cultures and they wear them with ease and without pretension. They do not slip in and out of self-conscious patois and hang Caribbean or African flags from their doors; they have no need.

'We'll have to leave it there.'

Our sessions always end abruptly. It takes a while to explain what I have never talked to anyone else about, especially when the someone else I am talking to has no idea about anything I am saying. I walk out of my appointment, take a few deep breaths and head to Waterstones. It is there I discover James Baldwin's *Go Tell it on the Mountain*.

Slam Champ, 2007

My home is in the pages of second-hand books and, increasingly, on stages at poetry nights. I take a certificate home which says I am officially the London Poetry Slam Champion; soon after, or maybe just before, I begin a Creative Writing MA.

Deep down, I know I should not be attempting to write anything, let alone attempt a writing course; I am not entitled. Performance poetry is one thing, fiction another. The two books I wanted to write have already been published – *Go Tell it on the Mountain* and Junot Diaz's *Drown* – and both shook me up, albeit in different ways. I have nothing new to say.

I should not be writing anything. But I am not writing because I *want* to write; I am writing because if I don't, something in me will perish.

I hang the Slam Champion certificate on the wall of my cramped bedsit in Russell Square, which overlooks Gay's the Word bookshop. I have not given my address to my parents, partly because they have not asked, partly because I do not know what my mother would say if she visited – and then looked out of the window and saw those shameless words. My sexuality is something of which we do not speak.

I wrap a towel round my waist, find my keys, leave my room and go down into the communal bathroom. I go back up again to retrieve my phone. Living here means going up and down the stairs several times and hoping not to bump into neighbours in the toilet.

I feel comfortable in this neighbourhood. Living here means leaving through the front door and finding myself right in the middle of a bunch of tourists and students, none of whom seem to know where they are going. I fit right in with my dreamy meanderings through Bloomsbury streets, bumping into lampposts while studying signs and people. Living here means walking everywhere – never getting a bus – and feeling at the centre of this bustling city, feeling like I've made it. It also means noticing how many cabs wait outside the basement flat next door late into the night, and knowing that the police will raid soon. It is wondering why the landlord's assistant does not mind if I skip a week's rent; it is not asking too many questions, knowing that soon, when this place is converted into upmarket flats and the rent quadruples, I will have to go.

I add a slim volume to my bookcase. It is a novella written entirely in verse which I was given as a leaving present from the job I quit – the only permanent, full-time job I will ever have. I am certain the shelf creaks with excitement at the new addition.

I spend more and more of my time reading novels and performing poetry. I spend less time worrying about who I am – what I am – and I begin to introduce people to my boyfriend, including my new classmates.

Moving On

Since leaving my parents' home, I have moved close to a dozen times. Most memorably I spent a year abroad in the Dominican Republic, working at a school. This home I will write about for many years to come. This home, the only place that still shares some conflicted space in my head, where I was still not comfortable with my sexuality but felt completely at home because of the tight-knit, supportive community around me. It is the only place I both dread and yearn to go back to, knowing that it will have changed from how I remember, knowing that the people there could shun the person I am now, simply because of who I choose to love.

My other homes have been in London: Central, North and West. I have grown to love my current home, Camden, as it is one of the few places I feel just as comfortable in a dashiki as I do in a tracksuit or a bow tie and bowler hat (or all three).

I have also grown to accept my body as a home, rather than a temple. Temples are sacred; you visit once or twice a week, or five times a day – depending on your tradition – and you sacrifice lambs to it, or maybe pour some alcohol down its walls. Homes are where we store our memories and our secrets. We invite lovers into our home. Our homes throb with the bass of our speakers – or those of the neighbours. Our homes gather wear and tear, and this gives us 'character'.

I went to The Fridge once, as an adult, on one of their rare gay nights. I distinctly felt like I did not belong; the techno and me… well, we just did not get along so well, especially after a guy in a vest bumped into me and spilled my drink all over my white v-neck shirt.

I have also eaten at a restaurant in the much-gentrified Brixton Village, where you can buy a hamburger for over ten pounds. I did not belong there, either, though I did belong for a while on nearby Coldharbour Lane, haggling over some overripe plantain.

I have been to predominantly black club nights, predominantly black and gay Christian fellowships, and to Black Prides in London and Washington, D.C.; I have longed for, but escaped, a full sense of belonging there, although I have found comfort and security.

I have been around poets, running workshops and working in schools, sharing my experiences and enabling others to do the same. Here I do find a home – but only for a while before I need to retreat into my other home: the home of reading, of staying up late and writing, of travelling to places and discovering myself in others. Perhaps – as the poet Edward Brathwaite questioned in *The Arrivants* – my home is not easily found in Paris, Brixton, Kingston, Rome… I must create my own home with all that I have; with my body, with my words, with my yearning.

> *I want you to know*
> *there is no square mile*
> *that I haven't trod down*
> *in this opaque city*
> *looking for you*
> *and finding freedom*
>
> *I want you to know*
> *there is a banquet*
> *at the end of your tongue*

a restaurant rising
from deep within
which you can, finally, call home.

(from 'Listed Buildings', 2013)

Victor Has Not Died!

By Cheikh Traore

The 'Cool Britannia' era of the late nineties and the period that followed the millennium year were marked by many advances in gay rights. It was also a time when we witnessed bold political moves advancing race equality and the recognition of multiculturalism as a positive thing for the country. Black people also contributed to advances in gay rights. A few did so in the political arena and will probably have their names written in history books. But countless others contributed to our empowerment by building our consciousness in subtle ways which we need to appreciate and replicate today.

The news of Victor's death came as a dizzying blow. It left us feeling like orphans; realising that from now on we would have to find direction through life by ourselves. He was a pillar for our community of gay men. He was a role model, perhaps because of his successful professional career. He offered his peers many reasons to hope and believe. Like most of us he had chosen to reinvent himself and dream new dreams in a place that belonged to no-one. Among our group there were many 'returnees' – people who had grown up and spent formative teenage and university years in West Africa, and who, in the nineties, were able to hop on flights for England or Scotland thanks to the rights afforded us by our accidental birth-histories in the old continent. Others were not returnees: they had come to live in London, often by choice, and through the luxury of having wealthy parents prepared to sponsor their studies.

Just like Victor's, our life-trajectories reflected the ups and downs of history and the new world of the eighties, the nineties: the end of Thatcherism, the fall of the Berlin Wall, the opening of European Union borders, the legacy of global economic policies in Africa. The world was in a state of flux, and as young university students in Nigeria, Ghana or Senegal we knew that we had to take our chances. Thanks to policies imposed by the IMF and World Bank, public services like education and health went through a crash in these countries. Salaries and pensions for doctors, engineers and teachers were no longer attractive. After medical school, a huge number of Nigerians simply left the country. For thousands of our contemporaries with degrees it was a much better option to go elsewhere, to shores where we could get better rewards for our skills.

One of the high moments of the nineties was the coming to power of Tony Blair. It arrived with lots of optimism. Britain was a 'cool' destination and London was the place to be. Looking back at the cover-art of our favourite music CDs, it was clear that London was a massive cultural hub for modern Black music. Elton John and George Michael were topping R&B charts the world over. Acid Jazz, New Jack Swing, ragga and lovers' rock, London was the place where new styles of Black music flourished, before spreading across the globe.

The 'Cool Britannia' era also came with media debates about 'gay rights'. It was a period where the image of Britain became even more contradictory: a deeply conservative country and yet a place replete with radical thinkers and islands of rebellion. London had famous gay clubs, some only a stone's throw from equally famous Catholic and Anglican cathedrals.

For our peers the emerging gay rights debate felt like an elitist concept, intended for a select crowd of intellectuals during TV shows like *Newsnight*. Just like politics in general, one could easily be put off by the cold nature of the debate, but still we tuned in. There was lots of talk about Section 28, a piece of law left over from the Thatcher era that banned discussions about (what was described as the 'promotion of') homosexuality in schools. Gay rights activists were facing sharp and at times accusatory journalists ready to rip their demands and ideas apart, piece by piece. It was also the time of the notorious Stephen Lawrence murder and the huge debates about in particular institutional racism that followed on from it. Britain was like a giant lab for human rights, and the whole world was watching.

All these events would affect our lives more directly decades later. At the time, for those of us following them from afar, the vividness and passion with which they were publically debated made coming to London seem a very attractive proposition.

One has to marvel at the power of the invisible hand that found people in the maze of London and brought them together in Victor's kitchen. We had a few things in common; we were men, we loved men and we were African. Work struggles and family tribulations were sufficient to threaten our fragile sanity. What made us happy was a get-together now and then, with jolof rice, stewed beef, beer and the company of half a dozen brothers. But the magic hand that linked us to each other must also have been sexual. Promiscuity is a pejorative, but we saw the proof that it could lead to building bonds and supportive networks. Within months of living here, exploring the city we found each other. Sometimes in odd places like cruising parks late at night, or the infamous saunas of Old Street and Bethnal Green. The guilt and unease at being in such places often took months, even years to subside, but eventually we got comfortable with these 'vices'. Our reunions once a month were enough to restore our sanity and make us feel good about ourselves again. Being in the company of people with similar struggles about identity. Eating. Drinking and listening to music. Simple things that made us feel grateful to be alive and living in London. Victor would welcome us in his flat; often on Sunday afternoons, often the day after another house-party filled with intrigue, drama and careless abandon.

The rituals were simple but well-orchestrated, with Victor acting as an unassuming therapist. His kitchen, a windowless room typical of the council flats in that part of South London, was always the favourite spot. He listened to our tribulations as he went back and forth between the small living-room, the kitchen and even his bedroom (into which some of us would sometimes disappear). Serving more drinks, opening the door to new guests, always with a welcoming smile, over the years he heard endless accounts of missed professional opportunities, glass ceilings and the ruthless employment market. Despite our hard-earned degrees back 'at home', most of us had to go to the back of the queue and do more studies: our African diplomas and degrees were often not recognised in 'Cool Britannia". There was always that venting of anger about trying to find

179

work.

As we swallowed more Grolsch and Stella Artois, the brothers would eventually relax. Soon, topics of interest would start to emerge: *So who was that gorgeous guy at the party last night?*

How come we had not seen him before... in this London?

Is he into Black guys or White guys?

Race, sex and desire were inevitable topics.

And then there was the usual banter between our tribal and national belongings; Igbos teasing Yorubas about honesty and righteousness. Nigerians teasing Ghanaians about who did the best jolof rice. West Africans ganging up together to tease Zimbabweans and Ugandans for not being 'cut'.

Male circumcision was always a matter for debate. And an irrational one, since none of us really chose to be, or not to be circumcised....

Victor was a psychiatrist. Perhaps this is why we felt so at ease to gather at his place to simply talk. The important thing for us was to talk to like-minded guys who most times had no solutions for our troubled tales and questions but at least understood them. We had constant challenges about being 'gay': the media images of gay and lesbian people felt alien to us, and the lifestyle described in *Gay Times* magazine was often equally distant from our realities. The numerous adverts with muscular and happy-looking guys on cruises to Mykonos and Crete. The holiday apartments for rent in Gran Canaria. They felt like far-fetched dreams that most of us could not even aspire to. We understood the clear commonalities we shared with white guys, but beyond sex, desire and the quest for love, so many things were different. We had to make up new ways of being gay for ourselves: after all, we were in London, the city that belongs to no one.

Victor himself had no answers, but it didn't matter: he knew instinctively that what people needed most of all was simply to talk. He didn't say much himself, but sometimes talked about relationships, which to most of us were a nice idea, but so difficult to put into practice. Most of us were viciously promiscuous, and we didn't see guys in relationships as a no-go area. Victor would often challenge us on that level: he not only talked

180

about gay relationships, but he himself was living in a relation-ship, with a Ghanaian man, Ernest. And before Ernest, he had been in another long-term relationship, with a Nigerian man, (Akin), another doctor who we knew. In many ways simply by being himself he provided many of us with a model, opening us up to the idea that a committed relationship was at least something to think about, one day.

How do people end up finding each other to create these intricate social circles?

Sexual adventures, cottaging or cruising in Finsbury Park or Bloomsbury Square were a common experience for some of us, but few of us would admit it even to close friends. Victor made it possible for us to talk about these things, to accept that, by virtue of being human, we had urges that needed to be satis-fied. As long as we protected ourselves and used condoms we didn't have to be embarrassed about our tales of exploration and lust. He was slightly older than most of us, and for him it was a matter of fact: London offered sex and men of all kinds on a silver platter. No matter how rich or poor you were, the city had it all on offer. The place was like a giant superstore offering huge discounts all year long. To be honest this was also why we liked the city.

There was fun in being young and experimenting with our 'gayness' in the anonymous London gaydom. But there was also sorrow, guilt and soul-searching when those busy, hedonistic weekends were over. Even after years of immersion in the gay scene many of us were still struggling with our sexualities and identities; and this is why Victor's kitchen was so therapeutic. We could come here with lingering questions and self-doubt, and seek others' understanding. Sometimes it was just enough to be reassured that it was okay to be Muslim and gay, or to be born-again Christian and gay. Or to be bisexual. It was fine to be different from most of our friends in White gaydom, who were often suspicious of people who expressed religious belonging too loudly. Many people felt insecure if they didn't match up to the standards of gayness that prevailed in the mainstream, such as fashion, music tastes and all these so-called gay 'icons' that we didn't even know; mostly White

American women: Liza this, and Barbara that. In this kitchen it was okay not to know those people: they did not define our gayness!

In the safety of this space we could ask some serious questions. Like, *'Why do we rarely kiss in public? Even in the safety of gay bars and clubs?'*

When does love become our chance to wake up from a bad dream?

On the day of Victor's forty-day remembrance service a significant portion of London's Black gay community headed to an Anglican church hall in Stockwell. We had heard that – unlike his funeral the month before – this service was open to all his friends. For those who could not pay tribute at the funeral, this was a rare opportunity to remember him and celebrate his life.

At the entrance a memorial booklet was distributed to every arriving guest by two impeccably-dressed ushers; two gay men who we all knew. On glancing at the programme, it was heartwarming to see that Ernest was on the speaker list. He was listed as a 'best friend'. Victor's parents could not make the trip from Nigeria for the service, but Alice, his sister from Chicago, came. As we made ourselves comfortable in our seats we couldn't help but remember that, a few months back, many of us were here in this same church hall with the same officiating Anglican priest. But the last time we were here it was a more festive occasion: a wedding ceremony.

Alice was the first to speak, after the sermon from the head priest and some hymns. She had relocated to Chicago recently, and was the only relative to speak on behalf of the family of the deceased. When she stood at the pulpit whispers went around, notably among the Black gay men in the audience: she was the only one who 'knew''; the only woman who was allowed into our circles. On several occasions she had attended those infamous Sunday get-togethers in Denmark Hill, and at other venues too. By virtue of her gender she was seen as an intruder by those who didn't know her. But her wit and humour always made her a very welcome intruder. She spent so much time in the company of Victor and his friends that she became part of

182

'us'. She understood all our jokes, and laughed with us, even when those jokes were not particularly kind to women.

Alice was straight. She had been a link between our two separate worlds: London's African community – which ignored the existence and contribution of its gay children – and the city's gaydom, which also wanted us to stay invisible. She was a known socialite in both worlds. We didn't know if she had lesbian friends, but rumours about her sexuality were rife. She did not mind and simply ignored them.

In so many ways, then, it was very fitting for her to be chosen as the person to give the keynote speech at the remembrance. She had also attended the wedding three months before in the same hall. It was one of those weddings that occurred in our community: guys well-known to be gay who suddenly got married to women. Invariably, all their gay friends would be invited to the wedding. And some would even appoint their male lovers as best men. And the male lover would later on become godfather of the children.

These practices were among the issues that set us apart from our white friends; and even from other Black gay guys. It didn't matter that we had different opinions on the matter: on this matter our 'gayness' was routinely challenged by others... Accused of duplicity, and even treason! Were we seen as less 'gay' than others because we were 'African'? We were similar to many in the Pakistani and Bangladeshi communities, where similar practices were apparently commonplace.

'This is what you African guys do... always.'

We didn't seem to care about the unsuspecting wives and in-laws, who often had no clue about their new grooms' secret sex-lives.

The tone of those remarks was often accusatory. We were the ones who always eventually got married to women and settled down with children into conventional family life. Especially when we reached our mid-thirties: we literally retired from gaydom and entered into an existence of conformity (and misery). For this we were made to feel like traitors to the gay cause. Few outside the community would understand the sacrifices we made to be welcome in all worlds. Perhaps it was wrong to *'have your cake and eat it'*.

It was ironic that our 'African' identity was reinforced in

London. Many of us didn't shout it from the rooftops when we travelled to Paris, where the French called us *Anglais*, or the US, where they called us *British*. London was the place where we met so many nationals from the continent in ways that could never happen 'back home'; an international crossing-point for Africans from North, East, West and South. And to confuse it all, geography, upbringing or birth were not suffi-cient or exclusive grounds to claim belonging to the continent: many Afro-descendants – born in the Caribbean or North America – also claimed an African connection and identity. London has to be special in our hearts; after all it is the place where African Liberation Day was created, and where it has been celebrated religiously every May since the 1950s.

When *Brokeback Mountain* came out, the movie was a hit in our kitchen discussions. Director Ang Lee had set the story in the sixties, but for us this story could well have been happening in the present, and perhaps even the future. We were so aware of the patriarchal societies we came from and the central role of family in shaping our lives and destinies. Issues of marriage, relationships with women and family usually set us apart from the very different lives of mainstream gay Brits.

Nonetheless, gay people would still get invited to the straight weddings of their fellow gay friends, and to the naming ceremonies of the children that resulted from those dramatic wedlocks. In fact many of the weddings we attended were graced by good numbers of queer people. Such was the case in this same Stockwell hall three months before the remembrance ceremony. Some of the men who were seen sashaying up and down the aisle at the wedding were here again. Looking more sombre this time, but still glamorous. Victor was missing in action at that wedding; rumours about his serious illness were getting confirmed.

Alice (the relative), and Ernest (the 'best friend') read their eulogies. Both looking solemn. Ernest was more shaken, unable to restrain tears. Perhaps his sadness was harder to bear because of the self-imposed censorship; he did not mention his three-year relationship with Victor. Their intimate life together – as lovers – was not supposed to be exposed at this event. Not even the fact that Victor died in his arms.

The eulogy from Alice was equally emotional, though she was more generally at ease and even smiled at times during her speech. She too did not mention the 'secret' life, even though she knew every lover Victor had had in the past ten years. She knew Akin (who was in the audience, and to whom she was a close friend). Almost every speaker mentioned Victor's successful career. It was impressive; before the age of forty he had been appointed as a consultant psychiatrist for East London Mental Health Trust. He never got to start the job, however, as his health deteriorated seriously shortly after he was confirmed in the post. The news of his appointment was a major event in our community. A signal of hope: we too could achieve professional success. A sign that our troubled relations with our families should not draw us back, and a reminder that after all we chose to be in London because we wanted to be successful. But we were also here because we wanted to be free. Free from oppression and willing to live life true to ourselves. We all knew the life of fear that would have been our experience 'back home'.

We sometimes joked that very soon our Sunday discussion club would move to a more upmarket location. Perhaps somewhere like Docklands: St Catherine's Docks; or in one of those new fancy apartment-blocks near Bishopsgate.

Neat speeches, well-chosen words, but without the truth about Victor's life and what it meant to us, they felt like a cover-up. They left the sour taste that our queer lives were secondary, not good enough to even mention, even at important remembrance events. The slightly joyful atmosphere at the start of the service had vanished by the time we left. A pillar of our community was gone, and here we were, feeling lost, and unsure that we had given him the right goodbye. We considered ourselves as his alternative family, perhaps even his real family.

In fact this remembrance event felt like a second death.

In this world we have no blueprint, but in this house we will define who we are...

When you are pushed to the margins of society, you either give up or you resist. Standing still is not an option. Looking for supportive communities was part of this resistance. The quest for the right community never stops, but in every newfound community we are enriched in ways that cannot be easily understood.

As the millennium year turned, more and more political talk of gay rights dominated the news. A major court case in Europe was won, and as a result gay people were now allowed to serve in the British military. Soon after that Mr Blair and his Labour party pushed for more advances in the law. Gay adoptions, an equal age of consent, protection for LGBT people at work and so on... He even appointed a Black gay Muslim man to the House of Lords! *Gay Times*, *Attitude*, *DIVA* and all kind of gay magazines were full of commentaries and speculations about what the future of gay Britain would look like.

For those among us with an interest in political activism there was a major dilemma: how did you get Black folks interested and active in this movement, especially the youth? The house-party crowd, and the club-goers busy looking for sex adventures, falling in and out of love week in, week out. Gay politics was the 'in' thing: could we let this trend just pass us by? Hundreds of Black queers religiously attended *Fruit Machine*, a popular Wednesday night event at Heaven night-club, but did they know how such nights came about?

Chris McKoy was one of those visionaries who saw London's nightlife as a vehicle to build consciousness. He did not live to see the advances in gay rights or race politics that were eventually achieved, but he undoubtedly contributed to that struggle in his way. He saw the commercial gay scene and places like Heaven as places of resistance. And it *was* a struggle, as Heaven's owners resisted his advances. For a long time throughout the nineties many London gay clubs were not ready to play hip-hop or ragga or any of the new genres of Black music which thrived elsewhere in London's mainstream heterosexual clubs. Chris stood up to club-owners, patiently and for many years, working for change. His message was simple: it was time for gay businesses to wake up to cool Britannia; it was no longer acceptable for gay clubs to be cultural enclaves catering only for White peoples' tastes. London is a free place after all; it belongs to no single group.

He died in the millennium year, at the age of thirty, shortly before New Year's Eve. Just like Victor he died while preparing for his biggest contract: a chance to host a New Year's Eve party in a major New York club.

He was a fun-loving intellectual, often seen reading broadsheet newspapers before his weekly performances at *Lowdown*, *Off the Hook* or the other clubs that crept up now and then in London's West or East End. He sometimes performed as a drag queen, and was always a hit. With his tall and slender frame, his Whitney Houston was always a success with the crowds. Most times he performed as a DJ and a club promoter, always on the lookout for venues that would allow him to organise Black gay nights. He skilfully combined entrepreneurship and activism. He learned his trade as a DJ from his Jamaican dad, and worked hard to infuse Black culture into London's club culture of the nineties. American culture dominated pretty much everything in London's gaydom at that time. It was a reflection of Britain; like the ostrich metaphor, its head steeped in US Anglo-Saxon culture and a body in Europe.

This was also the time when black gay folks in the USA had developed new genres of music, in particular house music. Chris was instrumental in making cultural links and bringing house music to Europe. But for a long time the nightlife remained culturally segregated.

The day he was finally accepted as a host DJ at Heaven, at first only for one night, he gained instant respect and admiration. From then on he became resident DJ at the legendary clubs of those days: Emporium, TRADE and others.

Victor and Chris probably did not know each other, most likely never met. Both died before they could release their full potential. Just before the millennium year. Both were powerful community-builders. Each, in very different ways, contributed to building the consciousness of hundreds, maybe more. Their legacy is a testimony that we can change the trajectory of marginalised people by doing simple things with love. They were powerful change-makers for themselves and others because they cared. They gave their time and opened their hearts to the possibility of love.

When I Was Six Years Old

By Paul J. Medford

When I was six years old my grandmother said
'Look at you! Standing there with your hands on
your hips – you can do that if you want – you're in
show business.'

When I was twelve and wearing too much Vaseline on my lips
she said,
'Put some on your eyelashes too! It will make them grow – you
can be whoever you want – you're in show business.'

On my sixteenth birthday she wrote in my card,
'Remember you are free – you can love whoever you want –
you're in show business.'

She saw, she recognised, she affirmed, she empowered.

London

By Mickel Smithen

Each time I hear or read any news regarding homophobia in the Caribbean, Africa or anywhere else I'm so
grateful for all of the Black gay support groups that
have supported me to date. Without groups like Black Connections (run by Pace, the LGBT counselling and mental health
advocacy group) and also NPL (Naz Projects London, the
sexual health group for BME LGBT) I wouldn't be the confident
Black gay man I am today. They gave me the confidence to
come out to my mum and my brother, who I felt needed to
know in order for me to get on with my life. I now have a good
circle of friends who I share many outings with to various gay
and LGBT venues and events.

I never stop going on about Black Connections and the NPL
projects because when you are new to London you need to find
and be around people you can relate to, and nine years ago
when I moved to London from Birmingham I really needed to
feel a sense of community, and to meet Black gay Afri-
can/Caribbean men who shared the same or similar coming out
journeys to the one that I was on at the time.

So now I'm more connected to the gay community but at
times feel rather excluded due to its inaccessibility. I am
visually impaired, and anything that is seen to be different the
gay community are very judgemental of, and will make one feel
very uncomfortable about as they ask stupid questions in a
rude manner:

'What's that?'

I explain it's a cane to help me navigate around the space.
Or their friend who is not from the UK will explain to them that
'he's visually impaired'.

I find it interesting that in London particularly the born gay
Londoners don't seem to understand the various disabilities
out there, whilst gay people from outside London and the UK
seem to understand instantly, and it's sad to think that gay

Londoners can be so ignorant. We talk about gay community and a real gay community is non-judgemental of anyone, regardless of their disability or race. We need to start to accept and love one another and then we'll truly be accepted in the wider community. Until then we've got a lot of work to do.

I'm a Black gay man and proud of it, but why am I not as close to my Black gay brothers and sisters as I am to some of my White or Asian gay friends? That's really interesting. At times I feel I seem to get more support as a performance artist from my White or Asian friends than anyone else.

My dream is that we can start to think outside the box of colours, stop judging one another, and start to support and embrace our differences within the Black community. I believe this will make Black gay people feel empowered and enriched because we'll then know we got each other.

Two pieces by Travis Alabanza

I am

– a collection of things you've told me –

I am the one who will draw you in, due to my exotic skin.
I am the one who stands tall.
I am not fat.
I am not thin.
I am achieving, I am respected
I am a performer. I am a writer.
I am a poet. I am strong with my words.
I am never wrong.
I am always wrong.
I am rarely right.
I always win the fight.
I am an award receiver, an ambassador.
I am loved.
I am also the dark boy.
I am the one stopped and searched at customs.
I am the one that needs a barrier around my hair, to stop those prodding hands.
I am the one that pays five pound extra just to have a tv channel with my people on it.
I am the one that is more likely to end up as a server.
I am the ones whose history spells out server.
I am the one in theatre who will only ever play a server.
I am your server.
I am violent.
I am the one who can't love wherever I want.
I am the one that excels in my field, yet isn't allowed in every field.
I am dark.
I am the one who shocks people with how I speak.
I am the one that is called less black for achieving.
I am a walking contradiction.
I am achieving yet I am dark.
I am gay, yet I am strong.
I am constantly pushed against.
I am confused as being sensitive when offended.
I am a mixed mongrel.

I am coloured.
I am a golly wog.
I am a nigger.
I am your nigger.
I am a faggot,
I am your faggot
I am a queer
I am a poof.
I am going to hell.
Yet I am good.
I am dark.
I am gay.
I am not cursed.
I am proud.
And I am, from this point on, going to remain the complex,
    multi-faceted
        dark
            queer
                rainbow creature I was born to be - and say:

            I am strong.

Chocolate

I love chocolate. All types of chocolate. I like the dark-coated Snicker bars, the M&Ms, Hershey Kisses and sweetly-coated Cadbury Stars. The bitter taste of 100% cocoa, and the honesty in the sting. The smoothness of the caramel swirl and the large Kit Kat chunky kinda thing. I like how I know that dark chocolate packs a punch, and that I brave myself for its harsh-tasting crunch. I like that out of all the chocolates dark chocolate is the strongest – it's been through the shit, and it stands up tastiest of the bunch. Only those that can handle the sweet bitter lips are the ones that stay standing and I'm first in line, only ever trying to find the chocolate among the Milky Way, XL bars worth the extra delay... I went through a spell, call it a Lent, when I had given you up – call it a bad experience with one bar that made me decide I'd had enough. From then on only the milkiest of ways fell on my lips, so I was never reminded of the Green & Black's hips – I thought that would heal me. Fill my wounds with white chocolate sprinkles and I'll forget that 100% cocoa exists... But god, too much white chocolate can make you sick. Only the brown M&Ms really can kick it, and I'm tired of explaining my heritage to the Milky Way cowboy kid – damn I miss dark chocolate's honesty-filled eyes, recognising my pain, man fuck these white lies. I don't want the milky chocolate house on the hill, give me the realest chocolate shit any day over that for real. So next time someone says what you given up for Lent? Damn straight it can't be anything but my chocolate-covered friends. So I went bought every dark bar on the shelf, gluttony over-came, and I bit and I squelched my way through every Kit Kat every Snicker bar as well – trying to replicate that dark foreign smell. And I know that no bar will ever taste the same, but damn, if I stick to dark chocolate – I'll not have to deal with a racist sucking my dick, ever again.

Inadequate

By P. J. Samuels

My friend called me yesterday.
'I am so sad,' he said.
'I don't see the point to living.'
This beautiful boy said 'I hate myself.'
And I said to him you're beautiful.
But that feels so inadequate.
I said to him baby boy, you are one of the best people I
know.
I said I want to make myself into spectacles,
place myself on your face,
and have you look in the mirror so you see what I see when I
see you.

Love reflected and multiplied.
I still wear the ring you gave me, simply, you said, because I
love jewellery.
I still have the leather bracelet.
The clasp is broken because I wore it so much.
I feel your kiss on my cheek though you are far away.
I love you.
You are beautiful.
I wish I could be the voice in your head so I could sing you a
new song.
I wish I could be the world so I could make it ok to be you.
Make it ok to cry because sometimes boys hurt too.
I wish I was a straw, and always there for you to clutch when
you feel like you are drowning.
A lifeboat, to take you safely to shore.
I understand. I am not your saviour.
But I wish I knew how to help the world handle that much
fabulous.
I wish I knew how to help you.

I wish I wasn't so fucking inadequate.
This city eats people up and papers over the cracks,
and carries on like nothing happened.
The pied piper takes more than children.
You are more than a blip on the radar.
You are powerful.
You are not a fallen leaf blowing in the wind, you are the wind.
You are not a cigarette in the rain, you are the rain.
You are lightning that rents the sky.
Thunder that rocks the earth.
You are all kinds of fantastic.
I wish I could make you see what I see when I look at you.
You are important.
Your life matters.
I know it's hard and it's heavy, but this too will pass.
Just hold on.
Do your days in moments.
And until you learn again how to love you, take mine.
Take my love and love you.
And hold on.
Please.
These words, are inadequate.
My love, is inadequate.
But you, my brother, aren't.
You're a rare and wonderful work of art.
You are the morning song of summer birds.
You are the morning.
The wonder of new beginnings.
The scar of survival.
The rainbow after a stormy night.
Just hold on.
Please.
Though it all seems inadequate,
I promise you brother
You are enough.
Just hold on.

Femininity in Men is a Source of Power

By Diriye Osman

W hen I first told my friends that I would be wearing a pearl-studded mock-Elizabethan gown for the cover of my book, *Fairytales For Lost Children*, they were doubtful. In the past I had flirted with androgyny by wearing women's jewellery and a dash of perfume but I had never worn a dress. To my friends, though the notion of a man wearing a dress meant having an extra pair of balls, it seemed essentially perverse. But to me the idea made perfect sense. My book was about gay Somalis exploring their sexual identities and gender roles, so why not riff on these motifs by donning a jewel-encrusted queen's dress?

I liked the flamboyant cheekiness of the concept, but when I went to the costumier for my first fitting that sense of cheekiness gave way to something more dynamic and surprising. As the costumier strapped me into the corset I didn't feel constricted. Instead, I felt – and looked – ice-cool, sensual, striking, powerful, virile.

In *Against Interpretation and Other Essays*, Susan Sontag argues that, 'What is most beautiful in virile men is something feminine; what is most beautiful in feminine women is something masculine.' To me, this is the most elegant breakdown of the Jungian theory of anima and animus – the feminine principle within men and the masculine principle within women.

Some of our most influential cultural figures – David Bowie, Grace Jones and Prince in particular – have straddled this dichotomy for decades. Miles Davis summed up Prince's visceral sex appeal as such: 'He's got that raunchy thing, almost like a pimp and a bitch all wrapped up in one image, that transvestite thing.'

In Somali culture hyper-masculinity is the most desired attribute in men. Femininity signifies softness, a lightness of

199

touch: qualities that are aggressively pressed onto young girls and women. When a woman does not possess feminine traits, it is considered an act of mild social resistance. This applies equally to men who are not overtly masculine but the stakes are considerably amplified. If a Somali man is considered feminine he is deemed weak, helpless, pitiful: The underlying message being that femininity is inherently inferior to masculinity.

Variants of this thinking extend across most cultures, belief systems, races and sexualities: Western gay culture is as obsessed with exaggerated masculine traits as the patriarchs of Somali clans. Femininity is predominantly perceived as an unappealing quality, a cancelling-out of hypervalorised masculine traits, with effemiphobia reaching its natural end-point on the online gay dating circuit, with the infamous 'No fems' or 'be straight-acting' tags that pop up on most profiles.

In the case of gay men one could argue that decades if not centuries of stigmatization have created a culture of conformity fuelled by internalized homophobia: The accusation – and it is framed as an accusation – that same-sex-attracted men fail to be authentically masculine has left an enduring mark. But where does that leave everyone else who doesn't fit the 'straight-acting' tag? After all weren't the Stonewall riots, the birth of the gay civil rights movement, kick-started by the transgender community, drag queens and effeminate young men – the most outcast members of the gay community? Shouldn't they be our heroes?

The case for effemiphobia often hinges on a threadbare argument against 'camp' overexposure. Prominent and popular performers like Paul O'Grady, Graham Norton and Alan Carr are constantly cited as stereotypes of what an imagined mainstream society wants from their gay performers: flamboyant, with outsized, unthreatening and mostly desexualised personalities. But it takes a tremendous amount of chutzpah to be as charming, cheeky and exuberant as O'Grady, Norton and Carr have been throughout their careers. Each of these performers has mined his experience as an effeminate gay man into comedic gold, and each one is now giggling all the way to the bank.

The position of these men as wealthy performers, however, obscures their outlier statuses, and their success is not an accurate representation of the daily stigma and abuse that many feminine men, whether gay, bisexual, asexual or straight, have had to endure from the straight community and certain sections of the LGBT community.

The American writer Dan Savage, who co-created the 'It Gets Better' campaign to tackle the issue of suicides amongst gay teenagers who were being bullied because of their sexual orientation, put it succinctly: 'It's often the effeminate boys and the masculine girls, the ones who violate gender norms and expectations, who get bullied.'

I contemplated these issues as I toiled with my dress to the photographer's studio. The outfit was heavier than I expected and I was sweating by the time I arrived. After I mopped myself down and gathered myself together the makeup artist helped me get into the dress. As she laced my corset I thought how strange it was that I, an African man living in the 21st century, would willingly strap myself into the kind of constricting garments that European women had fought so hard to resist a hundred years ago. I remained ambivalent until my makeup was done, until I glanced in the mirror and saw something I had never seen within myself before: a sense of poise, daring even. I had morphed from a shy, timid young man into someone who was bold, unafraid to take risks. I stood before the camera and gazed directly at the lens. There was no need for validation. The photographer didn't have to give me directions. I knew what I was doing. I struck confident pose after pose, proud of the fact that there was a hard-won sense of power in my femininity.

Because Elbows are Provocative

By Donovan Christian-Carey

The Headmaster's Bristol 411 thundered under the quarterdeck through the old stone tunnel's gates and continued up the inclined drive to the school's main entrance. There to meet him, Crain knew, would be two first- or second-year boys in their CCF uniforms, standing at attention. That entrance, with its dome, Doric sandstone columns and stained glass, was strictly not for the use of boys except on Remembrance Day. Then, as part of the special assembly, they would perform the stylized goose-step which was the school march, and march from the main hall, past Trophy Wall and Honour Wall, down the twin staircases and out under the dome, past the stained glass that bore the school motto and out through the main door. This was accompanied by the choir singing the school song, the words to which were rendered inaudible by the Richter-scale reverberations of the school organ. The effect, even the most sceptical boys had to agree, was always stimulating.

Crain was a fourth year non-boarder, the phrase 'boarders' and 'non-boarders' replacing 'Day Boy', which had in recent years not infrequently brought lessons to a sniggering halt with lisped comments from both pupils and teachers. 'Crain is a Day Boy, Sir' and 'He's only friends with other Day Boys, Sir.'

'Is this true? Are you a Day Boy, Crain? And do you have Day Boyfriends?' And most ignominiously, 'Did you come in the Day Boy's Entrance?' Not infrequently the Day Boy in question had been Crain.

This morning, while waiting for the bus, Crain had been swept up by the headmaster in his plum-coloured, throaty-sounding car.

Crain had no idea why the Commodore stopped to pick him up. He had never seen or heard of him doing it before, but he was grateful – not to be out of the rain, but to be spared the stares and whispers of the comprehensive school-kids on the bus.

At speeds substantially in excess of the speed limit Crain was motored to school. The Head had spoken softly and reassuringly about this being a time of great difficulty and change in Crain's life but that in time he would adapt and thrive. The outside world was a blur of razor grey, but embraced by the soft, warm, honey-brown upholstery, breathing the rich mix of leather, smoke and Limacol, listening to the head's round vowel-sounds and measured tones and the sternum thuddery of the six-litre, Crain's heart had slowed, his slim shoulders had unwound, and he felt calm and safe. The Commodore had continued talking as Crain brushed his own hair out of his face and watched the blood return to his pale fingers, making his now healthy-looking hands appear alien to him.

They arrived at Main Door, where two air cadets stood at attention. Crain got out of the car, thanked the Commodore, and was about to walk back to the Day Boys' Entrance when, to the bemusement of the air cadets, the Commodore gestured that he should follow him in through Main Door. The Head over-armed his keys to Air Cadet Andrew Clive. Amongst the many advantages of being on Main Door duty was the fifty-fifty chance that you would get to park the Commodore's car or even drive the Headmaster's immaculately-dressed and kind wife to the Tunnel Gate. This afforded ample opportunity to cruise slowly around the main school building past the quarterdeck to the quad and cricket pavilion, and to empty the ashtrays, liberating many only partially-smoked cigarettes; and most recently this could all be accomplished whilst listening to the Commodore's new CD player.

The car park was next to the swimming pool and backed onto a sprawling country park. This at its narrowest point became a path that led to Whitefriars Academy Girls' School, which had become a comprehensive ten years or so ago, but maintained close ties with its still-independent neighbour in all the ways it is convenient for single-sex schools to do, and the truants from which would usually join the boys in the park for a free smoke and a laugh. Andrew Clive maintained that he had had 'three fingers up Mandy Hemel under the willow by the trench' – although if you believed Clive, there were very few girls who he encountered that did not by and by end up with 'three fingers up 'em.' Crain had always thought it unlikely this might be at all pleasurable to any but a select few woman, but then what did he know? Nothing, and he had no means, he thought, of acquiring such knowledge any time soon. And so he had allowed three-finger Clive to regularly clasp him round the neck in a death-grip and assault him with his heavy-petting, badly-bitten-to-the-quick triple digits without dispute.

As Crain's head drew level with the mezzanine where the Headmaster's and Deputy's rooms clung precariously to the inner wall, the never-knowingly-understanding, always abrasive Mister Critchley spat down from above, 'Crain! Boy! Why are you using Main Door? Two demerits! My office imme...' He discontinued as first the Commodore's deeply tanned pate, followed by his deeply tanned patrician head, rose up into his view. Critchley turned and crackled away.

Tanned all over the Commodore was. Not some sunny, two-week-holiday patchy 'caught the sun' tan, but the all-over multi-layered kaleidoscope of perma-tan peaches, coppers, bronzes, browns, yellows and golds that Caucasian skin is capable of when exposed to three or four vacations in the West Indies every year for twenty years. The Head loved everything about the Caribbean; the heat, the sun, the food and black women, and he loved to sunbathe nude. The fact of the matter was that he generally loved to *be* nude, and his tall, broad-shouldered, lightly-sunbleached-hair-dusted, hard-bronzed, casually unclothed form could regularly be admired by those with an inclination to do so, swimming, exercising, or showering. When he encountered students or staff he was neither embarrassed nor brazen but easy in his nakedness. Except he was not naked, exposed, vulnerable: he was noble nude. The impression of the man was completed by his genitalia resembling nothing so much as the fat cock-and-balls effigies that adorned every locker, book, desk and wall in his school like a talisman.

In his office the man with the tan lit another Peter Stuyvesant.

'As you may know, each year I take a group of the boys to the West Indies for six weeks in the autumn term.' Crain nodded his awareness. 'This year we are going to Grenada. If you wanted to go it might be possible because a previously-booked boy has had to pull out, leaving a vacant place partially funded by his non-refundable deposit. If you decide that you'd like to go I'll have Mrs Powel get your aunt and uncle in for a chat.'

Crain's wit was tumbling around on his mind's ocean and being dashed on the rocks of his own anxieties. His blood began congealing.

'Of course you don't have to decide right now,' the Commodore continued, with powers the envy of Poseidon that at once commanded the ocean be calm. 'Just let Mrs Powel know by the end of the week. I think it would be a very valuable experience for you which you should embrace. The boys that come away with me often bond and mature in a manner which benefits them in many ways. We have a lot of fun and learn a lot. It is a... life-affirming experience, and I encourage you to consider this offer very carefully though it be outside your comfort zone.'

'I will, Sir.'

'Sometimes the only way to gain perspective is to do something radical. Do you believe that?'

'I am not sure, Sir.'

'Good! That shows that your judgment is unimpaired' – again his measured laugh – 'and this reassures me that I am choosing the right man for this mission.'

Crain resisted the impulse to widen his eyes in terror and instead opted for an expression which he hoped read as '*a year prefect awaiting orders, Sir*'.

'I would like you to show around a new temporary student the school will be hosting. He's not short on character. Beyond that he defies adequate description, so it really is best that you just meet him. You may find his confidence infectious and illuminating.' With those words the sun, which had been missing behind leaded clouds for days, burned through with intense brilliance. The heavy, button-studded, leather-backed door to the headmaster's office began to open, a shift of air briefly kissing their whole bodies as the room overcame its pressure differential. Then, continuing with a sigh across the milk-chocolate-coloured deep-pile shag, it revealed in the ornate frame the most incredible individual Crain had ever seen.

The Commodore had not been the first to note the ineffable quality of Gillard Janus. The stained glass, the sunlight and the sounds of a thousand boys and that pipe organ were at his disposal, and were so aligned as to bear him in as if he were the Queen of Sheba upon a litter. Indeed it was a resemblance Gillard cultivated. He had found it a useful first impression to make, and one that required surprisingly little effort. Beauty and strength, a combination with universal appeal, formed the keel of his being. Crain rose from his seat, trapping errant electrons. Gillard stood at attention and smartly saluted the Commodore and was given an 'at ease'.

Gillard was a vivid, tropical-coloured abstract watercolour of a schoolboy, an hypnotic three-dimensional zoetrope confection, shimmering, floating, intoxicating. He maintained their attention on his immaculate American manicure as the salute, over-articulated, flowed at once into an elegant, out-stretched handshake. While Crain could not decide if Gillard was wearing nail-polish he brought his own hand up to complete his half of the social ritual, and with that contact came the discharge of now-immediately-repatriated electrons with an almost audible crack. Crain's not-unnatural impulse was to flinch back. However as he did so he felt Gillard's hand solidify around his own and firmly hold him in place.

'Hello, my name is Gillard, I'm pleased to meet you,' said the elegant black boy, smiling broadly in his zoot-suit parody of the school uniform.

Like all the schools of its kind at the time, this one had a superficially healthy demographic spectrum but was not yet multicultural: the dominant culture of the institution remained one of privilege barely concealed beneath threadbare tweed. There were a handful of black pupils at the school, (although some of them may still have been 'coloured'), but Crain could not imagine Gillard fitting in with them or any of the pre-existing cliques. It was true that even a minor British fee-paying school had in any intake year the progeny of aristocrats, diplomats, politicians, gangsters, millionaires – both nouveau and antique varieties – and, threaded through these warps of money and privilege, (legitimate, traditional, coveted and acquired through favours bought and stolen), were the wefts of

parents for whom the term's fees represented a disproportion-
ate percentage of their income, and some who found it difficult
to pay. There were also some bursary pupils and a few state-
sponsored boys. But like the prisons that schools like this are so
often compared to, if the institution is functioning correctly
'no-one need know what you're in here for'.

The Commodore spoke. 'Gillard this is Crain. Crain, although I realise half-term is nearly upon us, and it would not
be appropriate for me to dictate to you your leave, I would
regard it as a personal favour to me if you would point him in
the right direction while he finds his billet. You have my
permission to take a free period until lunch, give him a bit of a
tour.' The Commodore was dismissing them, having assumed
Crain's compliance in the way that commanding officers are
wont to do.

Crain had heard the fragmentary rumours about 'Uncle
Commodore': that he hosted his many, many illegitimate half-
caste coffee-coloured babies at the school for various reasons
ranging from extortion to murder; and all the back-up harmo-
nies around those ugly songs. Could Gillard, Crain speculated,
be the Headmaster's son? There was no immediate visible
evidence to rule it out as a possibility, and although they did
not superficially bear a strong resemblance to each other, they
both wore an air of easy, confident authority and had a flair for
dressing. Even now Gillard was draped on his heavy chair
much more comfortably than a boy in a headmaster's office had
any right to be. However, having drifted too far from his mind's
calm harbour, his anxieties began to swell again. If he was the
Commodore's son why would the Commodore shackle him to
Crain of all people?

'Since the Commodore has such faith in you I am sure that
we shall become fast friends.' Gillard's voice was far back,
measured, musical and slightly clipped, British, not unlike the
Commodore's, and it too had the power to rest a storm. It was
an accent from another time that lent itself to imputation.
Gillard delighted in this: it was amusing to him that the rest of
the world frequently employed the query, 'Is he gay or is he
British?' and he was not displeased to be both.

His only nagging concern was that perhaps he had adjusted
too readily to the assignation, but then he had decided to avail

himself of the many daily-available opportunities to observe naked and semi-naked women in what to him seemed every other magazine, book, newspaper, and television programme, and that was an avalanche that would surely give environmental nurture a fighting chance against what he knew to be his nature. However he liked to keep an open mind: it seemed reasonable to suppose that this might just be the phase that anecdotally some pubescent boys were apt to experience and repress in later life, and that his own experience might not be contradictory to that narrative. In practice it meant that whilst choking down his self-prescribed, almost hourly homo-be-gone innoculant of female nudity, he was frequently in the company of boys and adult males who were prepared to risk life and limb and cash, crash cars and bikes, contort and compromise themselves mentally and physically, fail exams and jeopardize relationships all for a particular glimpse of naked female flesh, as though the next freely-available opportunity might not occur within their lifetime instead of the next time they bought a newspaper. They were also, it seemed, compelled to be as vocal as possible to reassure one another of their continued participation in the irrational game of Spot The Boobs when the boobs are literally everywhere.

'Nobody wears the hat.'

'What? You take that back!' For the first time since they had left the headmaster's office Gillard broke his stride, his high-stepping catwalk sashay. 'But boaters can be worn in so many ways.' He flourished the straw hat, the brim and ribbon of which mocked the word 'uniform', and in demonstration tilted the hat far back on his head and teased his crimped fringe 'like a virgin'. Then he pulled the brim down low over his eyes, hunched his shoulders and ruched his sleeves. Before Crain could stop him Gillard exhaled, 'Fosse! And of course my personal favourite and the workhorse of any hat repertoire – ' he flicked the brim with thumb and middle finger and stood up straight ' – jaunty angle – '

'SLEEVES!'

'Shoes!' retorted Gillard.

'Sleeves boy! Sleeves!'

'Who is this hysterical person and what is his problem in general and with sleeves in particular?' Gillard raised an eyebrow.

'It's Pritchard, he's the head prefect and he's – ' By this time Richard Pritchard or Two Dicks or Square Dick – the obscure and not-so-obscure names schoolboys assigned him – had covered the distance between them and was standing before them, snarling, apoplectic and red-faced. Gillard reached out to shake his hand and pulled the arc lever on what he knew was his winningest smile.

'Hello, Head Prefect! I...' he paused '...am Gillard Janus.'

'Demerits for you both, and you look like a prancing ponce. Are you wearing makeup? From across the quad I thought you were someone's visiting sister.' Gillard was indeed wearing makeup, quite a lot of it, in fact. Today he was sporting a dewy Little Richard with an ultra-fine copper, bronze and purple glitter at the left temple, brow, cheek and jawline in thin, discrete triangles.

The vice that Gillard was sure would eventually spell his doom was to lead people to the question. People led to a question seldom realise they are being manipulated, but the time-difference between the question and the prepared answer might one day be the difference between life and death. It was a phenomenon he characterised as the Harmony Hairspray effect, after a commercial he had liked as a child, its slogan '*is* she or *isn't* she?' Gillard enjoyed a great many things that were currently arbitrarily designated as feminine, and found it inexplicable that through the happenstance of his gender a whole other world of colour and fragrance was denied him. Unless he was prepared to pass it off as mere 'play-acting'. He considered that this was less connected to his gender identity than it was to his taste. More importantly, to his sense of self and its expression not seeking the sanction or the censure of anyone else.

'You need to smarten up, boy, if you expect to fit in around here – starting with your sleeves. Tell him, Crain.'

Crain mouthed the arcane directive that, 'No boy shall be seen with his sleeves rolled above the elbow.'

'So smarten up, my ladioo.'

Crain had long ago given himself permission to designate anyone who used the set phrase 'my lad' or any of its derivatives a wanker in perpetuity, and he felt it unlikely that this encounter would present a challenge to his preconceptions. Gillard's compliance was gracious but timed to synchronize with his inquiry, 'Why is that?'

The question seemed innocent, but an ear sensitive enough would have made out the barely audible micro-inhale at the end of the sentence. Gillard had observed that absurd rules can only be substantiated with more of the same.

'Because elbows are provocative,' was the second half of a sentence that he couldn't have bettered himself.

Gillard flashed Pritchard a dangerous look. A look designed to unsettle forty year-old married men, and it had. It also had the benefit of offering a great punchline. Amidst a coy ballet of batting eyelids and pouty lips Gillard licked his index finger, touched it to his still-exposed elbow and made a hissing sound, snatching his finger away to complete the illusion. 'If you think my elbows are provocative you should try my mouth. Are you all so starved of human affection that the merest glimpse of – '

'You should know better, Crain, than to go around with the benders. Everyone here has been taking it easy on you but if you start hanging out with bummers – '

Gillard had read the confused attraction in Pritchard. He was used to this response. His voice, serious and earnest: 'It needn't be like this, we can be friends.'

'Don't try to bum me up!' Pritchard's voice was high and incredulous. A foam was beginning to form at the corners of his mouth and even Gillard's prodigious powers could not prevent a cloud from covering the sun. 'Oh, right on cue here comes your day boy bum-chum, Crain, to overturn my demerits.'

'Is there a problem here, Mr Pritchard?' The baritone, calm and powerful, was mature enough to have come from a man twice his age. Tall, athletic, long-limbed, broad-shouldered, an achingly handsome conflagration of well-defined square jawline, dimples, cheekbones and large, long, dark-lash-fringed, pale aquamarine eyes sparkling with mischief and potential – the resemblance he bore to peerless Apollo was not merely passing but had circled back and passed again and again. Head boy, captain of the rugby, cricket, badminton and debate teams. An accomplished 'A' student who was not afraid to question blind obedience rationally and eloquently. His precocious adolescence had left his tawny skin unblemished and, although this now meant shaving every other day, he was pleased to have developed chest hair that withered to a pencil line accentuating the definition of his abdomen before widening to join the rest of his pubic hair.

To be both attractive and intelligent in an environment of entitlement might make some conceited or narcissistic, but here the occasional use of a popular spray-in light-activated hair bleach to literally highlight his naturally sandy-blond hair was their only indicator. He wore his straight peg trousers an inch too short, revealing white towelling socks and tassel loafers, all the better for demonstrating his Michael Jackson toe-stands, at which he was, of course, excellent.

'Are you okay, Crain?' His name was Hudson Britton, he was a Christopher Isherwood wet dream come true, and he was walking towards them. He was the son of an airline pilot father and East German figure-skating mother who was now a district nurse. They were not rich but they were loving and nurturing. His parents had rightly assumed that their emotionally well-balanced and intelligent child would flourish in any school environment, and they had chosen this school for their son more because of its proximity to their home than with any view to social or academic betterment.

Conversely Pritchard's father had abandoned him to boarding school, asserting, '*Listen thick-'ead, you don't know you fuckin' born. I left school and 'ad to graft with these when I was eleven. I would've give me arm to get educated, learn what they know, boy, but don't you come it with any of that shirt-lifting shit, I'll kick you up and down them stairs and out my door, boy, and if you ever came back I would take you up the farm and put a bullet in you, it's all they deserve.*'

'Your boyfriend won't be here forever.' Pritchard walked away muttering 'queers' under his breath and the weather changed.

Pritchard was right, although Hudson and Crain had entered as day boys from the town in the same intake. Their trajectories academically, physically, emotionally, could not have been more divergent but their early bond had endured. But Hudson would soon be gone. His academic prowess had seen him advance a year, and his late summer birthday made that year more like two, and he was cruising to the full Cambridge scholarship he richly deserved.

'I'm okay, Hudson. Pritchard was just beasting the new boy.'

'Hi, I'm Hudson Britton, head boy and Crain's best friend. I was worried because... It's just that, from a distance it looked as though Pritchard was going to hit you.'

'You are very perceptive. I like the way you think and so I think I like you.' The smile, and again the elaborate gesture-to-handshake manoeuvre that met Hudson's firm, friendly counter and raised him with a dimpled smile of his own, bringing the total number now on display to three and causing Gillard to exclaim, 'Frak! If my pimp sees you it's all over for me and I'll be touching gentlemen's elbows in dark alleys for loose change.'

'Okay, ignoring for the moment your dubious relationship with the man who lives off your immoral earnings, you know 'frak'?'

'I love 'frak'. I wish more people used the word. Have you got a BBC?'

'Model B. They used to say 'frak!' in *Battlestar Galactica* too.'

'What computers have they got here?' Gillard asked.

'There's a PET and an Apple II.'

'Do you want to go to a party tomorrow? I have this friend and her parents are away. She's the most bizarre character: she says she's a princess, she's a terrible fag-hag, but she does know lots of girls. And please say you'll come with...?'

Crain's initial thought was: who on earth was it that Gillard might find bizarre, but the thought was interrupted.

'Her name is the Princess Plenty Plenty Mittahsalty.' The boys all laughed. 'I know, right? Please come... there will be girls there'.

Hudson could see that Crain was waiting for him to politely decline on both their behalves. Recently, however, Hudson had had the vague feeling that there might be fewer opportunities for adventure than he might have wished. A feeling he was about to combat by accepting an invitation to a party from an exotic black boy he'd only just met. Crain was baffled but Hudson insisted:

'Come on, Crain: we've always done exactly what we've been told to do and that's fine, but soon I'm going to uni and I don't think I've ever done anything off the road-map.'

Crain had never been able to deny Hudson and had never really wanted to so he nodded.

'Excellent. Because if I'm honest, Crain, you look like someone who could really do with a party, and I know the girls are going to love this strong silent vibe you have.' Gillard reached out and gently brushed the hair from Crain's face. Crain didn't mind. 'What are we doing after lunch?'

Hudson himself had private study revision with FAT Thomas. Frank Arthur Timothy Thomas's parents could not have known that he would become a morbidly obese teacher who 'never checks the study room.'

Crain told Gillard that they had games, 'But I'm remnants.'

Hudson explained that students who didn't participate in games were referred to as 'games remnants'.

'Truly the treasures of this place most certainly lie in its trove of picturesque turns of phrase. I don't think it's healthy to refer to yourself in the pejorative. I think of you as crucial, Crain – my first friend here.' He smiled again, that smile still radiant and ultra-bright, but now less pyrotechnic. For Gillard had mastered the subtle anatomy of his smile, including the very tricky eye-smile. 'And I will hear no ill spoken of he who I call friend of mine.' The stress was on the possessive. 'So, just to be clear: what you're saying is that we have the day off! Then let us blow through this place.'

'You mean bunk off?'

'Well, it's hardly bunking off. The Commodore gave us a morning pass and by your own admission you were going to be free in the afternoon, and I need two good-looking boys to squire me around the local sights.'

Gillard linked arms with Crain and Hudson, who exchanged looks.

Hudson suggested that they go to his house since his father was away for another two days and his mother would not be home until after school.

By the time they reached the bus-stop Crain's misgivings had begun to ease. Thankfully Gillard had stopped walking arm in arm with them. People were still staring and whispering but he and Hudson had competition as to who would be the object of people's attention today. Gillard high-stepped, pouted and posed as he walked. He explained: 'In the future there will be cameras at every street corner and on every lamppost. Everyone will be on TV all the time, and in that world I intend to shine. So I practice.'

Crain, hypersensitive to such things, became aware of the cat-calling girls in A-line skirts first. Two black girls and two white. First the black girls chorused, 'Hey, batty-bwoy, you are a disgrace to the black race,' kissed their teeth, and began throwing bits of screwed-up paper.

Crain and Hudson tried to ignore them. Gillard knew that he could not, and now, as always, it was just a matter of timing. Then he heard the cue he had been waiting for: 'Oi mate...mate... oi, you...' One of the young white girls called, 'If you don't mind, can I ask you a personal question?' Gillard turned and smiled expectantly. He appraised the girls: so confident, so insensitive to the pain of others. He primed a high-yield scorched-earth detonation. 'Can we ask you a personal question?' Gillard nodded his compliance. 'Are you gay? You are, in't you?'

She sat back down as though she had completed a deft syllogism, and it brought paroxysms of laughter from the girls and several other passengers.

'Why ladies, how observant of you. Yes I am. Honi soit qui mal y pense.'

More laughter. 'He admitted it,' they smirked. But Gillard continued, his voice still sweet and steady:

'And now can I ask *you* a personal question? When was the last time you washed your cunt because I can smell it from here.' The words napalmed the upper deck of the 82. There were gasps and murmurs of indignation and one of the girls began to cry. Gillard surveyed the battlefield with an imperial demeanour to ensure his foe was completely vanquished. But he knew that pain can only give birth to more pain so he said, 'Listen, ladies. Now that I have your full attention: being oppressed isn't nice, is it? Yes, I am different from you. But when you ridicule that difference you legitimate the very people who have been oppressing your sex for centuries, and you diminish yourselves and your children.'

With that he turned on his Cuban heels and sashayed down the aisle and down the stairs and off the bus that had stopped as if for his sole convenience.

The two boys hurried after him. 'You were amazing in there,' Hudson said. 'They're still talking about what you said.'

Crain said, 'That was so cool.'

'The forces of orthodoxy must never be allowed to mandate our behaviour or in the future the government will be able to ban people from wearing hats just because they don't like the hats people choose to wear. When in another age, one within my living memory, those self-same forces decreed it all but mandatory for almost everyone to wear one, and who is to say which one is better?'

'You really like hats, don't you?' Crain was teasing Gillard, and Gillard was aware what an extraordinary personal achievement this was for him, and was happy for him.

'Hats are important. They prompt very specific responses in a great many people. Black hat, white hat, Roundhead or Cavalier, cowboy versus Indian.' He put on his boater and focused his attention through them to the lamppost some metres beyond. 'It's all about the hats. Jaunty angle!'

'And you talk about the future a lot too.'

'The future is easily as important as hats. I can't wait to get there. In the future people's every other thought will scroll across their chests like pages from Ceefax.'

'What I want to know,' Hudson inquired, 'is, how did you know this is where you needed to get off the bus?'

'Because this is where I needed to get off the bus,' Gillard said simply.

'No, what I mean is, how did you know this was the stop nearest to my house?'

Gillard just smiled. The boys were now in the high street. Gillard took Hudson and Crain to McDonald's and bought them all Big Macs, fries, drinks and apple pies, which he requested as if they were in Fortnum's, and then they went to Hudson's house. It was a place that Crain had spent a great deal of time in recently, and Mrs Britton had told him that he was welcome to come over, 'Even ven Hoodson iß gone,' and she had squeezed his hand. In Hudson's large, hessian-walled, tidy bedroom the boys laughed and lounged on Hudson's bright orange continental quilt, jumbo cord bean bag, or futon, while they listened to his cassette-taped music collection. Crain had always admired Hudson's intuitive ability to stop the tape, whether it were fast-forwarding or rewinding, at exactly the song they wanted to hear. They played *Frak!* and *Elite* and made the BBC Micro's speech ROM say rude words phonetically.

Hudson asked Crain, 'Are you going to come to the Caribbean with the Commodore and us?'

Crain's aunt and uncle had allowed him to attend the school because it was *'what they'* (his parents) *'wanted,'* but repeatedly made it abundantly clear that they would not put up with him bringing home airs and graces, knowledge or enlightenment. The sermon would continue, *'You remember: you might go to school with these rich kids but you ain't one of them.'* They would generally wait until he was almost out of the room to add, *'Just like his 'ucking mother! Always got to do you one better.'* And he had learned it was preferable to be far enough away not to have to hear, *'I'm sorry love, I know she was your sister but she always thought she was better than the rest of us'* or, *'But it weren't just her! It was 'im an'all! Skiing! for-fuck's-sake.'* The liturgy concluded they would slurp their strong tea and nod at one another sagely. To not enjoy the tea Crain had discovered left you open to accusations of despising the proletariat. *'Is it not refined enough for her majesty? The sooner you finish at that bloody school the better, and the sooner you can get your head out of the bloody clouds and get a job and start paying back some of the money me and your Aunty have spent on you these last two years.'* He didn't want to raise the subject of a tropical jaunt with them because of the seething resentment that his only inheritance from his parents had been his exclusive education. His cousin, with whom he now shared a small, airless room which smelled of boiled vegetables, was 'doing just fine at the comp, thank you very much.'

Hudson's spacious bedroom didn't smell of vegetables, cooked or otherwise. It, like its occupant, smelled freshly-laundered, with a difficult-to-place, subtle, medicated mix of sandalwood and lavender.

'I think you should decide to go, Crain,' Gillard said. 'Whether you *actually* go or not is irrelevant. The decision is the important thing. Look at it this way: the only good thing about caregivers that don't, is the fact that they don't care what you do or where you go as long as you don't bring any trouble back home with you. So you may as well do what you think is best rather than trying to please them because you won't. Believe me, I know.'

'Is the Commodore your father?' Hudson asked.

'Is that what they say about me here?' Gillard laughed his musical laugh and, turning to Crain, he said, 'We should all go to the West Indies, it will be fun. Hudson and I will make it our mission over the next week to convince you to come. Right, it's getting late. Do you think your mother would mind if I used the phone to call a taxi?'

Hudson called to his mother, 'Mum? Can Gillard and Crain stay over tonight?'

'Ja, zey musten telephone home first, to check alles klar.'

But Gillard said, 'I can't tonight. Believe me, it is my best, strongest policy *never* to turn down the opportunity to sleep with two good-looking, blue-eyed white boys. But I have to go home tonight.'

Neither Gillard nor Crain had anyone who would be remotely concerned by where they might spend the night, but they both went through the telephone charade anyway.

After he left, Hudson and Crain went straight to bed as instructed by Gillard because, 'Tomorrow is going to be full-on and you are going to need your rest... and maybe an overnight bag.' He blew the boys kisses from the back of the black cab, and as it drove away it began to rain.

The next morning the first herald of Gillard's arrival by taxi was again the sun, and he met the boys on the quarterdeck with, 'Oh god, a rainbow! How I hate them!' Gillard was preparing to deliver the rest of his '*in the future rainbows are the arching harbingers of doom*' routine when he heard the sound, a crack that amongst the reverberant stone walls seemed to come from all directions at once. 'What was that?'

Crain knew that the sound was that of a discharge from one of the school's Combined Cadet Force armoury of ten Lee-Enfield rifles, the firing of which was strictly proscribed, the ammunition inaccessible to the boys.

Gillard and Crain scanned around for the source of the sound.

'Hey guys, I think I've been shot – '

Gillard and Crain turned in time to see the light leave Hudson's eyes and his body falling slowly, silently to the long-grassy scrub-ground, a red disc on his forehead. Falling: falling... In tinnitus silence the Zapruder scene played out its trauma-coloured endreel.

Gillard's howl of shock, pain, rage, guilt and humiliation, was muted and futile: the evanescent spectrum of oppression continued to warp the world to its tyranny, pitiless in the face of Gillard's pleading. Brought to his knees, crawling beside the body of his new friend, pleading impotently in the shadow of the Bitfrost, broken, blood-soaked and disconsolate. The boy without a history had had freedom to be without shadow, all scintillating dazzling highlight. Now in shadow all subsumed, in the future this history might be all there was.

Crain viewed Gillard's sobbing, hopeless attempts at resuscitation as though through the underside of a glass-bottomed boat. Floating serene, he looked down. What he expected to see was the brutalized, gruesome wreckage of his anxieties. Instead, here in the drawback precipitant to a harbour wave that threatened to be even more massive than the one which had smashed away his life with his mum and dad, he could survey his memories, reflected in the smooth, exposed, undulating seabed of the harbour of his mind.

He remembered confiding in Hudson that he was at the mercy of the fear and guilt that, although he worked on it every day, so far personal tragedy had not revealed within him any previously-undiscovered potency, as the folklore would have it.

Hudson had thought for a moment and then climbed out of his own bed and onto Crain's futon by the bedroom door.

'Move over.'

He hugged Crain for a long time in the darkness, and then told him it was incomprehensible that he couldn't see just how brilliantly amazing, kind, wise and honest he had *always* been, and enduring misfortune without mutation or mutilation was beyond his admiration. 'I'm Hudson frakking Britton and you are, by far, the best thing about me, Crain, my friend.'

Crain had laughed and fallen asleep with Hudson's head and steady breath on the nape of his neck.

He remembered last night, when they had talked about

Gillard and how he might facilitate a little innocent disorder in their orderly whitebread world and teach them how to talk to girls. He knew the tsunami would explode overhead soon, shattering him to pieces: he could already hear its roaring rage and loss and police sirens.

The subsequent inquest would hear how Pritchard had secreted several bullets during a CCF target competition, and had used his Head Prefect keys to take a rifle from the armoury. He had, he said, intended to shoot at Gillard and scare and humiliate him but due, he claimed, to the misaligned rifle-sights, had instead missed and shot and killed Hudson Britton.

It also revealed that Gillard, who had been hurriedly removed from the school, was not a spy or the son of a diplomat or truck driver, nor even of the Commodore. He wasn't even the ward of the man he had claimed to be his guardian: they were in actuality lovers, and to conceal the affair, and add veracity to his claim that Gillard was his ward, the senior Whitehall civil servant had used his not-inconsiderable power and connections to place his underage boyfriend in a minor public school. The mandarin was brought down by the scandal, as indeed the government of the day nearly was.

The boys never got to meet the Princess Plenty Plenty Mittahsalty. The holiday to Grenada was cancelled after a coup and subsequent invasion. With the 'unfortunate business' relegated to the past, the Headmaster's tan, like his school, was unchanged, and Crain was alone again.

My Dad Always Wanted a Daughter

By Paul J. Medford

My Dad always wanted a daughter
He had four sons.
They say,
'When all you have is lemons, you make lemonade.'
My Dad called me Polly Poos
My brothers called me Boy Sally.
Daily I performed in front of the television.
Nightly I entertained them in the ad-breaks with my songs, dances and fashion shows.

Sometimes they applauded.

Sometimes they threw things if I was obstructing *World of Sport*.

They knew and loved me before I knew and loved myself.

Bullets

By Tonderai Munyevu

Now, when I watch that kind of man,
Standing, while someone kneels in front of him,
In a basic rhythm, I don't feel the same.
I feel different. The past doesn't flash before my mind
As it used to, an act of remembering what it felt like
To imagine a future with them, the men.

Mom worked at the Terescan Hotel. That was her plan, her get-out clause for pastures new. She figured she would meet with the right type of clientele there; make contacts who could help her get to England. She needed a plan and it had to be foolproof. A year maximum. She had convinced the General Manager there that she should be Head of Housekeeping, even though she had never set foot in such a department, being used as she was to being the customer, the one served. The one inspecting how good the hospitality was, and offering side-glances if it did not meet with her approval. Mom had been a businesswoman, a nurse, a doer and a maker – all to make ends meet. But now, if she was to make it to England, it was no good to be a businesswoman, a nurse or a doer: more was required. Contacts and friends had to be made, and quick, and the Terescan was as good a chance as any.

And then there were the expenses which had to be cut down. A three-bedroomed house on the corner of Pat Palmer and Ashdown Avenue in Malbereign was not sensible for a single woman nearing forty with three growing kids, (more like growing mouths), hungry to be fed like little birds in a nest waiting their mother's return – better yet, like hungry toothless lambs waiting to suck on their errant mother's tits – waiting for high school – well, the older ones anyways. I was the youngest, too busy being the youngest to know about secondary school, playing with Ludo the family dog and tugging on *Gogo*, the maid-cum-nanny-cum family cook. Anyway, Mum was a single

223

woman nearing forty, although no one could ever tell. She was more a single gal – not girl, but *gal*, which implies confidence, which she had; beauty – the kind that doesn't fade, founded as it was on mountain-high cheekbones; and guts – the real ones, which made hard choices without fear of consequence.

That's what she was. Not a single woman, mother of three, nearing forty. She made those tough decisions, and soon enough she was at the Terescan Hotel, head of the housekeeping department, thirty-inch waist adorned with a satin petticoat, over which lay a custom-made skirt held together by a red belt, sometimes the thick, wide, elasticated one with the butterfly clutch, sometimes something only slightly gauche, always a beautiful blouse, lips in red hue, hair a glistening short perm.

What of the three-bedroomed house? Exchanged for a small bedroom in a house-share in the Avenues, not necessarily the most salubrious part of Harare, but sacrifices had to be made. The children? To the townships with their father, not the sort of parent to inspire confidence, (too much lager, too many fast women and custom-made suits, frequent visitor to the local shebeen). But whatever he was, she was fond of saying, he was their father: who else should or could do it? Other women would have bristled at the thought of such a thing but not Mum: she is the sort to do as she pleases. Anyway, children must know their father. At least *Gogo* would be there to do the cooking.

The kids would go to high school near their father, all except the young one: he must not be interrupted; he will keep the same school till the end of primary school, when a new plan will be made. Who knows where she will be by then. Or what she might have *become* by then. It wasn't so far: a short combi ride from the Warren Park townships into town, then a school bus to Malbereign – forty-five minutes, an hour maximum, it would be simple. Twice a week he could come visit the Terescan and enjoy himself with a quarter-pound chicken and chips, and tea and scones, which the chef took great delight to send out for him – a cherished ritual between his mommy and him.

That's how it started.

Now, in a darkened room in XXL or Chariots

The smell is different, no longer the teargas
Choking me, caressing the back of my throat,
Me gasping, coughing, a sort of convulsion, maybe not.
What good is remembering, the act of it?
Being so grown up now, what good are these thoughts?
Looking at the boundaries transgressed, with the men.

The first time it happened – it must have been a Wednesday or a Thursday, for I always reserved my visits to Mom for the ending of the week, (but never Friday: the hotel was too busy then, and Mom would not have approved of me hanging around grownups at the Terescan on a Friday. *Friday?* No) – I had not heard anything about unrest. There had been no warning; we had no inkling. But this was a city in which one could rent a crowd, or even a mob, if there was benefit in it. The city was, as always, quiet, sunny, calm. The kind of calm Harare is renowned for. A calm that does not betray that something can happen here. Something dangerous, deadly even. People have been known to disappear, suddenly not to be found – it's hard to remember that now: others tortured, and all in the condensed balm of the Sunshine City. But strange things could happen and *did* happen. And in the bus, laughing and joking with my friends, pre-adolescent – I was eleven years old then – there we were, approaching town, ready to disperse like scattered seeds to our various abodes.

Here is where memory begins to fail me, to trim off the edges – a migrant remembering home, another time and another place, where they do things differently. Can one ever forget? What I do remember were people. Maybe I remember a crowd, hearing the voices of a crowd, maybe not – it is hard to recall; hard to know what happens to your senses when you are recalling. I think I heard sounds of crowds. Were they chanting? I'm not sure, because really the calm remained – as if we were in a fog, a dense yet clear fog, which you can see through – with sounds and tastes still intact, our schoolboy laughter occasionally crackling through like a fire lit by twigs, then suddenly a loud bang. *That* I remember: I remember that well. Maybe it was a shot. Then another, and more, in quick succession, and the smell of burning – and now the fog seemed to disappear and everything was real again, now came screaming, running and yelling. Us bundling up together, even strangers; women's voices in the crowd telling us kids to run and hide.

I was in delayed motion, not really knowing what was happening or what had happened. Still thinking I can make it to the Terescan Hotel and see Mom and devour that quarter-pound chicken drenched in salt and vinegar. And maybe hang around with Mom, feel her warmth and her Christian Dior-perfumed dress. It was the beginning of the missing – the chasm that would be created between Mom and me for years when she finally made it to England. But now this missing was in its infancy, and in this moment I was adamant I would reach her and see her just this once this week.

But the women's voices pierced my ears: I could hear nothing else. One touched me as if to wake me from a dream. Looking at her it was clear that I was in trouble and she knew how she would keep me safe. She motioned to me to run. I didn't: I started to walk, slowly. Then another shot, which now I heard as clearly as if it had been next to me. My heart beat faster – this I remember clearly: images flashing in front of me of men and women running, of army trucks thundering; whistling, crying, and a commotion whose speed and rigour I had never yet experienced. Suddenly I was in motion, struggling to breathe in the enveloping teargas. I found a place, some public toilets under a car park. I ran in, seeking some sense of quiet and a temporary release from the gas, and before long I was strangely still, listening to the commotion outside. I stood waiting for my heart to beat less and my mind to engage a plan to see Mom.

Then a man came in, and walked to the urinal.

Now I go to those places where Us/We go.
Looking for things deeper than I or he the man,
Standing with his dick out while another man kneels
In a rhythm that grows ever more frantic and breathless, can understand.
While the man pretends he is a queer gangster enjoying the spoils,
While the kneeling man pleases his younger self's dream of the men.

*

Was I getting used to it? It had become a ritual, a play for one. The same urinal every single day after school – or was it every other day? It is hard to recall. Time lays to waste so much of what happens, what *happened*. And distance too. Distance creates a kind of bridge that must be climbed with both fortitude and trust, not knowing what will be found on the other side. A bold untying of knots. Yet sometimes memory is crystal-clear: things remain just as they were. A Londoner remembering a foreign country, a foreign childhood, the broken melody of a song sung elsewhere. I remember it as a sort of play. Me visiting the site. Me as the star and audience, (the kind of plays I used to star in back then!), secretive but not hiding. Feeling the thrill of something new, within me and out of me. A real sensation I had never felt before developing: growing adolescence. I had seen my cousins naked, and my brother. But not this, this was altogether different. The power these men possessed intoxicated me. Fuelled my mind with things I yet did not and could not understand.

Years later I came to know of the pleasure of pleasing a man. How a man is simultaneously weak and powerful. How tender his dick could be, and functional; and how, together, two men can become more than friends, more than brothers – a love deeper than I could fathom, and sharper in its intensity than anything I had ever tasted or felt. How addictive it could be. Back then I stood and waited for it all to make sense, and for the meaning to be something less painful than what I was already feeling, I knew enough to keep this a secret. And with each new day I visited this place came another sensation.

Sometimes the men would watch me, see what I wanted, what I intended. I saw it all: those coming in and heading briskly over to the urinal, undoing themselves quickly, unleashing a gush which sounded like a torrent. Those leisurely strolling in, as if all the time in the world was theirs for the taking, sometimes whistling a happy tune and greeting their fellow brothers in this most functional of moments. And those who came in quickly to get the job done, but on noticing me became performers, eager to show off what they had, and see how far they could get with me. These men scared me the most: I wonder if I ever will recover from those gazes. Being para-lysed by them, not knowing what to do and how meaningful those moments were. How do I progress this into something fun-loving and tender? I mean now, as an adult. In what place does this bullet lodge? When will it become something clearer, without the fog, (which now is part of a lifestyle), or the screaming voices, (which are now the judgement and self-loathing that accompany every tryst), so that when I walk away from Him/ They/We I feel more than just being stunned by the act of fucking?

Now I remember as if it was yesterday
Standing there waiting at the urinals for a grown man
To come unzip himself, his thick, large, hanging lizard
Or maybe a human pipe, with water –no – urine gushing out,
Him – them, using their hands, their fingers, the thumb and the index
And the other to shake and dry. Not boys, but men.

Secondary school finally came. It was a missionary boarding-school atop a mountain hundreds of miles from Harare. Boys my own age, prayer, the mountain music, tinned and preserved food tightly stored in an army-type trunk, the mystical occult of the mountain people, all for a while masked the scent of manhood in my head, the stench of beer in that urine, the gushing sound of it which writing this now fills me with a heat that is hard to ignore now I can kneel in front of any man, and smell and engorge my senses with that aroma.

But back then January, February and March passed on. Then a month in the city, back to my old ritual. From the boys at school I now knew what a dick was and what it was capable of: how hard it could be while throbbing and tightening; how much pain can be inflicted when the beholder is at the mercy of his erection, until in the end he is weakened by his come, forcing its way out of him like a discharge of bullets from a soldier's gun when nothing else can be done but shoot. Back to school, where May, June and July raced by in the mountain chill, then back to Harare again, to the same routine. You see, nothing changes much in a place like Harare: tall buildings don't suddenly rise, beggars remain where you left them and the city boys keep moving. Was I beginning to tire of these scenes? I can't say so, for any opportunity I had led me there.

Then again back to school, where September brought the Coca-Cola-sponsored school dance, October the regional choir competition, and finally the exams in November. Now we were free until January, when the new year would commence.

That December I had one last chance to patrol the place with the men. Mom had sent a letter and Daddy had agreed that we would spent Christmas with her in London. So it was city workers, cleaners, township boys, soldiers and business-men for the last time this year. Had to fit my ritual around getting ready for London. People said it was cold there like we had never seen before. That walking down the pavement your feet would suddenly just freeze. At times I wished I wasn't going to such a place. What was wrong with where we were? But simple economics made that question a stupid one: to survive one had to move, like the hordes of wildebeests cross-ing the Mara River for pastures green. Then I thought of Mommy and her beautiful face: surely she had become white now. I couldn't wait to see for myself my very own white person, up close.

Still, my ritual place was full of excitement. Once I think I saw a man who could have been a politician, or a millionaire, (bodily functions do not discriminate); another time a soldier came in. A real one, with a red beret. A soldier with a real gun, *loaded*, a trigger he could pull at any moment. He stared at me for a long time, too long, as if he knew how fragile my life was, yet with love, maybe compassion, or more. Desire? I must have been at my most beautiful then, in callow splendour. I vowed to return to this place, this private ritual place in my heart and in Harare, a place I would not betray. A few weeks in London, then back with stories to tell and maybe more.

But I had not reckoned with my mother's love for us: that she would make sacrifices while coiling a dream in her to hold us tight; and that her grip would not loosen again, however much I had made a place for myself, a ritual place of belonging – with the men.

That is, I remained in London, nursing an ache for some-thing that would dislodge this bullet so tightly lodged in my head, travelling through my body with frightening regularity and exquisite sensation.

*

Now I remember me, only eleven then, knowing without knowledge;
Feeling without fear, and the bullet that lodged in my brain –
Between seeing and the sensation that travelled through the nose,
The throat, it quickened the heartbeat, raced like a hunger pain,
Bypassing the belly itself to my growing loins, to the heart of it.
Lodging itself permanently, resting, in wait for a trigger.

Great Greatness

By Anu Olu

Tradition
The way of our people
The way it always was
Must it be my way?
My mind fails to recall the time I requested for this title to be
bestowed upon *my* journey.
Great expectation imposed is rarely strapped to a mounting
heap of self-fulfillment but too often left to sluggishly sail down
the lake of self-loathing.
Was this the way I wanted it to be? Great greatness.
This barometer of excellence is broken – it does nothing.
 Its mechanisms shatter individuality. Its spilt mercury poi-
sons.
 Its talons destroy boldness in the unlucky; they are forced
 under its slicing measure.
I will grow old in my body.
These hands will wrinkle in vain.
I will not bury my name and all the expectations that you have
attached to its meaning
When asked what man I will be I merely answer with desires
and wants-to-fly

To soar, to explode, catapulting into triumph; to implode, to be
victorious, to return with great enemies slain.
Who defines great greatness?

Our fathers? Our mothers? The distant yet familial well-
wishers, church-goers, Mama Ali?
Our lovers? Our brothers?

Perhaps it is the ones that lie beneath the weight of our libido.
I intend to be an honest over-achiever until the day I die.
Is it tradition that must preordain my choice of labour?
Perhaps the call of my culture must predestine who is chosen for me to night-timely side-by-side.
Who decides who will be recruited to see me through the lull of this life?
The gods/The spirits/The prophets/The elders. Those that came before me?
I shatter my dreams to nourish the wants of others
I silence my satisfaction for pretences unknown to me.
The end is far. The future is near. I can no longer await the unequivocal arrival of the fruits of my fear.

Queer Nation:
An extract from
Battyman. A memoir

By Topher Campbell

L ights down, sweat pouring from the low ceiling. We stand in tight Levis, bare chests smooth-skinned, muscular, worked out to perfection. We display ourselves proudly, stallions pivoting from hoof to hoof. We parade around the tiny dark club full of explosive power. We: the power of youth. This is a primal ritual of sexual competition mixed with bonding, celebration and excess. An essential part of my Saturday night at the turn of the 21st century. Queer Nation, my home from home, was in Substation South, Brighton Terrace, a busy side-street off Brixton Road. Its subterranean cavern of black walls and low ceilings, bathed in the sounds of Chicago House and New York Garage, was the place for cutting loose and free-falling for me and many other lost souls.

1998-2004. It always started something like this. I'd be at home on my own. The usual blandness of Saturday night shit pouring from my tiny television. I knew I had done the same last week or at best a few weeks ago. I knew I needed to give it a rest but the tug, the desire was too strong.

I'm sitting on my sofa, penniless or between freelance paycheques, musing on yet another boring Sunday. Uninspiring 9 pm gives way to a couldn't-care-less 10 pm.

11 pm.

11.15.

'You going QN?' The first text message.

'Out tonight?' Another text message.

'Coming?' Another...

'QN?' Another and of course another and another...

'No,' I answer. 'Not tonight' and 'Giving it a miss'.

11.45.

The last Victoria Line train south from Finsbury Park to Brixton is at 12.20.

Okay, quick! Where are my just-washed Levis? Underwear or no underwear? Boots or trainers? Boots are good as they gave my arse a lift. I had bought the most perfect pair of boots in LA eight years earlier at a 'Swap Meet'. I drove out into Canyon Country and came upon a large dusty field with people selling crap. Amongst this crap was a box full of the sexiest boots I had ever seen.

They reached halfway up the thigh, secured by a single thick leather strap that wound its way around the leg and then fastened at the tight top. The boots were in a great big boots box full to the brim with boots.

'Earthquake Boots fifteen dollars apiece, son,' said the burly guy in a genuine Midwestern accent. Fifteen dollars! About eight quid! In London they would sell for eighty. I was on a pauper's budget so it was really a case of boots or food. I bought the boots.

I LOVED those boots. They were steel-capped so I enjoyed wearing them when travelling. They set the alarm off in airports. I had just had them resoled to give them ultimate lift.

Trainers are cool too. Easier to dance in. They stay comfortable all night. Adidas are my fave. Worn in tribute to my hiphop brothers Run DMC and LL. Not that I ever listened to Run DMC. But I regularly fantasised about LL. Still do. That muscular Blatino body. Those thick suck-a-dick lips and that smile. Really...? (sighs... clutches pearls) Adidas made me more light on my feet. The only problem was that they would get filthy dirty by the end of the night as they suffered the abuse of multiple trampling. They were useless if it was raining. The best thing with trainers was that I could spin and turn on the dance-floor with devastating effect. Always useful when you wanted to show you could do more than just bob from side to side, nodding inanely like a puppet dog. An unfortunate side-effect of two or more pills.

11.50. I try the trainers on with Levis and no underwear. Now boots and no underwear. The boot-straps always took so long. What about boots *with* underwear? You always needed decorum at the end of the night if the jeans became loose. Top of the arse on display in night-club good. Top of the arse on display on Brixton High Street or the night bus home not so good. It all comes down to how sexy do I feel? Maybe if I take some undies and shove them in my pocket I could change into them for the journey home? Maybe not. I might be too high to concentrate.

12.10. It's boots and no underwear, spiced with Palmer's Cocoa Butter on the body. A simple tight tee completes the look. This is summer-wear but of course autumn and winter need a jumper or coat. Anyway, less clothing is better: less worry and no coat-check fee. Wallet. Keys. Phone. That's it. No watch, and only a chain and earring for jewellery. The less you have, the less you worry about.

12.19. Excited, I run down the steps toward the southbound platform. Who knows, tonight might be different. Instead of ending it high and horny and going home alone I might go on some new adventure. One problem: people think I am an 'It Boy', therefore not easy to approach. It doesn't help that I adopt a 'don't fucking come near me face' when I am out because deep down I am just an insecure child... Really..? (raises eyebrow) My 'fuck off' face also helps to ward off weirdoes and the desperate. Of which there are many. Nose stuck firmly in the air, I only went for what I wanted: other 'It Boys', who were very rare indeed. Result: loneliness.

The Tube Ride.

I always pretend not to notice anybody noticing me but I see them all. Finsbury Park itself is a non-event. The odd straight couple board on their way home from visiting the in-laws. A middle-aged Asian man with bad shoes and a nondescript haircut sits next to the very attractive girl with shiny clothes on her way to expensive Mafia dives Browns or Mayfair in Holborn.

Do I look too gay? I keep a normal facial expression. My tight jeans, (sometimes with rips in them), coupled with my heavy boots were a giveaway if anyone cared to look and look closer. I hate the thought of being identified as gay. I like to think of myself as different, unique, special. It's just that this 'uniform' was the right thing for the night. But it's still a uniform, right? I wanted to signal that I was also sane and alpha to other men in the club, I guess. This was straight-up subtle sexy gay club-wear. So I thought.

12.45. Oxford Circus. Things get more interesting. On pile the drinkers from Soho. Some in suits, some out to get pissed, some way drunk already. There is noise, laughter, heavy banter and heavy petting. I've always thought it crazy that we Brits are considered reserved on the Tube. The hungry eyes of gay men search furtively for reciprocity as they head south to Vauxhall and its tiny gay scene dominated by the Vauxhall Tavern, the Eagle and the legendary fetish club The Hoist. No sign of the temple of mega-hedonism that Vauxhall was to become a few years later, spearheaded by superclub FIRE.

I get nervous. I am not the best at casual conversation and I don't want to be recognised. The problem is made worse because I never remember anyone's name. I heard somewhere that Richard (Dickie) Attenborough had the same problem so he called everyone darling. Darling didn't work for me.

'Hi, Topher, isn't it?' said perfectly decent guy I don't re-member.

'Hi, Babes,' I replied.

'Going to QN?' 'Babes' asked enthusiastically.

'Yeah,' I replied.

Awkward silence.

I look up. Around me the full tube with its furtive glances is a place of silent conversations. Some you don't want to have.

12.50. Brixton tube station at last. I come out into darkness. Someone hands me a flyer. 'Roots and culture'. I swear that guy has been there for ten years. 'Babes' runs off to meet other 'Babes'. I cross the wide road. The streets are sparse and the usual cocktail of speeding cop-cars, late-night stragglers waiting for nightbuses and the occasional homeless guy litter the streets. I don't care. I have one target and it's moments away.

There's a queue. Good sign it's gonna be busy. Hugs and kisses for those I know. Handshake for those I am acquainted with, and a slight glance taking in all those I want to get to know. The club-line etiquette. Heat rising.

Now I have to get through the two gate-keepers. First there is Leroy. I join the guest list queue although I didn't put my name down. Leroy was a mystery. Bouncer by night and postman by day, that's all I knew. He looked thirty-five but was probably forty-five. He's a reassuring sight. Heavy-built with a serious no bullshit manner, he polices the outside of the club with assured authority. Drug-tolerant and flirtatious, he sees everything.

'You. No,' he said to the short, five-foot-nothing guy in front of me.

Fag in hand, the guy started kicking off in a queeny South London accent: ' Fuck you! I been comin ere for ages. Patrick knows me! I fuckin built this club!'

Such power in one so small.

'You're banned,' Leroy stated flatly. Another bouncer gently steers short guy away.

'She tinks she cute!' said short guy, cutting the air with his shrill voice. 'Girl – ' He turns to me '– I am no trouble-maker. I just don't like people dissing me!' He is bundled out into the street.

All this while Leroy was saying, 'Hi, how are you?' as he patted me down. 'I'm good,' I replied, just too excited about the coming night. 'Go on,' he said when finished.

I didn't bother looking back at short guy and didn't spend but a moment thinking about whatever misdemeanour he did or didn't do. I just hear him as he walks off talking on the phone as I go downstairs:

'...Yeah, that ugly black bitch at the door... She tink she run-ning tings...' Really..? (upward inflexion, shakes head)

Gate Keeper One. Passed.

The stairs went down ten steps, turned a corner, and then down another ten steps. I turned right at the bottom and there on a stool, Buddha-like, was Patrick Lilly. Gate Keeper Two.

I'd known Patrick for over ten years. Ever since my old boy-friend Keith (Lenny) Lennon introduced me to him at the dawn of Queer Nation 1 in 1990. This, the original Queer Nation, was in the Gardening Club in Covent Garden. Another subterranean pleasure pit, though altogether more light and breezy than its current incarnation. QN1 was publicised on a hand-drawn flyer that depicted a little rotund smiling man going for a walk. Maybe it was Patrick. How sweet. It's now an Apple Store.

At QN1 there was an innocence and playfulness. The club had more light, there were less drugs about, and we were all just starting out. People got pissed, not high. Patrick's vision was of a multi-ethnic polyamorous space where people could work up a sweat and listen to some of the best tunes not heard on the late 80's Eurodisco-drenched mainstream gay scene. It was also a place for Black folks, white folks and misfits that wasn't about R&B or dancehall.

Patrick Lilly is round. He has a round bald head. A big round body and little chubby hands and he knew it. He was like a squat frog but he also held a fascination for me. I was attracted to his work ethic. What the hell did a promoter do anyway? How did you get a club venue and DJs and flyers and sexy boys? My straight-laced theatre-directing background couldn't get my head around it until I did it myself. Of course.

'This one is okay,' said Patrick dryly. Patrick always saw the desperation in me to get in the club and get fucked up. But then I wasn't alone in this quest, and although he was a promoter trying to make money, in his own messy way he was also a cultural entrepreneur trying to build a community... and he loved black dick. So what better way for a fat white man to get as many shirtless hot Black guys around you than open a sweaty, soul-drenched nightclub?

Patrick gave me a paper stub. I gave it to the cashier.

Gate Keeper Two. Passed.

I squeezed around the coat-check queue, opened the black double-doors and exhaled.

'*Who's been breaking your heart been breaking your heart...*' – dropped by Supadon, the self-effacing Black DJ with the coolest name. The tune greeted me like the song of sirens beckoning me on to an adventure, and for the next six hours I followed the Three Phases:

PHASE 1 – THE ENTRANCE

I had arrived at just the right time: the 12-2 hour. Any earlier the club would be empty. Any later the pace of the club would have accelerated and I would have to catch up. Arriving late shifts the balance too near to desperation.

I walk around. Black paint on brick walls. Pool table near the entrance. The space is split in two. On the right an oblong dance-floor. Darker corners at the other end. DJ box in the middle on the far right. On the left a bar with a cigarette machine and a huge fan. The two sides of the club separated by a long cage installation and a brick wall. A sign that this was a sex-club on other nights of the week. All good for hiding, grinding and posing.

Familiar faces are everywhere. There's Neville and Deleon, Eric, Vivian, Jeff, David, Luke, CJ, Sean, Kenrick, Paul, Courtney, Ken, Jim, Obi, Merran, Saun, Chris, Alan, William, Delano, Rodger, Roger, Miss Carney, Courtney, Tall Crazy Guy, Short Crazy Guy and everybody's favourite couple, Gem and Deji.

Part of The Entrance ritual was making sure all the regular faces were there. Each one to be greeted by: 'Hey babes, how are you?' Kiss on both cheeks (a must) and a little catch-up about nothing. 'You alright?' – the 'i' in alright is drawn out. 'Yeah, I'm good, how are you?' 'I haven't seen you for ages, dear.' 'I was here last week.' 'Really...?' (mild fake surprise) 'I hardly ever go out these days.' If all the regulars are there it's gonna be a great night.

'I thought you weren't coming, dear,' some would say dryly. Liking the fact they had caught me in a lie.

'*Reach Reach Reach Reach ...Reach out for love....*' Little More Mix kicks in just about here with its trancelike driving beat.

PHASE 2 – SCORING DRUGS

'D'you know anyone who's sellin?' asked Vivian. Which was unusual as he always seemed to have his own supply.

I am on the dancefloor now. Enjoying a Martha Walsh 'Carry On....' remix dropped by Luke (Howard), one of the great London gay House DJ's and a QN fixture... '*...a new day dawns...*' Vivian had muscles and looked great. I like muscles. With a do-rag on, Vivian, though a little camp, managed to look thuggish. We spent a lot of time fucking in the 90's and early 21st century, or rather I spent a lot of time fucking him.

239

'I'll find out,' I replied. I went hunting. Sometimes this hunt was fruitless and frustrating. The usual dealers should arrive in the best hour, but now and then they don't turn up at all. Not tonight.

'How many?' asked 'A'. I thought for a moment.

One was a non-event. Two was a steady night with a decent end and okay come-down. Three was a hopeful night and meant I was going to score.

'Four,' I replied. Might as well go for it.

A disappeared. Ten minutes later A returned. We danced really close to each other. Our hands embraced. I squeezed £20 into his hand and he put four white pills into mine. I danced with A some more to complete the deceit and then I rejoined Vivian, who then went off to see A himself.

Hungry for my high I went to the bar and bought two bottles of water. Vivian was back on the dancefloor. We drank water, took a pill and waited.

The tiny club was rammed. It was a crush and fight to get anywhere. Black and white men and one or two women were getting on with the serious business of working up a sweat. Hands were being thrown in the air. Boys were spinning faster. The cruising getting more direct. Arses were being pinched (mine), poses struck and faces were fixed in hope on other faces.

PHASE 3 – TOPS OFF IT'S ON

'You feeling anything?' asked Vivian.

'A little,' I replied.

We danced.

Then fifteen minutes later my limbs got looser and my body tingled. Waves of softness flowed through me. I felt lighter, more open. I suddenly found myself... there. The music became deeper. The bass went from being a heavy, deep, shattering pulse that went through me to being... *in* me, part of me, the lyrics were about me and the lights, the lights were like warm fire, bright like beach Sun. They wrapped themselves around me and illuminated my soul. Not dangerous, not frightening. No; just radiant and milk-chocolate warm and fierce and open. Like the most welcoming of smiles on the most beatific of faces.

I held Vivian close to me. Felt his arse. He sank into me. His hard body, shoulders, back, sighing, giving. Giving in. It felt good. I held his shoulders and tugged at his shirt. He took his top off. I did too. I looked around, and all over the club tops were coming off like rockets being launched across a dazzling blue sky. Everyone looked so great. They were my friends. I loved them all. Muscle glistened through sweat. Hungry eyes met hungry eyes and the possibility oh the possibility of release was just there just there beyond, in his body, in him...

There wasn't anywhere to go after that but down. So that's where I went. Down to the Underground. Deeper.

And Deeper.

And Deeper.

Deeper Love... Deeper Love... Deeper Love DEEP DEEPER LOVE...

Jeffrey Hinton is on the decks now. Jeffrey is a pixie and likes to cuddle. He has a little pixie voice with a London accent, and an intensity when he communicates matched by none. He also gives me a reason to live because he plays the last set at QN. One that matches the need to fly.

I took another pill and another. My pupils exploded with sights as multi-coloured light cut into the writhing and gyrating. This was a place for show-offs, and loads of show-offs parked themselves right here on the middle of the dance-floor. Each one displaying his signature dance. Kenrick lolloped and slithered in an out of people. Tall Crazy guy flung his arms and big long body forward and back not caring who he hit. Gem and Deji, who never fail to be the featured couple of the night, bopped from side to side facing each other, huge arms poised as if about to box in a ring... Paul Allard just fell over... and Space. Space flew by again and again, sometimes dressed in a silver thing or a white thing or a dustbin thing, his movement skimming the surface of the music like Jesus walking on water.

Queer Nation was forged out of a desire to create a music sanctuary far away from the techno techno techno heard everywhere else and made popular by Amsterdam duo 2 Unlimited. Techno was a place where white gay men ruled with their tribal aesthetic of uniform motion. QN's inspiration came from New York clubs The Sound Factory, Paradise Garage,

Body and Soul, The Warehouse and The Shelter. All places I, a Deep House music pilgrim, sought out hungrily on my Virgin Airways flights to NYC in the heady '90s. QN was made possible through inspiring sounds imported by Norman Jay at High on Hope in West London, whose fire in turn was lit by legendary Frankie Knuckles, the supreme Chicago House pioneer. I craved an antidote to the British battle between Blur and Oasis and the omnipresence of the Spice Girls and Take That. In image and sound Blair's booming Britain with its Mosses, Hirsts, YBA's and inyerface theatre failed to entrance me. I wanted to gorge from another deeper well. There were Black folk in them there boom beat hills. Gorgeous Black men and I wanted to be among them.

I'm floating along the city streets now. Entranced by motion. Over Waterloo Bridge we go. Past the National Theatre. Tonight I love the National Theatre. The National Theatre is really really lovely. The wide black Thames sparkles beneath us. The expansive view, on one side Big Ben and on the other Tower 42, mesmerises me. The buildings are centuries apart and I am here in this timeless moment with Vivian beside me. In a minicab. How fabulous is this. The promise of great sex hangs in the air. It occupies the space between us, exciting us as we sit silently.

'You alright?' he says to me eventually. His voice quiet, almost a whisper. Relaxed.

'Yeah...' I sigh as all the world floats by and I just don't care.

On reaching my small first-floor flat in North London I close the door behind us and watch his strong legs and perfect butt climb the stairs from the communal front door to my apartment. I open my door, he walks in and I follow. The music, though long silent, still beats through my Body and Soul. I look at him and smile, my dick hardening, and with the anticipation of a child at Christmas I think how fantastic, how fabulous, really, it is to be part of this tiny gang. The joyous Queer Nation.

Thug Ass

By Rikki Beadle-Blair

T hug Ass *was commissioned by Topher Campbell as part of 'The Mangina Monologues', a series of mono-logues written by Black Men, gay and straight, celebrating the pleasures of the arse. Other contributors included Christopher Rodriguez and Deobia Oparei. The Mangina Monologues was premiered by* rukus! *at the Soho Theatre in London's West End in 2009. The character of Thug Ass was performed by Ayo Fawale.*

A bare stage in darkness. Spotlight up on THUG ASS, a handsome, muscled, masculine-identified black British man in his mid-twenties with an urban style.

THUG ASS

This battyhole ain't no pussyhole, a'right, blood? This bat-tyhole ain't no male-pussy 'mussy' mangina, none of them tings, you get me? This here do not mince, you get me? On the street, this here strides. Bowls. This here limps like I been shot in a drive-by, this here pimp-rolls like a Don with a twelve-inch Dong. Ain't no sugar in this tank. Ain't no lightness in these loafers. Ain't no gay in this gait. This right here is a thug-ass ass-of-a-thug. Just cause a man check for man-dem, don't mean you gotta be some kind of gyal, innit? Don't mean you can't be solid. This battyhole's solid, feel me? This battyhole's tight. This battyhole's a no entry zone. This battyhole is a soldier's battyhole. You won't catch this batty switchin' at Booticilious, blood, ain't happening. You won't find this batty bumping cakes with bitch ass booginas in batty-rider hot-pants at the Mardi Gras, bruv. You'll find this batty in a low-slung pair of baggy Moschino jeans, backed up against a wall at a blues, soaking up bass. You'll find this batty hole winding with a screwface sister in a Brixton Basement on the downlow on

the QT. This battyhole is keeping it real.
I know what you lot's thinking, innit? If this muthafucka's
so down-low how comes he's even heard of Bootilicious?
Yeah, maybe I heard of it – what? Maybe I even been there.
What? Maybe you seen me there last night. What? Strickly
observational, bredren, you get me? Strickly anthropological research. This thug ass belongs to a thug with an interest in human nature. Well, everyone likes a freak show
innit? You hear bout these tings, don't cha? In chatrooms
and that, bout clubs where you find mans and mans all being whatever, gay like, but when you picture dat, it's like,
whassit, *Queer as Folk,* just a whole heap of white bwoy-
them waving them arms to techno. Not this soldier's style,
seen?
But then the other day, my man's on the common yeah, just
kicking back on a bench, having a smoke, yeah, leaning back
with him hands behind him head, so – in order that him bi-
and tricep them catch the moonlight, yeah... when this
proper little fucking chi-chi man comes swishing past. Taking lickle princess mincy tippy-toe steps, like he's grinding
coffee between him legs – and just the sight of him and this
sphincter just clench up real tight. My man's like, Ra guy –
why some people have to come so stereotype? Just cause
them like mans does that mean them have to act like them
saving up for a sex-change? Just cause you go a certain way
don't mean you have to bring down shame on your whole
race, is it? Unnecessary, blood, you get me? Ain't like it's
even sexy or nuttin' – If a bredren's out checking for mans,
then he's checking for *mans,* innit? If my man want a gyal
he can get the real thing, no sweat, trust me, dread, believe.
Bitches them love my man. Phine brotha, caramel skin,
pumped guns, pecs, abs, gold chain, gold tooth, head
shaved, white white trainers with the price tag and security
tag still in place – and just the right amount of tattoos and
scarifications in all the right places. When this alpha male
hits the street in the Lexus, gash a fall from the trees, blood
– pure gash! Falling! Like peaches in a twister. So when
we're in the park past midnight, looking to scratch that particular itch – you know that my man is checking for brothers. Sisters can just step, you get me? So when this fag butt

comes switching, giving it the big Look at Me prance and pout, we just ignore our treacherous erection and my man just cut him eyes like and kiss him teeth so...

(kisses teeth)

Only it well backfires, innit? Cause the bitch just stops and says, 'Excuse me?' In – no lie – the queerest fucking voice on this planet.

My man's like, 'What?'

He's like, 'Did you say something?'

'Say so'ink?'

'Yes, say something... I thought you said something.'

Yo, this fucking faggot is *bold*, man. He don't know what kind of brother this might be, My man might be fresh out the pen, ready to jump up and lick him down, one tump and he's out and we're gone with his wallet and watch and that belly-button ring. My man inhale him smoke, turn away and exhale him smoke, don't say nothing, but the pussy-raas is staring, so my man just shrug: Whatever, like. Dick is proper uncomfortable, all twis' up and aching like, but he ain't touching it, this pussyhole might get the wrong idea. Might think it's throbbing for him.

Yeah, right. Like we'd be interested in fucking a sissy like this. Yeah, he's built nice and tight but my man ain't about to fuck Flo-Jo, you get me? My man is out looking for a Carl Lewis. Mind you, you heard things bout Carl back in the day, but at least the brother's a brother, feel me? Yeah, he had something fishy going on with them eyebrows but that brother was fucking hench, blood. That brother was all man. Ahhh! Seen! That's why I'm all fucking stiff, innit? Cah this chi-chi man's making us flashback on Carl. My man was a proper shortie when him first laid eyes on Carl Lewis, but, can't lie, man, there was straightaway a fascination. My man was captivated and we was sprung. Something stirred. Not the same part that's stirring now – but something, yeah? Something deep.

This punk bitch is still staring. We can feel it. My man wants to cut his eyes back at him, stare the fucker down, say 'What?' But he don't. Just inhales, exhales, watching the smoke float out like steam.

So he goes, 'Don't I know you?' My man's like, Shrug.

He's like, 'Ain't your name Darnell?'
Inside, my man's like, 'Fuck!'
Outside he's like, Shrug.
How the fuck does he know our name?
He's like, 'I'm Andre'.
Inside, my man's like 'Andre?'
Outside he's like, Shrug.
He's like, 'As in lickle Andre?' My man's like, 'Fuck!'
Inhale, exhale.
He's like, 'Your mum and my mum used to do nails together at the salon, you used to call my mum Aunt Sylvie. You remember? You used to stay over sometimes?' Darnell remembers, alright.
Shrug.
...Lickle Andre... in't thought about that breh in years, but back in the day we used to think about nuttin' other and no-one else. We used to sleep in the same bed, used to feel the heat of him just there and listen to his breathing and we was in Hell, swear man. He was torture to know. Shit... Lickle Andre... Ain't so lickle now. Look at them thighs!
He's like, 'I wondered if I'd ever see you here.'
What's that supposed to mean? Then he's like, 'I used to get a vibe back then, but I used to tell myself, 'Well, maybe this is just wishful thinking, innit?''
Darnell looks at him, and he's like, 'Wishful thinking?'
Andre smiles, 'It speaks'.
And Darnell blushes. *Blushes*, man! Shame or what? Fucking blushes! I'm like, Pull your shit together soldier! But you can't control blushes. Once again we're sprung.
He's like, 'Hey, Darnell.'
Darnell's like, 'Sup.'
And he like smiles even more impossibly wider and Darnell's blushing and I'm clenching and our dick feels like it's going to explode and take out the whole of Clapham Common.
My man Darnell looks round and it's quiet, so he's like, 'Wanna sit down?'
Andre's like, 'I'd love to but I'm meeting someone.'
Darnell's like, 'Cool.'
Andre's like, 'No, it ain't, it sucks. But I don't like to keep

people waiting and if I sit down with you I don't know when I'll get up again.' He grins. 'You always did blush easy.'

My man's like, 'Whatever.'

And instantly hates himself, As well he should – I mean what is he, a fucking Peckham gyal? 'Whatever?' What so solid soldier says 'Whatever'? Andre ain't bothered about it, Andre's moving things right along. 'You can come with, if you want.'

Darnell's thinking, Come with where? But just says, 'Is it?'

Andre says, 'I'm just meeting a friend, you won't be a gooseberry or nuttin'... He's cool.'

I'm wondering if his friend's a pretty boy like Andre. I seriously don't know if our system can take two of 'em.

Andre's like, 'We're going to Bootilicious.'

Darnell's like, 'Booty...?'

He's like, 'licious..? The club?'

Then he's sees my man don't know what he's on about and he goes, 'It's a gay club. R'n'B, hip-hop and ragga.'

Darnell's well taken aback – he's like, 'Ragga?'

And Andre pulls out that smile again –   That's a secret weapon, that smile – and he's like, 'Ragga.'

Darnell says, 'So... Do they play...' and Andre whispers jokily, '...Murder Music? Nah, but there's plenty of slackness. You'll be right at home. You should come.'

Darnell's like, 'Nah, man, I'm cool.'

Andre's smile drops. 'You sure?' Darnell's like, 'I'm cool.'

There's a silence, when nothing moves, and then Andre says, 'Well, if you feel curious or whatever, yeah, it's down Vauxhall under the arches, just look for the queue with the niggas and the wiggas. Tell 'em at the door you're with Andre and you'll get bumped to the front.' There's another silence.

And then Andre goes. 'Well...' and then there's another pause and then Andre goes, 'I'm late. Peace.'

And Darnell's like, 'Peace'. Watching Andre's cakes going dunk-a-dunk dunk down the pathway and Andre's gone – and here's we are. Alone. And my man Darnell realises – his smoke's gone out.

MUSIC

Okay. I know Andre said this place was ragga but this place is *ragga*, yo! Yeah, my man Darnell likes to keep it ghetto, like standard, yo, but some of the dudes up in this place is *hood*! Brothers who if you saw 'em round the way you'd have to stop yourself from crossing the road. *Hood*! It's like, 'Ain't that T'shaun? Ain't he got like three baby-mamas? What's he doing in a gay club? Dealing?' And then bam, T'Shaun's lipsing up some dreadhead in a black and gold Nike tracksuit – like lips and tongues and throats and everytin' and it's like, 'Damn! T'Shaun, breh! That's kinda gay!!' Darnell's trying not to look too bug-eyed an' that, just kicking back by the wall, wishing he had a thicker gold chain and wondering where the fuck Andre's at, when there he is – Andre! All white teeth and long lashes and shiny smooth skin and he's yelling over Mary J Blige, 'You reach, then!' And Darnell's shouting back towards his ear, 'I reach!' and they're grinning like a pair of fools. Then the deejay drops another tune and Andre's like, 'Ooooooooh, girl! My song!' I'm like,
(tensing up)
'Girl'?? And Andre's grabbing my man Darnell by the hand – not the arm, mind – the *hand* – and he's leading him to the dance floor! My man Darnell don't dance! My man don't let no man lead him nowhere – specially not by no hand! I'm so tight I could empty a tube of toothpaste. And then we're on the floor and Darnell's dancing! To Beyoncé! Darnell! Darnell's throwing shapes, blood. Darnell's danc-ing with a man! Singing! Working up a sweat! Stripping off his vest! Kissing Andre!
...Darnell's kissing Andre. On a dance floor. In South Lon-don. Half-naked in public. Darnell's kissing lickle Andre. Lord Jesus.
Back at Andre's place the kissing ain't stopped – at the bar, in the mini-cab, in the lift, on the landing through the front door into the hallway – just one long kiss. And now on the floor, by the bed in a room decorated with Whitney, Darnell is laying back gasping for air while Andre kisses his way down the length of his torso from quivering nipple to trem-bling knee... up along his ripped inner thigh and suddenly, with one swift move, Andre's got Darnell's legs over his

shoulders and I'm like what the fuck is that in my face all pink and wet, and it's Andre's tongue! I'm like what the fuck are you doing in here? I've never seen one of them things before – I've been totally mugged up and I'm so surprised that I almost forget to clench! Until I pull it together and I'm like –

(muscle gorilla pose)

Get the fuck out of here! It ain't going without a fight, though – it's wiggling around and lashing out like a fifties horror movie –

I tell you, man, tongues is *strong*!

But tongue know it's wrong – tongue in ass may feel good, but it don't belong

And tight thug ass is in effect – and the tongue is gone!

Hell no! Not on my watch! I'm catching my breath now, thinking I need me to have some serious words with my man Darnell. I don't know what he thinks the next chapter of this story is, but it's time to remember that real men don't play that... Then I feel something else and I'm thinking what's that? What the fuck is that? I can't believe it! It's a fucking finger! It's a FUCKING FINGER! Darnell! DUDE! Wake the fuck up! We're getting tossed up, man! I'm pulling on my deepest darkest mojo to get this fucker out of my grill but the finger's all slimy with something and I can't get a grip – and I realise, it's coated in lube! I'm getting lubed! What the fuck is going on? Ain't this picture upside down? I mean, look at my man Darnell and look at Andre and you tell me – who's the bitch here? This is not a punk ass! And then the finger quits wiggling and it's gone and I'm like Oh my Lord, Oh my God... here comes the big one. At first I'm ready for a fight – I'm all Vive La Resistance, You Shall Not Pass – but you know what, then I get to thinking... this might be my department but this ain't my business – if Darnell's too drunk to care, why should I bother to hold things down on my own? So, I take a tip from the civil right dudes from the sixties and I just go limp and let nature take its course.

It's funny – you don't realise, over the years – just how lonely things have got, you feel me? It was sorta nice like to have company drop in for a bit. And he was wearing a pretty cool raincoat. And I have to tell you – my man Darnell was loving it! Hooting and hollering and making a whole heap of noise! Oooh, Daddy! Yeah, Papi! Toss me up! Turn me out! Do me Do me Do me, man! It was the longest sentence he ever spoke since he first said, 'It wasn't me'. It was good to see my man let himself go. It was alright. It was sort of fun, like. Different... the first time. By the third time it was starting to be in danger of becoming an addiction. I was starting to look forward to it.

So it's morning now. And we're lying here in the warm sun and cool breeze through Andre's open window and I realise something's changed. And that's okay. 'Cause nothing's lost. I ain't lost nothing. I'm still working for the Don. Still a thug-ass ass-on-a-thug. Just every now and then – like seven nights a week and matinees on Saturdays? I get to be a punk ass too. Nothing lost, everyting gained. But I ain't no pussyhole, you get me? Unless you're name's Andre. And then, Papi... I'm whatever you want me to be.

FADE TO BLACK

Retrograde

By Donovan E F J Morris

5, *6, 4, 6, 3, 4… Hmmm… 7 – no, 4 ½… Ronal marvels, amused how the turn of a body, a shift of weight, the elevation of a shadow could change the curve of a* back, the swell of a belly and so diminish the attractiveness of a man, downgrade him 3 points; disappointed, he dismisses the man attempting to attract attention on his right.

Am I being too harsh? Isn't everyone doing the same?

He considers his own rating. Age: 46 (downgrade -1) but looks early-to-mid-30s, aided by his lush black (dyed) locks (+2 upgrade) – 35 being the perfect median. Luckily genetically athletic – classic T, broad shoulders, slim hips – his rounded chest and biceps shows he is no longer a stranger to the gym (+2 upgrade). Although the pressures of work had caused his aging middle to spread over a nearly four-pack (- or +1, dependent on the marketing), at least – to paraphrase Stevie Wonder – 'his legs were sturdy', exuding muscular strength (+1 upgrade); that unrealised sprint career continually paying off. Despite previous affirmations Ronal had only recently, with the help of his therapist Leo, come to believe that his embarrassing hereditary traits were features. This was particularly true of what had been called his 'crowning glory', his round and fulsome arse (he still couldn't quite view it as an upgrade, although he had been reassured countless times that he needed a large hammer to drive a big nail).

Ronal squirms, his mouth an oval of sensuality as, heavy-lidded, he looks down at a man knelt venerating his nine-inch nail. This final attribute (+3 upgrade – particularly if on show) probably bumped him up to a 7½, possibly 8. He was of course discounting his abundance of melanin, which he knew for swathes of men totally desexualized him (serious downgrade). He shrugs off the thought, consciously un-tensing his shoulders. It was not that he was especially short of admirers – he strokes the occipital of the head nuzzling between his legs – but he felt weighed down by the constant battle between regard and disregard for his being exotically 'other'. Was this man here because of or despite his ethnicity? A soft moan escapes Ronal's lips negating serious concern; adhering to his own mantra, given to Andrew and other long-term lovers when they questioned his culturalism:

'You have to both ignore but be constantly aware of the blackness.'

Andrew had baulked at this perceived reprimand, and, rather than explore the nuance and complexity of the issue, Ronal had, as usual, backed down, assuring his partner (then of three years) that he had not been insinuating racist intent. Now, as then, he wonders if his insecurity about colour causes him to sell himself short for fear of being alone. He again looks down at the man before him who barely meets esteem baselines of above 5, (although an enthusiastic tongue tries to persuade otherwise). Suddenly disenchanted, Ronal disengages with the obligatory strokes of thanks.

Jack Daniels in hand he reconnoitres for new sexual campaigns, moving deeper into the subterranean arches that everywhere serve subcultures so well, allowing them to operate safely beneath the criticism of social acceptability. He eyes balding heads, (6, 5, 7, 6½), greying temples, (7½, 6, 6½), and the beginning of expanding girth, (7½ wuff, possibly 8), that for him often scored above the young, insouciant, fit & buff, (4, 5½, 7, 6). The acrid perfume of nitrites tickle his nostrils, complementing the dank visceral visuals, the musty smell, forbidding, but also liberatingly manly; creating the perfect fusion of fantasy and security. He feels intoxicated. The primal beats of Deep House reverberate, heightening his senses, elevating his pulse as he revels in the atmosphere. Sex fills the air, pre-cum, post cum, possibilities, comings together. It was the wealth of possibilities that he really enjoyed. That, and The Men.

They were all here: the muscled, the sallow, the defined, the bellied, grey, stocky, bearded, bald, lean, not so lean; wan Asian students (3-6) eyeing smash-faced Eastenders (2-8); trilling Middle England youths (4-5) flittering around Middle Eastern

gentlemen (5ish); pale Hoxton hipsters (6 ½) kissing Mediterranean muscle-boys (8+), geeky academics (6) frottaging
stocky American financiers (4). Even the ever-present Methu-
selah-like Jewish grandfather with his sagging skin, blood-
hound eyes & orthopaedic sandals (1) had his (admittedly few)
admirers, one man's poison definitely being another man's
meat. It couldn't just be men so desperate to hook up that they
strayed far from their sexual norms and fantasies, nor just
opposites attracting. There seemed to be more; a craving to
connect, a need for conjunction, to join together, a grasping
after an affirmation of life. It reminded him of his beloved rave
days when camaraderie exploded with Ecstasy, before the
Internet started the decline of the gay social whirl. Ronal hoped
that it was something primal; that when stripped down, despite
the disparity of bodies, all men were more adorned with
certainty in their own skin. He suspected it more likely that a
buff muscle boy (at least when clothed) had as many insecuri-
ties as a middle-aged (slightly) bellied accountant. Whatever its
cause, the comradeship he felt gave him a great sense of
comfort. One that kept him returning, had sustained him when
after thirteen years he had found himself surplus, supplanted.

'I really don't think this is working anymore.'
  *These were the words that Andrew had used after what
had seemed a successful trip to Ikea to buy shelving.*
  *'I think you'll find this will work just fine,' Ronal had
answered, pulling the shelving out of the packaging, not
realising that Andrew was dismantling their carefully-
constructed comfortability.*
  *'I mean us,' Andrew had continued. 'I still love you, but I
need something more.'*
  *'Something more?' Ronal had mumbled distractedly,
opening screw packs, unaware that his world was being
disassembled as he assembled.*

*Two years later Ronal still battled to suppress the rage that
had fired in him when he had learnt that the 'something more'
was a slender, smooth, twenty-seven-year-old Nigerian
Afrocentric film-maker/Pilates instructor Andrew had met
four months earlier. Ronal had been attempting to quench*

this fire with alcohol when he'd stumbled into the club one night. His usual reserve lowered by shots on top of bourbon on top of beer, he had not turned on brogued heels when asked,

'You know its underwear/boots only tonight?'

Slipping out of his Gap chinos and Brooks Brothers' button-down, Ronal had almost unselfconsciously divested himself of his carefully-tailored image. His mother had colonised his blackness with her many mantras, which distilled down to: 'Same same, but better'. Elocution lessons at seven, tutors at nine followed by a private school part-scholarship she had worked three jobs to ill-afford had propelled him into the middle classes. His homosexuality had thrown her, but when he had brought Andrew home, all floppy hair and clipped Etonian tones, she had simpered, pleased, colonisation completed.

Heading for the bar he had sought an unintimidating body to join before topping up his confidence, not yet quite drunk enough to extinguish his vulnerability. He was offered a beer. Needing something stronger he chased it with Jack Daniels and surveyed the room craving a cigarette. The black walls and dim lighting created a gloom that comforted, allowing him to feel hidden. Multifarious bodies sat, stood, lounged and wandered unselfconsciously around him. His chest constricted, reserve threatening to overwhelm him.

'All these men, it is a wonderful sight, isn't it?' His bulbous neighbour at the bar leaned across.

'It is... definitely... interesting.' Ronal turned, fumbling with his glass, not quite ready for interaction.

A hand grazed his thigh. He flinched, pulling in his belly. He looked down. The hand belonged to a sexy Al Pacino circa Serpico. Blood pressure rising, confusion bubbled, his gaze pinned by dark eyes that questioned invitingly. It wasn't possible, he had thought, but the man's hand still caressed his thigh.

'Hi,' Ronal exhaled, unsure how to proceed.

'You are sexy man,' Serpico replied, his accent as heavy as his hand, which was continuing an upward creep. 'You are very sexy mans.'

Despite the obvious delusion Ronal flushed. Involuntarily

reaching up for validation, his hand rubbed against a muscled chest, his fingers grasping abundant chest hair.

He later learnt this godlike man was named Jorge, an architect visiting from Venezuela. Jorge had not cared that he was no longer 'slender', getting chunky around the middle, exercise no more than the odd Pilates class. Jorge had not felt his salted beard too messy, nor thought his shoulders needed shaving or (as Andrew had implied) that he was really too dark but not black enough. Jorge had led him away and tickled his hairy back with his tongue, caressed his moobing chest, buried his face appreciatively beneath his belly bulge; had made him feel more than just 'stubby and brown'.

Sex with Andrew, always Protestant, had over the years become perfunctory; snatched before morning meetings or Sunday papers, edged out by theatre visits, around catching up with friends, an adjunct quickly dispensed with. He and Jorge had explored unhurriedly, foraging deeply, uncovering entombed delicacies of pleasure. At the moment of release Ronal had shuddered violently, quiet tears overrunning his cheeks. An avalanche of emotion tumbled from his prised heart as Jorge held him close, breaking their fall. They clung tightly together, each absolving the other's need. They spooned, cautiously clambering over the barrier of language, speaking of Andrew, learning about Marcello, sharing morsels of their lives, not wanting to leave the intimate feasting with anything unsavoured. Their unexpected intimacy dissolved time, too soon the club was closing; they had to leave. Jorge back to the southern hemisphere, Ronal back to the flat he scrimped to no longer share, but for once not contemplating the cause of this.

In the months following Jorge's departure Ronal had returned to the club many times, with each a feeling of emancipation growing. He made new connections, both physical and mental, nakedness somehow removing differentials, the cut of one's jeans seemingly more divisive than the swell of one's belly or the sag of one's buttocks, with similarities outweighing differences when social camouflaging was eliminated. In the club he found freedom, acceptance and communion. It was never the same as it had been with Jorge but he always found

255

release. The cygnet Jorge had birthed flourished with each return. After folding away the woes of the world and putting them temporarily in a black bin-liner with his clothes he could be reborn, renewed. Here he could be whoever he wanted to be. Encouraged by the attention of others he had remade himself: month by gruelling month his waist trimmed, stomach hardened, biceps and pectorals grew. Admiring glances and inviting smiles boosted his confidence until he was comfortable with, rather than was embarrassed by, his body.

Assurance emanating from his veneration/blow-job, Ronal steals back into the ranks of sexual warriors, eyes seductively hooded, a smile nearly playing on his lips. It was a look that Ronal had seen successfully worked by others, flirtatious invitation veneered with indifference. He jostles through the undergrowth of flesh, appraising, being appraised. Eyes scan chests, (7), bellies, (4½-5), groins, (6), eyes, (8), evaluating attributes, searching for that spark of attraction that might answer their yearnings. He acknowledges recent acquaintances. Avoiding others, he skirts two Ghanaians, (4, 6) who mock-grasp after him. He laughs, completing the ritual. He sees a rugby-built, blond bearded possibility (7) in the distance and starts a stealthy pursuit. Bodies press and release around him, merge and congregate, florid patterns in the dim rufescence. The mesmerising glint of a Prince Albert causes his eyes to linger. Looking up, his bearded beauty is gone, swallowed amongst the bodies. Pulled into another scene, a circuit proves:
Never mind, plenty more men in the barrel.
Gliding on confidence garnered from alcohol and admiration, Ronal pans, unsure what he seeks but confident that, just around the corner, he will see that face, hear that laugh, feel that warmth, be lost in those eyes, be spiked. Ronal pushes around a cluster of rutting bodies, men grasping after him hoping to detain; stumbling onwards he stops, eyes wide. Before him a handsomely beautiful black man perches, legs akimbo, confidence visible. He is 'The Lesser-Seen Black 9'; younger, taller, broader, fitter and better-looking. A fine bone-structure suggests Igbo descent, his unblemished skin, (dark but not too dark), glowing. On his bowed lips he wears thuggish

insouciance; on his feet, Ronal guesses, correctly, Hi-Top trainers, ticking all the 'Ethnic: Black' attractiveness boxes. The Black 9's almond eyes make sagacious acknowledgement.

Damn! Damn! Damn!!

Ronal's spirits, self-grading and esteem slip as he sidles away, diminished, pretending not to notice eyes that had flickered interest slide over him dilating upon seeing The Black 9. A familiar shroud of disquiet slumps across his shoulders. The feeling that, despite a wealth of equality laws in the UK and a US president of colour, there was not enough room for all the blackness. Despite all his 'remaking' he immediately feels like an ugly duckling.

His life-strategy had always been to constrain his stubby brownness; using twill, tweed, flannel, education and money to show that he was the same; prove his worthiness of inclusion. Stripped of his usual accoutrements he had re-dressed with muscle and attitude but here is The Black 9: 'Same same but better'.

I need to Jack up my game.

Ronal often turned to Jack in times of trouble. Jack could help in any situation, a friend he could rely on. Jack always made him feel younger, fitter, brighter, better. The first sip of the warming amber liquid begins massaging away his shoulder knots, and by the third his neck is relaxing, extending. Out of sight of his nemesis, two infusions of fortitude unknot enough for Ronal to affect a disinterested nonchalance against the bar. Men brush by probingly close, needing deeper clarification in the dim light. A few reach out, weighing up his potential, most (3, 4½, 2) he brushes away, smiling dissent; some (6½) he allows delay. All move on, no ignition sparked.

Obviously time to circulate.

Finishing his drink, Ronal smiles a grimace at his new neighbour, a slight young Asian man, whose receptive gaze makes him feel slightly paedophilic, and launches into the whorl and whirl not quite ready for 'Daddyhood'. The press of flesh is less now, the mood quieter; chatter underscores the still-pumping bass-line as cliques form. Softer eyes casually review, relaxed, no longer working the crowd; consociated, romanced, sated. Zenith passed, zeitgeist waning, few notice Ronal's passing presence. He, however, notices that his bête noire is still present, attitudinised majestically, stealing attention.

Ronal begins circling, scouring with lustful hope lustreless eyes that had previously annulled, seeing again disappointing dismissal. He reappraises slack musculature, desiring the already disregarded, his sexual manifesto eroding as his craving for contact increases with each pass. The Black 9 has The Rugby 7 in his thrall, their sinuous dance tantalising vicarious onlookers. A Floppy-Haired 6 Ronal had been stalking joins their sway. Ronal declines further, thrusting his breast while inwardly crumpling.

There is nothing happening for me here, I should just leave.

Ronal circles again and again and again, desperation etching into his soul. Each circuit bruises, The Black 9 an irritant in the corner of his eye, taunting, collecting more acolytes, a Blue-Eyed 5, a Skinhead 6, the growing coterie capturing the best of a depleting pool. All that remains are bottoms in the air and the hard to love. More men congregate around The Black 9, sexual heat radiating out like a bushfire, alighting other smaller groups.

His circling slowing, Ronal joins the hover. He grabs an offered bottle of poppers, proffering his body as tender. The bottle is fresh, the rush almost overwhelming, filling his brain, infusing his body, heightening every sense; every nerve soars with the recorded diva. He doesn't stay long, irritated by a touch that dissatisfies. His heart pulsates, rhythmically tuning into the bodies surrounding him, all of them throbbing to the revving beat.

Ronal simmers up the ranks, pulled into ever-closer orbit of The Black 9. Hands pushing, pulling, tweaking, mouths licking, squeezing, sucking, all frantically using every seduction technique at their disposal to ensure involvement. The musky aroma of craving percolates, increasing arousal. Ronal is pushed up against muscular solidity. The Rugby 7 glances back, considers and pulls him closer. Ronal's thigh grazes The Black 9, whose eyes flash wantonly. Nitrites suffuse, dilating blood-vessels, engorging lusts. Electrons jump across skin electrified under many touches. Eyes roll back in heads no longer needing to scan, beyond grading, revelling in the crescendo of sensations. Ronal feels glorious, connected, truly alive. Around him bodies entwine, a writhing tumultuous mass interlinked in celebration, hands, fingers, mouths, tongues, register only as pleasure, elevating ecstasy, grades forgotten. Ronal's urgency builds, all outside concerns fall away, problems at work (gone), mortgage worries (gone), his usual abiding feeling of loneliness (gone), his striving, his searching, his struggle, all gone, nothing matters except his current contentment. It is all-encompassing; he neither looks back nor thinks forward. He is just here, totally present within a wonderful continuous moment. This is why he returns time after time; this connection with the universal life-force. He feels wanted, needed, and loved, an unstoppable supernova. He is a glorious 10.

'*The best in town.*'

Streaming sweat prickles his body, running down his face, stinging his eyes. Shallow grunts escape through gritted teeth as his body begins to tremble spurred by adjacent spasms. Head back Ronal finally cries joyful exultation, testimony to his convulsing body overflowing with pleasure. Gratification echoes around him, a chorus of release, The Blue-Eyed 5, The Floppy-Haired 6, The Rugby 7 and finally The Black 9 add their voices to the cacophony of discordant praise.

Paroxysms abate, breathing slows, cum, sweat, poppers & beer permeate mingling with joy, satisfaction, relief, despair, regret staling the air; some achieving their desires, not all desiring their achievements. New kinships develop, most temporary, some permanent. Muted chatter accompanies uplifting vocals that pump around a room now deflating with exodus, ties of desire loosening, lives being returned to.

Post-euphoria, Ronal rests sweat-saturated against The Muscled 7, head buried, sucking in the smell and taste of the curly blond hair plastering his mouth. They regain breath in unison, extending their moments of knowing. Looking up, Ronal catches The Black 9's sanguine gaze.

What do those eyes want?
I don't fancy black guys
But this man is beautiful
But he is the enemy
Abuser, name caller, hate chanter
The reason I had to change schools, to escape

259

Why I live in the West, keep myself contained
Why I settle, stultify, suppress
Why I fear...
Disrupting Ronal's reverie The Rugby 7 growls, grinning thanks. Ronal facsimiles the same, pulling away, unhappy to break their bond but glad to escape the disconcerting scrutiny of The Black 9.

Ronal pulls on a cashmere hoodie, (part of a newly-acquired urban edge), pushing discombobulating thoughts of The Black 9 out of his head. Club nights were for unfettering, not for the challenge or questioning in those almond eyes. Tonight The Rugby 7 had been the salve to his soul, had allowed redemption and enabled release, which was all he really needed.

Reciting the modern Trinitarian formula, '**keys, wallet, phone**', Ronal saunters out revitalised, feeling strong, attractive, powerful, re-armoured, ready to do battle with life.

I Told Them a Tale

By Adebisi Alimi

Screaming in the background;
Crying and tears
A narrative I cannot explain
Words on my lips but too powerful to be spoken
Dialects strange to say but gagging to be spoken

In my own words I told them a tale

Excitement from the past, anchoring the future
Laughter so sweet it made me cry
Poetry flows like stream of life
Passion like the fire that burns to give life

In my own words I told them a tale

A tale of joy, of battle won and lost, a tale of love, of pain felt and loved

I told them of the passion to consume and be consumed
Of the unending desire to be wanted
Of the fear of being lonely and the burden of being with someone

In my own words I told them a tale of growing up with the shame of being different

Of the desire to belong but the longing to be different.

I told them of the words my mother told me.
'Why are you bringing shame to the family?'

In my own words I told them of the words the kids at the playground called me: 'batty boy', 'faggot', 'adofuro'

They hurt. I cried, I ran home, I wanted the day to end.

In my own words I told them the words my lover told me
'You are the best thing to have happened to me'

In my own words I told them the words my friends said
'Thanks for giving us a voice'

In my own words, I told them about the break of dawn

I told them about the tales at moonlight

In my own words I told the children of tomorrow the tale of
ever evolving world of today

I share with them the tales of the motherland. The tales of
'Ubuntu'

In my own words, I am shaping their world today with the
tales of yesterday.

David & Robin

By David McAlmont

'One man's creed is another man's psychobabble...' – me

Have you ever noticed that when you focus on your breathing the idea that inhaling and exhaling can ever happen unintentionally seems bizarre? Then your mind strays elsewhere and the breathing just carries naturally on without the help of your thought. Scientists can explain my existence to me with exhaustive erudition and informed conviction, yet I find breathing lungs, beating hearts, operational bones, and blood coursing through veins utterly miraculous and mysterious - even as I think these possibilities absolutely bonkers. Yet I would much rather have these things happening to me than not. Circling the nearest star aboard this immense vehicle, Earth, within a skin casing which somehow contains and maintains this bewildering, functioning system of bone, flesh, blood and vulnerable organs, sounds like one hell of a trip, and that is exactly what my life is... one hell of a trip.

When I express myself thus, there are as many opinions on my views as the persons who hear them. Those opinions occur against a backdrop of billions of events per second, in a range of dimensions, particularly if you subscribe to the Richard Dawkins view that life is 'queerer than we suppose'. It is never a certainty that you will all agree with my worldview, or my take on myself. Even if I simper, 'I only know that I am amazing because I believe that we all are,' there are still those who will counter that I am just full of myself, and still others who will say that I am just plain wrong.

My own identification with the views of others is never a given. Compassion is underrated, even if it sometimes appears to be in short supply. Despair is an option, but I think that some of us are granted a merciful self-perception. People like me always find their way back to being fascinated, not disappointed, by what they are. But 'people like me', that could mean anything. Who is like me? I am a fingerprint, unique, yet another exception, a one-off. You only get one me. So, people like me? People with whom I have something in common? Perhaps.

My individuality is founded upon the soaring concrete towers and pebbledash houses of Brutalist Croydon, the quaint rose cottages and seaside guesthouses of sleepy Gorleston-on-Sea, the eccentrically faunal, fruit-rich brown waterways of humid, coastal Guyana, and the densely cultural boil and ceaseless scrum of subterranean, sky-scraping metropolitan London. My individuality is shaped by the sum of everything that I have seen and been in those various locations and others, where I have been abused, beaten, criticised, delighted, disgraced, educated, engaged, exposed, feted, fought, hated, honoured, included, indoctrinated, insulted, loved, ostracized, presumed upon, ridiculed, sent up.

Envy has often been mine. It can generate a range of incorrect impressions regarding one's lot. Often an individual considers the circumstances, perceives the advantages, counts the blessings of another, all based on an insufficiency of information: a newsflash, a headline, a quote, a photograph of an arrival at a party, news of a happy couple's wedding, a harsh exchange of words, a passing glance, even a once-deep, now-forgotten conversation on a druggy, muddy festival field. Thus the question, 'But are they happy?' carries a lot of weight, because there is little way of grasping how it truly is for someone else, based purely on what I think I know about them. Unless I find a way to exist in an alternative dimension, which is to say the alternative dimension that someone else is, I can only barely assess how life is for anyone other than me.

I believe that the masterstroke in my trajectory was my mother's. She gave me two powerful names, David and Robin. David is the name on my birth certificate, yet she never called me that. She has always called me Robin. It stems from a Guyanese family tradition; my mother was born in the countryside, on the west coast of the Berbice River, in a little village called Golden Grove. She was christened Iris Beatrice. She later changed her name by deed poll to Edith Elizabeth, but the family have always called her Girleen. I have always known that I was named after a singing psalmist king and a songbird, by a woman who, as a child, was known in her small Berbice village, Lovely Lass, thronged by the lush backdam and the silty wat'side (waterside), for her rendition of Nat King Cole's 'Walking My Baby Back Home'. In Croydon, in Cardiff where my father studied law, in Norfolk, and Guyana, she raised me on Nat, Tony Bennett, Perry Como, Bing Crosby, Dionne Warwick, Sam Cooke and Art Garfunkel. Consequently, music has always seemed like my birthright, and it has proven to be my salvation.

At the time of writing I am convalescing at a friend's house in Tooting, South London after a sensitive operation. It is a wonderful place to recover; just south enough and culturally varied enough to represent the London I still believe in. I perceived my operation as the conclusion of a chapter, a book. I see my emergence from the anaesthetic as a new beginning, waking into a dream of success and good fortune. The house that I am in is a perfect setting from which to launch these aspirations. My host is an enormously achieved, award-winning thespian. I could say actor, but there are actors and then there are those, like my friend, who better suit the title thespian. There are writings by the Dalai Lama, Marcus Aurelius and Nelson Mandela in the bathroom, and on the walls there are posters and photographs from a prolific career that continues. It is an environment where everything seems possible.

If my self-loathing were brimming, as it has been known to, I would perhaps be given to comparing and despairing at this time in this location, but instead it is my self-esteem that is brimming, after years of soul-searching and negotiating my way out of pains – creative, emotional, mental, physical, and psychological – that have been so often self-inflicted. I have developed a necessary spirituality, and attempted to cultivate a higher power. If life had been a walk in the park these things would not have been essential. But life has not been a walk in the park; it has been more like a succession of chapters from a Tolkien epic.

I have a lot in common with my Tooting host: he is half-Caribbean, half-African; he is a creative renaissance type; he is dark of skin; and he is gay. But then again so much about us is different. I am only technically Caribbean; I am arguably half South American. My friend's mother is from Barbados; my mother is Guyanese. My friend and I have Nigerian fathers in common, but I haven't seen my father since I was six, and anyway my father is Yoruba, whereas my friend's father is Ibo. My friend makes his living as an actor; I sing for my supper. My friend is a father; I have never biblically known a woman.

So how does one define oneself? Moreover, are those who would caution the definers of self against self-definition right to do so? One might say that there is a lifelong war on: a weight of human expectation: religious belief, societal constructs, the neighbours, first impressions, the ambitions of others and one's own, social misalignment and sociopathy, all confronting and challenging human individuality daily. It is only when I am displeased with myself that I accuse myself of being a 47-year-old man. Moreover I still feel very much a boy and cannot quite compute a personal adulthood or locate enough evidence of that adulthood within myself. I am always amazed that people claim to see past my skin colour, or to not notice it at all, but this is because my colour has so often been pointed out to me, insisted upon, required of me; sometimes with the best possible taste or sometimes with the most tasteless offensiveness.

In my early twenties, after an incident where I nearly drowned at Highgate Ponds, I remember quipping to the man who saved my life, 'I am not black; I am Burnt Sienna!' The statement was greeted with uproarious laughter. I was half joking, but by then the idea of black and white had begun to strike me as simplistic, especially years after I had been exposed to my artist sister's different tubes of watercolour paint: ivory black, mars black, lamp black, titanium white, ivory white, Chinese white etc. The blackest people I have ever seen were descendants of Indian immigrants in Guyana, South America; according to my mother they came from a place called Madras. But even they weren't the colour that Windsor and Newton watercolour tubes contained. Neither have I ever seen a zinc white human being, except of course at the circus, and then they were only professionally so.

In London it is apparently one of the best places in the world to be black, but discussing black experience with Londoners who are not is rarely deemed essential in this city. The minute you mention colour you get a distinct feeling of affront. 'You're not black are you, Dave?' a friend so-called once joked. 'It's that fucking black chip on your shoulder!' snarled another, when I presumed to take umbrage at his mother referring to Aboriginals as 'coons'. 'She's an old woman!' he admonished. He also declined to understand my lack of amusement when he told a boyfriend to call me a 'stupid black bitch!' because I'd forgotten a commitment I had agreed to.

That I am black is supposed to mean less these days than it once did, but what did it mean then? And could that explain why there are those who have counselled me against visiting Russia for reasons of my blackness; not that it hindered the 2013 all-black cast of the RSC's Julius Caesar from going to Moscow, where people from the Russian provinces approached them in the streets to request photographs.

There was another time, in 1992, at a pub on Finchley Road in north London, when an A&R man who was interested in signing me to his label was amazed that there was such a thing as a black gay, and astonished that there were thousands of black gays in London, as I had pointed out with amusement. He thought I was terribly brave to be honest about being those things. To me, it seemed that singers like Holly Johnson, Jimmy Somerville, Marc Almond and Sylvester had already paved the way, so I didn't feel particularly brave about discussing it. Nevertheless, it was still 'a thing' in the early nineties. Nonetheless, it still is.

I remember the first time I heard the expression 'batty man.' My mother was gossiping about one of the church brothers. I always felt nakedly visible at the mere mention of the 'perversion', as if another's invocation of the word made me shimmer with hidden sin. I remember a group of preachers performing the laying on of hands at a remote church retreat in the white sandy region of Demerara, Guyana. I approached and asked for relief from my depression. I remember the preacher putting his hand on me and praying for 'this demon of homosexuality' to be exorcised; I remember accepting the prayer, but wondering why he thought my depression was related to homosexuality, an explanation I had not offered for it.

There were a few incidents like that. There was Sister Phyllis at my Pentecostal church in Georgetown, Guyana: a sweet, well-meaning woman. I had confided my sexuality to her and she had taken me on ferries to exotic-sounding places to be prayed over by powerful men of god who expected me to vomit my demons up – literally. I remember her being horrified when I announced that I was returning to England. Her stance: 'There is plenty of gay there!' Instinctively, I had kept my intended departure from Guyana secret until the very last minute. She made it plain that she would have done everything in her power to keep me there. Remarkably, sisters in the congregation who had never looked at me twice flirted coarsely with me that Sunday morning. Back then in the late nineteen-eighties people were getting out of Guyana by any means possible, if at all possible.

I had to get out of Guyana. I was there for nine years and every day – yes, every single day – I was called 'anti-man' by strangers, even before I felt the questionable desires that would mark me out as such. It was always expressed so gleefully; I became a nine-year joke. It wasn't only my youthful effeminacy that was mercilessly lampooned on the streets of Wismar and Georgetown, but also the size of my lips (Lipticus, Liptibatus, Blubber Mouth), and the size of my feet. Every day I steeled my nerve to leave the house. It was most painful when I was walking with my mother or my sister, mortifying for them and embarrassing for me. It instilled a lasting fear that in the Caribbean they can smell the gay on me, and it reeks as high as rotten tilapia. The members of the concrete churches I attended in the capital tended to be kinder, yet they always bore my salvation or exorcism in mind.

I have subsequently pondered whether it was those slings and arrows – from schoolchildren, men on corners and lawless women, which upset my sister and distressed my mother – that 'turned me'. I no longer think that. Frankly, I do not know why I am 'anti-man' as they loved to spout, and, just as frankly, I am not possessed of an aching need to have the proclivity explained, even though the explanations are frequently entertaining. I have an explanation of my own: that gay men are a naturally selected support-structure for the breeding species. One day I will probably explore that idea in another essay.

After high school I was too dark and too effete to get a decent job in Georgetown. The only work I could find was unpaid work at British West Indian Airways, for which I was given a seventy-five percent rebate on a flight to any of its destinations, which included London. Astonishing! Every day I traipsed to work in cheap clothes, supported by my mother's nursing wages, living in her dilapidated tenement house in Lodge, a hideous, badly-irrigated area of town landscaped along crude bauxite streets, to work in a pretentious, air-conditioned, would-be chi-chi environment where I was treated like the unpaid staffer that I was. The people I worked with had a self-importance to them: working at an international airline in Guyana, a country that everybody was trying to get out of, meant that they had the keys to the kingdom, as it were, and they acted like royalty. I relegate that perception to mere impression now. It is entirely possible that I was feeling profoundly 'less than' at the time.

It was in that ambience that I decided to become a star: it seemed like the only option. I knew that London was the place to make that happen. I got my passport from the British High Commission and determined to flee the 'land of six peoples united and free' on the northeastern seaboard of South America. I lackeyed for the next three months at the airline, got my rebate, borrowed some money from Sister Dalgety, and promptly fled. I gave myself five years upon my return to concrete Croydon to achieve stardom, and it worked out just as I intended, although the five years included mopping up vomit in old people's homes in Surrey, and liability claims handling.

Upon my return to England I had given Christianity seven years, from thirteen to twenty – the perfect number apparently – to cure me of this hideous queer malady. But then one afternoon in a Streatham Hill bedsit I realised that I had made persistent use of my direct line to the good lord above, through fasting, vows and prayer, and he had persistently declined to change me. Obviously he wasn't going to, and the intensity of my feelings couldn't accept this bizarre notion that homosexuality meant that god had 'called me' to be celibate. I had absolutely no patience with such a god; I just couldn't take him seriously. Clearly I was bound for hell, but it became my express intention to have a bloody good time on earth until my inevitable encounter with the devil and his angels.

I left southwest London for northwest, to become gay. I didn't do a Lot's Wife and look back. In the event I flourished: I dressed more adventurously, more androgynously; I gravitated toward the militantly irreligious; I went to gay bars and clubs; songs like 'Back to Life' by Soul II Soul and 'Musical Freedom' by Adeva seemed indicative of a new life opening its arms to me. I made gay friends and lovers. It was amazing. It took a few years for my fear of the Lake of Fire to subside, but it did. I was meeting good people, and once again my impatience with the draconian Pentecostal Jehovah deepened because I couldn't believe that these decent, likeable human beings were going to burn eternally for taking pleasure and finding love in each other. I decided to go to Middlesex Polytechnic to study performance art and to audition for a band.

I began to fantasise a cool notion of a successful black, gay, soul singer who sang openly about love between men; strange, because when I imagined such a thing I was not thinking that the singer in question would be me. With the success that came I became a vocal Black Gay. I broadcast it from great heights. I trumpeted it on television and in the broadsheets. I wielded those aspects of myself like a mighty staff. Although people were interested in my music I shoved my colour and sexuality in their faces with impunity. Looking back I think I took that path because I had endured years of having those qualities treated as curses.

These days those days seem like an eternity ago. Life has become exponentially better, especially since I unclogged the better channels of my existence of the booze and the party additives that encroached upon my stardom. I am singing more and more, I have become a vocal coach and an art historian in training at Birkbeck evening university, something I never expected to do. The Black Gay monolith of my early twenties has given way to Everything That I Am. I look at newspapers very little and television not at all. I read a lot, study hard and create incessantly; I write a lot as well. After years of loving James Baldwin, essayist, I decided that I would quite like to be an essayist; I quickly concluded that the only way to become one was to write essays, lots of them.

Ultimately, I can only be thankful: thankful that I am a son of life's longing for itself – as Kahlil Gibran would put it; thankful that my South American mother and my African father met in the United Kingdom; thankful that my father's motile sperm fertilised my mother's inviting egg; thankful to my mother for naming me; thankful that I have had nearly five decades of life on earth; thankful that I have a voice that works and a brain that is inquisitive; thankful that I have been the youngest in my class; thankful that I have been the oldest in my class; thankful that I was the only black boy in a Norfolk school; thankful that I was the only English boy in a Guyanese school; thankful that I was a poor boy from England in a school of wealthy Guyanese children; thankful for the love that enabled me to survive all the insults; thankful for the oasis from verbal abuse that the Pentecostal church provided; thankful for the sensitivity that allowed me to care about myself when others attempted unwittingly to destroy me.

I am thankful to the airline that would not pay me but would get me out of Guyana; thankful for the aunt in Croydon who took me in under duress and then unceremoniously threw me out; thankful for the Surrey recruitment agency that sent me to the care-homes of Carshalton where I discovered what I didn't want to be; thankful to the Streatham church that arranged a nice bedsit for me in Montrell Road after the horror of the bedsit in Burlington Road, Thornton Heath; thankful for the insurance company that had the same effect; thankful for the *Time Out* magazine column that showed me where the gay men were; thankful for the militant, socialist, atheist, gay father figure who nurtured me in the north of London and enabled me to become fabulous; thankful to the public schoolboy alongside whom I worked at London Underground who told me about university grants; and thankful to the other public schoolboy whose tale of drunken flunking of an art history degree switched a light-bulb on in my head.

The gratitude lists are endless. Suffice to say, like Kim Basinger, I am thankful to everyone I have ever met. And of course I am thankful to my mother for giving me the names of the singing Hebrew king and the enchanting songbird who became the fundamental icons of my blessed existence.

My Favourite Game

By Paul J. Medford

My favourite game as a kid was packing.
My favourite toys were my suitcases.
My parents bought me a Wendy house and erected it in the garden.
'Why didn't you buy him a wigwam ? He's a boy,' asked the neighbours.
He asked for a Wendy house my mother told them. 'He knows what he likes.'
I loved travelling from my bedroom to my Wendy house in the garden
With my suitcases full of entertainment, excitement and joy.

Four poems by Dean Atta

The Mix Up

Cypriot relatives called me, 'The black one.'
Jamaican family called me, 'English bwoy.'
And here I am asked, 'Where are you from?'

Not Cypriot and not Jamaican
My British passport
Lays my strongest foundation

Parts of me are still lost at sea
Shackled to painful memories
Parts of me are bullet holes
In abandoned buildings
In a more than thrice-conquered Mediterranean island

British soldiers patrol my border

Racism is rarely a downpour
You never know whether to put up
Your umbrella for the drizzle
But when you get home you realise
You are soaking wet.

I Come From

I come from shepherd's pie and Sunday roast
Jerk chicken and stuffed vine leaves
I come from travelling through my taste buds but loving where
I live

I come from a home that some would call broken
I come from D.I.Y. that never got done
I come from waiting by the phone for him to call

I come from waving the white flag to loneliness
I come from the rainbow flag and the union jack
I come from a British passport and an ever-ready suitcase

I come from jet fuel and fresh coconut water
I come from crossing oceans to find myself
I come from deep issues and shallow solutions

I come from a limited vocabulary but an unrestricted imagination
I come from a decent education and a marvellous mother
I come from being given permission to dream but choosing to
wake up instead

I come from wherever I lay my head
I come from unanswered questions and unread books
Unnoticed effort and undelivered apologies and thanks

I come from who I trust and who I have left
I come from last year and last year and I don't notice how I've
changed
I come from looking in the mirror and looking online to find
myself

I come from stories, myths, legends and folk tales
I come from lullabies and pop songs, Hip Hop and poetry
I come from griots, grandmothers and her-story tellers

I come from published words and strangers' smiles

I come from my own pen but I see people torn apart like paper
Each a story or poem that never made it into a book.

Losing My Mind?

It was a secret between us, he told me not to tell; that's when the silence fell
No one in the family spoke about it
A collective denial about their uncle, brother, child
Was it pride that stopped him asking for help?
Sworn to secrecy, I watched on helplessly, as he slowly lost his sanity
He wasn't the same man to me; the father figure he used to be
The stories he told me would never add up; two minus one and my uncle was gone
In the hospital he looked worse than ever but we hoped, in here, that he would get better
Suddenly we took this seriously; we were there for him
Spoke openly
We're not dealing with this perfectly but we're trying our best as a family
It's always a taboo, whether it be you or someone in your family, we suffer silently
We don't realise that it's so common, that mental health is such a hidden problem
Afraid that they'll judge us or our loved ones, we don't tell our friends, our colleagues or the system
We don't ask for help when we truly need it, act like it's not real until we believe it
Until it's too late, in hospital or worse, died because of pride or denial; that's somebody's child
Could be your uncle
Could be your dad, your mum, your aunt, your sister, your son, your brother, your cousin
It could be you
It has been me but I got help when I needed it
My uncle was a warning to me and I heeded it.

Steal This Poem

Steal this poem
Rob this poem
Put me out of a job with this poem
Download it
Upload it
Brag about how you stole it
Blog a review of this poem
It craves your point of view, this poem
Criticise this poem
Praise this poem
Copy and paste this poem
Donate lines to this poem
Predict the rhymes of this poem
Preach this poem
Teach this poem
Keep children out of reach of this poem
For fear they will understand this poem
Discover and demand this poem
Keep it in its place, this poem
Devalue and deface this poem
You might as well erase this poem
No, don't do that please, save this poem
It will learn to behave, this poem
Doesn't need to be paid, this poem
Won't expect too much, this poem
Of course you can touch this poem
Feel free to degrade this poem
Exploit and enslave this poem
How dare it fight back this poem?
Chemically attack this poem
Drug this poem
Diagnose this poem
Examine and expose this poem
Make this poem illegal
Tell this poem it's evil
All eyes on this poem
Exorcise this poem

It tells no lies, this poem
You despise this poem
Reprimand this poem
Disarm this poem
Make unfair demands of this poem
Train this poem
Rename this poem
Offer money and fame to this poem
Blame this poem
Scapegoat this poem
Forget about who wrote this poem
Go to war for this poem
Kill more and more in the name of this poem
Denounce this poem
Vote for this poem
Learn how to cope with this poem
Tell your president, prime minister or your dictator
Whatever power they have, this poem is far greater
Succeed with this poem
Believe in this poem
Please take whatever you need from this poem
Put your name on it
Hand it in as your coursework
Graffiti it on walls
Permanent marker it on toilet doors
Tattoo this poem
On drunken nights out
Spew this poem in the gutter
Mutter this poem
Scream this poem
Dream this poem
Wake up in the middle of the night and scrawl this poem
Recall this poem
The first time I went on stage and received applause for a poem
I knew I would continue to do it for my ego
Now I even do it for money
I'm not any kind of revolutionary
Most days I feel depressed in spite of my success
Most days I feel lost and lonely and writing can only help me so
much

Like a broken clock, I look all right if you catch me at the right time
Most of the time I feel helpless and writing feels pointless
But sometimes I'll write something I think might be worth sharing
And I'll share it
So I wrote this and I'm sharing it
So you can have it, if you want it
And if you don't, that's alright too

Either way, this poem is for you.

Thoughts of Chairman Leee

By Leee John

My roots ran wild through the halls of Hackney Hospital, Kensington Palace, Monte Carlo, the home of Nelson and Winnie Mandela, jetting off to be reborn in the USA and back again to Finsbury Park, North London, UK.

...A fun-filled life which is still full of rock and soul. I'm always asked the question, 'How was life before Imagination?' (my soul funk group of the 1980's). I reply: 'I've gone back to my pre-Imagination days energywise.' I love to multitask, but keep each project as a prime focus so it doesn't suffer. When I was a lot younger I played in three or four bands, played recording sessions, had a recording contract at fifteen, had a day job, gigged at night and later did temp jobs when music was lean for money.

It was and always has been fun, joy, tears, laughter, struggle, frustration with the cruelty of the business that is Show Business.

...The essence is education: keep learning your craft. The secrets are in the past, in the artists who came before us and how they survived, or didn't. Their legacy, depth, knowledge and artistry show us you must have a dream, so you can score your own goal and reach the highest heights. Even when you fall, for that moment your experience of life will help to pick you up – that's if you're determined to reach for it.

...To me nothing beats 'organic' – that freshness, originality: going where you shouldn't creatively. I see myself as 'me', not a victim of sexuality, or colour, or any bias. The world and media can be cruel. This can contribute to increased personal fears, but I pray and say I am me, myself, individual – and also surrounded by my team, who help sustain me centre stage. To quote the phrase, 'No man is an island, no man stands alone.' I say in time your skin, your brain, your being becomes tougher through experience. Of course through age you develop other aspects, some good, some bad – e.g. cynicism, being defensive, affirmative, leadership skills (which doesn't mean you're a control freak). A good argument with strong points can lead to new reasoning, new reactions and different thoughts. 'Time is always the master and healer.' I always relish the ideas of the future, keeping the dream alive.

...Too busy being 'you' is what's it's all about, not being a clone follower.

To end my Thoughts of Chairman Leee: the great actor, singer and activist Harry Belafonte once said to me and a few others when we joined Artists Against Apartheid, 'As the world turns, we turn it.' My reply: 'WE TURN THE WORLD'.

Turn Out the Lights

By Z. Jai Walsh

t iles
echoing laughter
crowds
ticket barrier
beep beep beep SEEK ASSISTANCE
jump it
'A Good Service is operating on all lines'
escalator
down deeper and deeper
busker
more crowds
'Mind the gap!'

Nate watched the tube-train surge into the station, the hot, dirty air expelled from the tunnel ahead of it hitting his tear-stained face. He caught the driver's eye, hoping for some sign of forgiveness, or perhaps permission.

I have to do this. It's best for everyone. I'm doing it for Aston

Forgive me Father for I have sinned

Nate closed his eyes, saw himself stepping off the edge of the platform to meet the front of the train, his scream mixing with those of the other passengers on the platform

for Aston

to spite Quinn

He saw the train rolling over him, crushing him, pulling him into the hidden workings underneath the car

Aston

Quinn

The train was here now. He stepped forward.

One hour earlier.

It was Jomo's fortieth birthday party. Aston was deep in

conversation with the birthday boy, the pair effortlessly dominating the room. Jomo, 6' 4" and a dead ringer for the sprinter Harry Aikines-Aryeetey, was wearing grey Superdry joggers that hugged his massive thighs and beachball booty. A Michael Sam St. Louis Rams jersey clung to his muscular torso – a present from Aston. The room had echoed with wolf-whistles when he peeled off his T-shirt to try it on. 'Sex siren. Walk!' someone yelled out with a finger-snap. 'Put your baps away love, they're sagging,' someone else teased, to a ripple of laughter.

Aston was a few shades darker than Jomo, his long locks contrasting sharply with Jomo's close fade. His frame was leaner than Jomo's NFL player bulk, vintage distressed jeans and crisp white shirt accentuating what he was working with. Nate gazed at Aston's large, expressive eyes, (Manga eyes, he liked to tease him), those long slender hands, as he gesticulated elegantly, trying to convince Jomo to join his Big Brother programme, mentoring homeless gay youth, so many of whom were BME.

A more jealous, insecure person than Nate would have been standing right next to Aston, would have his hand proprietorially around Aston's waist. Just in case. But Nate knew Aston was his.

So why did he feel so uneasy?

Quinn was smirking at him from across the room.

They met at that year's UK Black Pride, Nate's first. He had gone alone, having spent weeks trying to decide on an outfit, wanting something that would capture the attention of the Nubian God he knew was waiting for him out there, somewhere. He'd selected skinny jeans that showed off his well-developed legs (honed from cycling between his flatshare in Canada Water, and his job at Selfridges on Oxford Street), and a longline vest that exposed his smooth, pecan butter arms. During the quieter periods in menswear he'd tried on a snap-back cap (too hood), a beanie (summer – too hot!), and a bucket hat that made him look even more like a kid than he already did. In the end he decided to forego a hat and let the sun see his soft, dirty-blond curls. His 'good' hair. Despite being twenty-five, he still found himself getting age-checked when he bought alcohol. He tried to use self-service checkouts whenever he could to avoid the embarrassment. Nate stood at 5' 5", with a light dusting of freckles across his flat nose. His lips were wide and full, and although his ears stuck out a little too much for his liking, he liked his high, bubble-butt booty. It certainly attracted a lot of attention in the staff canteen at Selfridges, where being gay and mixed-race was virtually mandatory.

As well as sisters (femmes and studs) and a sprinkling of white folk, there were brothers of all colours at Pride; here mischievous faggamuffins with their asses hanging out, balancing snapbacks on their heads at unlikely angles, and there the more conservative preppy brothers, so much better than everyone else. He spotted the odd leather daddy too, but nowhere near as many as he'd seen in pictures from American Pride parades.

Then there was Aston, towering over everyone else, his long locks piled up high on his head, spraying out like a Texan oil well. He was decked out in white skintight jeans, his bare, chiseled torso looking like it had been precision-carved from onyx. Light glinted on his expanses of pectoral and deltoid muscles in the afternoon sun. A big-boned black woman with a buzz cut was standing on a milk crate painting his face to look like an Egyptian pharaoh. Nate watched, hypnotised, as she filled in a solar disc on his forehead.

'You're next, golden boy,' Aston said, catching his eye. Nate blushed, and glanced around. The throng of people surrounding them kept moving; Aston kept looking at him, eyes twinkling. 'Yeah you, Nestlé Caramac. I been watching you.' Aston held out a hand. 'C'mere.'

Hesitantly, Nate stepped forward. 'Sorry, I didn't mean to stare...'

'Hold still!' the woman painting Aston's face said crossly.

'How can I,' Aston said, still gazing into Nate's eyes, 'when my heart's beating so fast I can feel my chest bursting open.' He took Nate's hand, and pulled him in closer. 'Whagwaan, bwoy?'

'Oh, for fuck sake,' the woman said, drawing a brush heavy with gold glitter across Aston's eyelid. 'Tell me you ain't gonna fall for that darlin',' she said, addressing Nate.

But Aston had already pulled Nate in for a kiss that was as

long as it was deep. Nate went limp in Aston's embrace.

'Pull the other one, it's got bells on,' she muttered, giving Aston a hearty slap on the shoulder. 'You're done,' she told him, standing back to admire her work. 'And so have you been,' she winked at Nate.

Later, they walked down through Piccadilly and Haymarket to the concert in Trafalgar Square. Aston hadn't once let go of his hand. *He picked me,* Nate kept thinking. *He picked me.*

'Coming to HustlaBall later?' Aston asked, passing Nate his water bottle. Nate drank greedily from it.

'I've never been,' he said. 'I mean, I've seen videos on Xtube. Tyson Tyler's performing, right?'

'You love your dark breddas, innit?'

Nate blushed. 'I like light-skinned dudes too,' he lied. 'What about you,' he continued, trying to keep his tone neutral. 'Do you only like light-skinned dudes?'

'I like you,' Aston grinned, tweaking his nose. 'Caramac.'

Nate fell silent, looked down. *He picked me.*

he picked my skin.

my skin.

'We don't have to go HustlaBall,' Aston said after a while, picking up on – if misreading – Nate's discontent. 'Come up my local with me, you can meet my bredrins.'

'What about Hustlaball?' Nate asked. 'Don't you have to... work?'

Aston laughed. 'I'm not a go-go boy. I'm a social worker.'

He smiled, and kissed Nate, right in front of the National Gallery. The crowd in the Square cheered for someone on stage, but in Nate's mind, they were cheering for him.

They took the Tube from Trafalgar Square to Oxford Circus. The Bakerloo line was stiflingly hot and crowded, fifty-year-old trains that had seen better days. Tourists piled in at Piccadilly Circus, pushing Nate and Aston further into the side of the car. Impulsively, Nate flexed his glutes against the solid curve of Aston's thighs as Italians clutching bags of overpriced tat from Fortnum & Mason chattered excitedly around them.

'Oh, *rah*, you twerking on me, baby?' Aston breathed in his ear as the train picked up speed.

'I'm moving right down inside like the driver said,' Nate grinned. 'Making room.' The car jolted abruptly, and everyone stumbled. The Italians laughed at the novelty. Pressed together, Nate and Aston were all but oblivious.

They tumbled out of Stockwell Tube, manning up as they emerged onto the street and into a sea of Nike tracksuits and hijabs. They walked down Clapham Road for a while, before turning off onto a quiet side-road. Aston led Nate to a small pub called The Flying Horse. At the door, he rested a hand on Nate's shoulder. 'Hold your breath. Make a wish. Count to three – ' he kissed Nate's forehead '– Come with me and you'll be in a world of pure imagination.'

'Willy Wonka!' Nate exclaimed. 'My favourite movie! The original, of course...'

Aston pulled him in close, and whispered in his ear, 'You'll be free, if you truly wish to be.'

Four hours later, Nate was standing at the urinal, booze draining out of him. He could hear Frank Ocean on the sound system in the bar outside, singing about love and good times. Nate was swaying. It was all too good to be true. He liked Aston's friends: his gym-buddy Jomo, a bubbly, built brother who ran a vinyl record store across the street. Like Aston, he was an alpha male, a Big Bwoy, a man's man. Nate watched in fascination as Jomo and Aston chatted. To him, they were towering Nubian Gods. They were like two Victorian gentlemen smoking cigars in the study, talking of affairs of state whilst the women gossiped outside. Their conversation was an elegant wrestling match, one part gentle joshing, one part boasting, and one part mutual admiration. Because Jomo was Aston's equal, Nate didn't feel threatened by his abundant sexuality: Aston was showing Nate off, seeking Jomo's approval. 'You've done well for yourself son,' Jomo winked at Aston, and Nate's heart beat a little faster as he bathed in their approval.

Someone positioned himself at the urinal next to him. Quinn, the tall, dark-skinned brother who earlier had kissed Aston on both cheeks, yet pointedly blanked Nate. He wore thick-rimmed box glasses like Tinie Tempah (were they fake like Tinie's, or prescription, Nate wondered), red Chinos and a fitted black T-shirt that showed off his lean torso. His low 'fro was immaculate.

'Where are you from?' Quinn asked, unzipping. His tone was icy, his accent cut-glass. He came from money, or seemed to.

'Canada Water,' Nate replied, knowing this wasn't what he meant. Against his better judgement he glanced down: Quinn was well-endowed, and uncut.

'No, sweetie, where are you from?' Quinn was looking right at him, his full lips slightly parted. He took a long, lingering look at Nate's dick. Nate realised he wasn't pissing anymore, and that he was now simply standing there, stupidly, provocatively, with his dick in his hand. Quinn gave his a few shakes, and zipped up.

'Bath,' Nate said, hurriedly zipping up, turning away to wash his hands.

Quinn joined him at the adjacent sink, soaping his hands. 'Public toilets. Filthy places, aren't they?' Nate didn't reply. Quinn rinsed his hands off. 'Lagos.'

'What?'

'I'm from Lagos.' Quinn methodically dried off his hands with a paper towel. 'Or rather, my father is. My mother, from Abuja.' He tossed the paper towel into a bin. 'Where are your parents from?' He leaned back on the wall next to the paper towel dispenser, his arms folded, so that Nate had to reach past him to get to it.

'My Dad's Jamaican,' Nate said, looking away, watching his hands dry one another. 'My Mum... she's Irish.' He reached awkwardly around Quinn to the bin, all the time aware of his piercing gaze. Quinn reached out and touched Nate's strawberry blond curls.

'Such good hair,' he smiled.

Nate spun around to leave, almost crashing into Jomo. 'Whoop whoop,' Jomo laughed, mimicking a police siren. 'No fucking in the toilets.' He immediately registered the anger on Nate's face, and glared over at the smirking Quinn. 'Oh *seen*, the feds are here already. Colour Police division.' He put an arm around Nate's shoulders. 'Has he checked you against his Dulux colour chart yet?'

Quinn patted his 'fro in the mirror. 'Aston already borrowed it sweetie. He wanted to make sure he didn't pick up anything darker than beige at Pride.'

'Fuck you Quinn,' Jomo said cheerily, steering Nate outside. 'Ignore him,' he said, 'he's had his eye on Aston for years. Thinks Aston ain't on it because he's a dark bredda.'

'Quinn is a handsome dude,' Nate said neutrally.

Jomo squeezed his shoulder. 'He's a prick though. Plus, yeah, he's Aston's friend. That's what Quinn doesn't get: F.R.I.E.N.D.' He sat Nate down in a booth, and they both watched Quinn emerge from the men's room and head for the bar, the picture of insouciance. 'African mans –' Putting an arm round Nate's shoulders, he lent in confidentially and slipped into patois '– dem tink dem too nice, you know.'

Aston slid into the booth, sandwiching Nate between Jomo and himself. 'Get your paws off my man,' he said, kissing his teeth and slapping Jomo's arm away.

'Listen, yeah, I just rescued him from Mama Africa,' Jomo retorted, nodding at Quinn, who was tapping away on his BlackBerry at the bar.

'That was just random,' Nate frowned. 'Was he flirting with me, or what?'

Jomo choked on his drink. 'Rah man, flirting, you know!'

'He was looking!' Nate blushed.

'He wasn't flirting, Caramac,' Aston said.

'He thinks,' Jomo said enthusiastically, ''cos my bredrin here loves down his lighties, it's like some massive betrayal of the race. My boy is white, he knows he ain't got a hope with me, but Aston... so near yet so far.'

''Llow it man,' Aston said, toying with his glass.

'And you know what, he votes Tory. Raasclat pussyhole is in that gay Tory group,' Jomo laughed incredulously, tossing a peanut into the air and catching it in his mouth. 'What is it, LGBTory? Fucking jokers, man.'

'You know what, Quinn is cool,' Aston said. 'Real talk, he can be militant on shit he believes strongly in. But underneath it all, he's got a good heart.'

'He's a prick, man,' Jomo said, tipping the last of the peanuts into his mouth. Adopting a faux African accent, he said. 'Please, I must ease myself now. Please boss.'

'Eediot,' Aston said half-heartedly, as Jomo squeezed past them. They watched him bounce to the men's room. As he passed Quinn, Jomo winked back at them, seized Quinn in a bear hug, and roaring like a lion, buried his face in Quinn's neck. After a brief struggle, Quinn broke free and slapped Jomo hard across the face. Jomo froze, and turned to Nate and Aston, making a pantomime out of rubbing tears from his eyes. Quinn said something to him, and Jomo fell out laughing. Nate grinned at their shenanigans. But then Quinn glanced over at them, and his expression instantly turned to ice.

'Quinn is cool,' Aston repeated, watching Nate's face fall. 'Truesay, he can be a prick...'

'Then why do you keep him around?' Nate asked.

'When Mum found out I was a battyman, she kicked me out,' Aston said, still toying with his glass. 'I was messed up. A lickle clueless yute. Quinn kept me off the street, showed me how to get a place off the council. Made sure I kept going college. He saved me from the streets, you get me.'

Nate stared at Quinn. 'So, he's not all bad then.'

'Quinn is cool,' Aston repeated, this time with the hint of a challenge in his voice. Nate broke off from eyeballing Quinn, and offered Aston a weak smile.

'Yeah, he's cool.'

A few weeks later they were sitting on the South Bank in the sun, after watching Top Boy at the BFI. The Hackney drugs saga had left Aston melancholic. 'I know those streets,' he said, gazing out across the Thames. 'I know that world. All the money in this city, man, and kids are still living like that. Our kids.'

Nate was silent. He'd grown up in Bath. His parents were both architects, and his childhood a cosy, golden-hued idyll. When he was fourteen, the family moved to London. A regeneration project, and they'd both wanted to be hands-on. At school, Nate had tried to adopt a rudebwoy style. But the real rudebwoys saw through it: they lived on the run-down estate his parents were going to gentrify, and Nate lived in a semi-detached house in a leafy Ealing street. He wore the right clothes and tried to copy their slang, but something always gave him away. He didn't pass. He might as well have been the wigger they said he was. *Just. Not. Black. Enough.* 'They've got you,' Nate said. I've got you. 'Our kids have got you, man.'

Aston stroked his hair. 'I love it when you say 'man',' he grinned. 'Just like a real yute.' Nate stared back at him, wanting to tell him, *I am real. I'm not a fake.* But he didn't know how to. 'It's like the riots never happened,' Aston continued. 'Like no-one learned anything. Walk around Hackney on a Saturday night and it's hipsters with beards and girls with names like Hannah and Molly hanging around outside chic retro bars. Our kids can't afford them places, and they ain't wanted there, anyway.' He put his arm around Nate's shoulders. 'I want to reach out to those kids, do something, be the change. But if things go on the way they're going, it'll happen again. The riots, it'll all happen again.'

'There's a boy at work,' Nate started, uncertainly. 'He's in Beauty, and he's really fem. He says he's never felt safer living in Hackney than in the last few years. He says gentrification is a good thing.'

'Is he from Hackney, born and bred?'

'Do you mean is he black?' Nate retorted, more harshly than he had intended.

Aston glanced at him. 'Quinn really got to you, didn't he?'

'I don't care about Quinn,' Nate lied. 'You think I haven't been hearing that shit all my life? Domino, mongrel, coconut, mutt, Halfrican... Caramac.' He broke off, biting his lip. 'Am I one of those hipster fakes to you, some middle-class kid trying to be down?'

Aston turned to him, pushing his long locks back over his head. 'You're Nate. You're a brother. You're real.'

The sun was going down over the dome of S$^{t.}$ Paul's. A tear rolled down Nate's cheek.

'You and me, Nate. We could have a life,' Aston said softly, lacing his dark fingers with Nate's pecan butter ones.

Jomo's birthday.

'Why Nathaniel, I'm surprised to see you here,' Quinn said, materialising next to Nate, peering at him over his glasses. He was wearing a salmon pink bowtie and leather braces. In his folded arms he cradled a glass of white wine.

'Leave me alone,' Nate said.

Across the room Aston was deep in conversation with a pretty Polish boy named Tomasz. Tomasz said something, and

Aston laughed; Tomasz hugged him. Nate flinched.

'These island boys,' Quinn smirked, 'they really are into their Polacks, aren't they?' Nate stared past him at Jomo's impressive vinyl collection. 'You know why, don't you?

Nate couldn't help himself. 'Why don't you tell me, Quinn? It's obvious you can't wait.'

'Oh, Nathaniel! Back in the day, a brother could elevate himself by hooking up with the Irish. 'No blacks, no Irish, no dogs'. But things have changed, those Caribbean queens are now second, third generation. A few rungs down the ladder you've got the Poles: white, but still immigrants. They're the whites they can get. That Hackney born and bred brother thinks flaunting his Polish boy makes him master now.' Quinn sipped his wine. 'I do believe Aston would split little Tomasz in two.'

Nate watched Aston watching Tomasz. 'You're a dick,' he said.

'Didn't you ever stop and think: why would Aston stop at light when he could go all the way?' Quinn smiled, tilting his head just so. 'Why, if Tomasz were a girl, he and Aston could pump out little half-castes like you.'

'Shut up!' Nate yelled, and the room fell silent. Everyone at the party looked at them.

Quinn was always there, hovering on the fringes. Aston's homey, wannabe lover, the life-saving friend in a way Nate could never be. *Bitch*. He had hated Nate from the beginning, for taking what was his. And Nate hated him back in equal measure, never more so than when Aston seemed to be drifting away from him, too caught up in his good causes and kind deeds to be the lover Nate needed him to be.

It seemed like there was something going on every night – a youth group, a committee, the gay teen kicked out of home only Aston could help. More committees, late-night radio talk shows, opinion pieces for this newspaper, or that website. And the endless phone calls! Aston was never off it, either counselling a distraught kid, or making plans with one activist or another. Their arrangements were made to be broken. Nate spent his first birthday with Aston dining alone in a fancy restaurant in Mayfair because a sudden emergency called Aston away. Sometimes Jomo would turn up in his stead, looking apologetic. Nate could easily picture the scene: 'Look after Nate for me, would you?' Aston would say, stuffing a twenty into Jomo's pocket.

He imagined Aston having sex with Quinn when he was allegedly at the hospital with a kid who had overdosed. Nate imagined sleeping with Jomo. He imagined Aston, Jomo and Quinn all having sex together, and laughing at him as their dark, sinuous bodies writhed together as one. Real Nubians, together, perfect. He always pushed those thoughts to the back of his mind, and waited patiently for Aston to come home, accepting the breathless apologies his lover proffered before falling into bed, too exhausted for anything but sleep.

The shy, freckle-faced boy on his own at Pride, the boy with a steady job who wasn't a rent-boy or a junkie, just wasn't a worthy enough a project anymore. One day, Nate thought: if you can't beat 'em, join 'em.

He put holes in their stash of condoms, using a safety pin like he'd seen some desperate woman do in one of the soaps. She had wanted to get pregnant to keep her man. Nate wanted to give his man a different kind of gift, one that would harness him for good.

'Aston,' he said numbly, one night. 'Look – the condom split.'

Aston stared at the ripped, sodden latex. 'You don't need to worry, boo, I'm clean.' And Nate knew this was true, because the last time they had planned on going to Bootilicious, Aston had cancelled so that he could volunteer to help run a free rapid HIV testing event at the club instead. 'I'm clean, baby,' Aston repeated.

Nate found he had a tear rolling down his face, surprising even himself. The sight of Aston's beautiful face, a picture of benevolent concern, all for him, did it. He thought of that face looking at another man that way, and more tears came.

'Hey,' Aston said, taking Nate's face in his hands. 'Don't cry, boo! What's wrong?'

Nate stared back at him, savouring the moment: he was once again the centre of Aston's world. He was everything. 'I was raped,' he said, almost inaudibly. Nearly involuntarily. 'When I saw seventeen. At a party. They drugged me and raped me. I'm poz.' The sobs came easily, part play-acting, part self-loathing, and right then he almost believed it himself. Aston hugged him close.

'Nate, can you talk about it?'

His head buried in Aston's chest, Nate shook his head vigorously. 'No, man. Don't make me. Please.' And he couldn't have said more. How could he say even more?

'Shush,' Aston said, stroking his head. 'It's okay, baby. I'm here for you.'

The moment of total intimacy was perfect, intoxicating. The thought of Aston having that with someone else sickened him.

'I think I knew,' Aston said softly. 'The first time we fuck-the first time we slept together. It was like you were afraid of me. Or afraid of men? I felt it.'

Nate didn't reply. Aston was, as he had hoped, self-programming to fit his story. Worst of all was the wait while Aston was tested, because then the concern had to flow towards Aston and away from Nate. But soon enough the results came back negative, and now, no longer a hostage to his own health, Aston could devote all of his attention on Nate.

The lies kept tumbling out, and Nate found he was pretty good at it. He used NHS Direct to embellish the medical details. Soon, he found that Aston was sad and attentive when he was ill, and happy when he was better. Sometimes Nate would stage a crisis and quickly follow it up with an unexpected recovery, and on those occasions, Aston would be really happy. He'd be ecstatic.

Nate grew used to the lie, and slowly learned to live with it, even if he didn't enjoy it. And then Quinn found out about Nate's status. 'He's one of my closest friends,' Aston said, 'I had to tell him.'

Nate could still see Quinn's expression, his eyes glinting behind his glasses, boring into him, right through him. He knew. He knew the truth.

Quinn knew, somehow, that Nate hadn't been raped, and that he wasn't HIV-positive after all.

'Nathaniel has an announcement to make,' Quinn said mockingly, using his phone to tap his glass for attention. 'He's a wonder of modern medicine. He's been cured!'

296

Aston stepped forward. 'Bruv, what you doing? It's Jomo's birthday man, have some respect, yeah?'

'But Jomo will appreciate this.' Quinn raised his glass to the birthday boy. 'He's a pastor's son. He believes in miracles.'

'You're not funny,' Aston said firmly.

'Allow me to introduce Femi,' Quinn said, and with a flourish, he pulled a short stocky man from the throng of revellers. 'From the clinic. He's brought a present.'

'I'll pass, son,' Jomo said, shooting a 'what the fuck?' look at Aston.

'Oh, it isn't for you honey, it's for Aston. You see, Femi's brought his kit from the clinic. He's going to test dear Nathaniel – '

'Quinn, you're going too far bruv.'

'Au contraire. Unlike Nathaniel here, I haven't gone far enough,' Quinn swung back to Nate. 'Take the test. Give Aston something to *really* celebrate.'

Everyone was staring at Nate. His legs turned to jelly, seconds stretching into minutes. He wanted to grab the wine glass from Quinn's hand and grind it into his smug face. He glanced wildly from Quinn to an embarrassed-looking Femi, to Jomo, to the faces of the other people at the party. And then, suddenly, Aston was right in front of him. 'I'm taking you home,' he said.

Nate froze, trapped by the multitude of eyes trained upon him.

'Nate boo, can you hear me?' Aston murmured.

Nate stared wildly back at him. Abruptly, Aston released his hands.

'Liar,' Quinn hissed. 'Liar liar pants on fire.'

'Yo, shut the *fuck* up, bruv!' Jomo bellowed.

Nate swallowed, turned and looked directly at Quinn. 'It was you,' he said, unable to help himself. 'You gave me the bug. You raped me.'

Quinn's smirk widened into a triumphant grin. Aston shrank away, his shoulders sagging. Jomo sank into a chair, his head in his hands. Someone laughed nervously.

'I told you he was poison,' Quinn said. 'When will you learn?'

'It's true!' Nate gasped, panicking. 'Baby?' He looked at

297

Aston, but Aston was staring at the floor.

'Nate, you better leave,' he said hoarsely.

Nate reached out for his hand, but Aston shrugged him off.

'Go away,' he said, his voice barely a whisper. But he might as well have screamed it.

'We could have a life,' Nate said, tears running down his face.

The other partygoers started to melt away, embarrassed. Some of them patted Aston sympathetically on the back. Others flashed Nate disapproving looks.

'We could have a life,' Nate whispered, but he knew it was too late. Quinn had his arms around Aston. *Fight or flight.* Nate had to get out.

The eerily serene female voice echoed along the platform: *'Ladies and gentleman, because of a person under a train there is no service in either direction between Elephant & Castle and Paddington on the Bakerloo line. Customers should seek alternative routes to complete their journeys.'*

'Sounds like someone else beat you to it,' Aston said, pulling Nate back from the edge of the platform.

'Let me go!' Nate sobbed. 'I'm bad, man. I'm fucking rotten to the core.'

'You ain't rotten, just bruised,' Aston said, holding on tight. The front of the train passed them. 'Why'd you do it man? Why did you lie all this time?' A set of doors opened in front of them, but no-one was in the last car.

Nate shuddered in Aston's arms, the reality of what could have been only now dawning on him. The train. His man. The track. *A person under a train.*

Aston pulled away then, but kept his hands firmly on Nate's shoulders. 'Talk to me bro. I need to understand whagwaan.'

'I'm sorry,' Nate said. 'I'm such a fuck-up, man. I don't know what's wrong with me.'

'No bro, not good enough,' Aston replied. 'Don't gimme that lickle boy shit this time. You overstepped, big time, you get me. Man up or I swear down I'll dash you on that track myself.'

'I need you,' Nate blurted, raw, exposed, perhaps for the first time in their relationship. 'I. Need. *You.*'

'I'm here,' Aston said, taken aback. 'I'm here, man.'

'But where have you been, man? Where have you *been*?'

Aston's hand went to his forehead, a tiny sign of self-doubt. 'Boy...' he said, stumbling, uncertain. 'I didn't know. Why didn't you say something?'

'How could I?' Nate said quietly. 'What you do is important. *I'm* not important.'

Aston pulled him in close. 'What I do, man... It's for us. All of us. Including you. You didn't have to pull a stunt like this to get my attention. You should be next to me, fighting with me. You didn't have to do *this*.'

'You'd want that? Even after tonight?'

Aston looked uncertain. Nate's heart began to sink. *You don't want this. You don't want me, now.*

Jomo came bounding down the platform towards them. 'Fucking Quinn, bruv!'

'Quinn's telling the truth,' Nate said, holding Aston's gaze. 'It's me who's fucked this up.'

'Shush,' Aston said, stroking Nate's head. 'Me and Jomo, we're the patron saints of lost causes, yeah. You should hear the grief Michael Sam here' – he jerked his head towards Jomo – 'went through with *his* boy back in the day.'

'You get me, though,' Jomo said. 'Why do we do it?'

'Love,' Aston said softly, walking Nate back along the platform. 'Hey, you, I hope you remembered to touch in with your Oyster.'

Nate managed a tearful smile.

''Llow that,' Jomo snorted. 'How we jumped them barriers like David Oliver in the sixty metres. I'm too old for that shit man. I'm a pensioner in gay years.'

They stepped onto the escalator, with Jomo taking up the rear. Nate looked up at Aston. 'I need to see Quinn, tell him I'm sorry,' he said. 'What I said was unforgivable.'

'Leave Quinn to me,' Aston said. 'He's got his own cross.'

Jomo leaned forward and whispered in Nate's ear, 'He cuts himself.'

'It's true,' Aston said. 'How else do you think he figured out what your game was? Takes one to know one.'

They approached the ticket barriers, and Aston touched his Oyster card on the reader. Everything felt heightened; the yellow disc loomed at Nate like a giant sun. Brushed metal surfaces glinted and winked. Jomo propelled Nate ahead of him, following up closely behind, so that Nate was briefly sandwiched between the two of them. The machinery whined, but it was no match for Aston and Jomo's combined bulk. The three of them ran out of the station, laughing.

'I'm gonna head back to the party,' Jomo said, hugging Aston. 'Else that lot'll rob mans blind, you get me.' He kissed Nate on the forehead. 'Be lucky treacle. And do me a favour, take the bus next time.' And with that, he turned on his heel and jogged off.

Aston put his arm around Nate's shoulders. 'So what now?' Nate asked.

'Home,' Aston said, leaning into Nate so his locks spilled over Nate's head. 'We could have a life, right?'

The Boy From Mushin

By Bisi Alimi

As a young boy growing up in Mushin, an area of mainland Lagos that is well-known not just for its musicians and actors, but also for its crime and druggies, I already had the forces of nature and circumstance against me. I was not expected to make it in life. Even the mere thought of hoping to make it condemned me to the land of dreamers.

Yes, and a dreamer I have been for most of my life. I was born a dreamer, I grew up a dreamer, and as I travelled across the world, (a place that has finally become my oyster), I was dreaming still. However, while many of my friends were limited by their dreams, I was busy dreaming beyond my limits. I think it was my lonely, dreamy lifestyle that contributed to the problematic relationship between me and my mother and my father.

There are many things I have come to realise that shaped that relationship. None are pleasant, but all have made me into who I am today.

I was born Adebisi Ademola Iyandade Ojo Alimi. My birth date was January 17th 1975. According to my birth certificate and what I was told, I was born at 12 midnight on the 17th. A few seconds earlier and it would have been 16th. So, as a dreamer, I have asked myself: why one minute? What importance would that one minute have made in my life? As a dreamer, I am still asking. However, I have come to see that I was born on the 17th for a reason, and I might not know it, but I am sure it has a role in what I am today.

My birth was abnormal: I happened to be among the few children born with the umbilical cord around his or her neck. There was no reason why this should have occurred; nor do I understand why we attach so much importance to it in my culture. However, one thing was clear: I walked around the world wearing troubles, challenges, inspirations and determination on my sleeve.

Prior to my birth, my parents, Rasaki Alimi (my father), and Idiatu Alake Alimi (née Dawodu), my mother, had two children already. My elder brother, Bamidele Alimi, was born seven years before, during the civil war in Nigeria. According to the tales from my mom he went through a lot and he suffered a lot.

Because my father was away fighting for Nigeria against the Biafran army, my mother and my grandmother had to take care of my brother. A very young mother, my mother struggled taking care of my brother at the peak of the war, and as I grew older, this explained the strong bond between the two of them. My elder sister, Remilekun Alimi, was born three years after my brother.

In 1975, when I arrived, there wasn't the possibility of a scan to know the sex of a child. One thing, though, was to become very clear: my mother would always remind me she never wanted a boy, hence she never wanted me.

And so I grew up a rejected baby. The one that was never expected so therefore not accepted.

I therefore blamed myself for coming along, and became angry not just with myself but everyone around me.

As little boy, I had to deal with the dynamics of religion in my family. My father is a Muslim from the south-western part of Nigeria, Oyo state to be precise, and from the historical city of Ibadan. A very faithful Muslim, he has never been to Mecca, but has spent all his life observing the other pillars of Islam.

As a faithful Muslim, my father made us all follow that path, encouraging me to study the Quran, though he was never forceful or demanding about it. I can say that my six-feet-four-inch father is the most humble, sincere and honest man I have ever known.

Many times I think my father's simplicity is his downfall. He is simple to a fault. He hardly argues unless he is arguing about football and politics, and most of the time those arguments are always with me.

I grew up loving football and politics. In principle I hardly agree with my father on many things, though he was a very strong supporter of Chief Obafemi Awolowo – one of Nigeria's most prominent politicians – as much as I was. At the tender age of ten I can remember my father introducing me to the politics of Awolowo: the principles of free education, freedom of the press, free healthcare and many others. I was a child of socialism. Though I may have grown up to see socialism in a different light, I will never forget that were it not for the social responsibility of my government, I probably would have ended up like the so-many young people on the streets on Mushin.

Awolowo gave my generation hope, and through political awareness my father kept his dream alive. Today I consider myself centre of the left politically. However, I take social responsibility as the core of what I do, and it serves as the core of my relationship with others.

Speaking of my father, I remember many times I have had to disagree with him about football. Growing up, I know my father as a staunch supporter of Shooting Stars, the famous football club from his hometown. If you think the English are crazy about their football then you have not seen the Nigerians of the '70s and '80s: the crazy, passionate fans that will take football rivalry to the home front.

As a little child I always wanted to find a reason to disagree with my father. Since I could not really disagree with him politically, I looked for a different reason, and what other reason if not football? So, to anger my father, I chose to support Abiola Babes. This is the source of much ridicule from him. One, because Abiola Babes is a football club from Ogun State where my mother comes from, and secondly because Abiola Babes was to Shooting Stars what Manchester United is Chelsea. But I loved the fact that for once I didn't have to agree with my father, and we could have a healthy rivalry at home. Sad to say, this was possibly the only thing I could relate to with my father. His weakness and silence meant that even though he was there all through my childhood he was pretty much invisible.

Another reason was that my father is a polygamist. He has another wife and that means he had to divide his attention among ten children. I need to state here that, as a father, he struggles to pay attention to one child, never mind ten. He was a typical example of the model of pre-colonial fatherhood that extended into the postcolonial era. While my grandfather had many wives because it worked for his agricultural profession, my father had no reason to carry on that tradition. He did, though, and the system of polygamy seriously affected not just my childhood but also that of my siblings and stepsiblings.

I also understand that while my father was playing out the social and familial expectations of what it is to be a man, he lacked real expertise in what it really meant to be a father.

There were many times in my childhood when I wanted more from my dad. Like when my mom beat me for almost no reason, or when she denied me certain rights. My father never based an intervention on rationality: he was always very passive.

However, there were many things I loved about this man I call my father. I listened to him many times telling us the story of his childhood. This is one story my father tells always with so much pride, and these are the stories that many times when I questioned his weaknesses made me look deeper and be proud of him.

My father was born to a very poor family in Molete in Ibadan, and had little or no chance at education. However, he wanted to learn. He had witnessed colonisation as a young child, had had the opportunity to hear white people talk and, according to him, he wanted to be able to speak with such knowledge and such eloquence. With little or no money, and despite education not being a priority in his family, he started saving money from his work as a young labourer to buy books. He started reading English literature at the age of fifteen. By the time he was seventeen he left Ibadan, taking with him all the books he had ever bought, and headed to Lagos.

He believed coming to Lagos would open a door of opportunity for him, and help him achieve his dreams. Yes, Lagos gave my father the options: banking on his standard six education and the knowledge he had acquired from self-education, he became a teacher at a very young age.

With a desire to do more for his country my father then joined the military, served in the Nigerian army during the civil war, and also fought in the Congo. I grew up seeing the picture of my father in full military dress displayed in the living-room. His service to Nigeria will go down as one of the reasons I have come to cherish this man I call my father.

Not only that: while I did not have the pleasure of seeing my father as a police officer, I often heard of how wonderful an officer he was. But by the time I was born my father had resigned from the police and moved the family from my mother's side into my maternal grandparents' house.

My mother is from the famous Dawodu family in Mushin. Her father was a notorious politician in Mushin. According to the stories, my grandfather (who died few years before I was born) was a very popular politician, a typical Mushin man, famous for his political ideology, and was seen as power-broker in my area.

In my mother's family education was not really a gift you gave to a girl child. The girls in the family had no education – apart from my aunty, who educated herself and moved to England in the '80s – and my mother only completed primary school – just. My father's second wife, she had her first child at the age of twenty-two. She gave birth to me when she was twenty-five, and that was after two children and one miscarriage. My father's first daughter is only about ten years younger than my mother, so she was fifteen years old when my father met my mother.

My grandmother was my shield from all the abuse I faced as little child. She was the only one I could run to when I got picked on, or got bullied by my brother. I know that as young man my life would have been a living hell if my grandmother had not been part of it.

My grandmother was also a disciplinarian, but that stopped with me. I never did anything wrong in her eyes. I was her baby, and I spent most of my childhood sharing the same bed with her.

When she died I felt I had lost a huge part of me. I was left lonely, vulnerable and angry. That was the first time in my life I had lost someone I loved so much. The second time was when I lost my boyfriend in 2007.

On the other hand I had to fight for my mother's love. I am not sure, and I cannot say for certain, why my mother abhorred showing such feelings towards me. There *were* times my mother showed me love, but never in isolation from my brother: I only got general love, nothing personal.

I have to admit at this point that there have been times in my life my mother has been very proud of me. Those occasions might be rare, and I look forward to them as much as my mother did back then.

As a child who spent most of his time alone I learnt to find distractions. Among the many things that I spent much of my lonely, fearful childhood doing was reading. I took to it at a very early age. I remember that I started reading *Mills & Boon*s at age nine. I think I took to them because of the romantic escapist tendencies they fed in me as a little boy.

Even as a teenager I daydreamed about what my life would be like when I grew older. Only growing up and learning that romance is not how it happens in the cinema or on the pages of *Mills & Boon* brought me back to reality.

Not only was I reading romances, I was also very much into academic books as well. I was told by my mother that I could tell the time as young as three, and that I was teaching my brother and sister the simple logic of reading the hands of the clock by age four.

While I wouldn't call myself a child prodigy, or even claim that I am particularly intelligent, it's a fact that being bullied made me turn inward and find solace in, and develop, my interior and intellectual life. This tactic also helped me cope with bullying outside of my family: I went through secondary school and university being bullied, but instead of being destroyed by it, I always told myself that the only way I can overcome is to be better than these people and show them.

I knew that the only way to be seen as better than my brother or get a commendation from my mother was to do well academically, and that was what I spent all my life doing, even up on till now, as I contemplate commencing a PhD.

While in primary school I had been playing with the idea of becoming a Christian. To put this in perspective: my father was and still is a Muslim. My mother was born into a Muslim family, but due to my aunt's conversion to Christianity, and her role as a reverend in Foursquare Gospel Church, and also given her status as the most educated member of the family, my aunt was able to assert so much influence on my mother that she converted her to Christianity. Prior to this time I had been attending Quranic School. I hated my Quranic School with such a passion that when it comes to going in the evening, all I will do is just cry. I remember many times being dragged there, or having my teachers coming over to pick me up, something I hated very much.

As I was experiencing unpleasant moments in my Quranic School, top of which were the constant beatings by the imam for not reciting the Quran very well, my aunt was at the same time taking us to church every Sunday. Sunday School offered everything that Quranic School took away from me. I found peace and love, my Sunday School teachers were welcoming, and every time I answered a question correctly I got a gift.

While dreading Quranic School in the evening so much that, though I would fake being ill, I would actually really get sick, I looked forward to Sundays and Sunday School classes, and it didn't take long before my bible stories replaced *Mill & Boon* in my life. I was studying the bible with such passion because I know that the more I studied, the more chances there were of me winning gifts. Sunday School also offered me something special about Sunday that my every-evening Quranic school could not. As I got increasingly excited about going to Sunday School, and more and more hated the idea of going to Quranic School, this also took its toll on my religious study in school.

Due to my father's religious preference, I had to attend Islamic Religious Studies. So that meant: more beating. I am not trying to say that Islam is an aggressive religion, but the process of impacting the religion on young people should be reconsidered. It is brutal, abusive and does not encourage a friendly atmosphere of learning. All through the time I spent going to Quranic School I felt seriously violated and abused, and my Islamic class in primary school became a continuation of this process of abuse and torture.

Any religion that is designed in such a way that it tortures children and abuses them should be placed under serious scrutiny. Islam became the extension of the pains and agony I was going through at home. It was very painful that as I was trying to look for a way to escape the torrent of hate I was facing at home as a kid, Islam was adding to this pain.

After enduring years of abuse in my Quranic School and from my Islamic religious class, I decided to stop going. I became the first person in my family to disobey my father. Not that it mattered, or that I would face any serious punishment: I could get away with murder as long as it was my father. It was easier than trying to get away with anything with my mother. So, I stopped attending Quranic School and kept on with Sunday school. I was just ten years old.

My leaving Islam was one of the bitterest experiences my father had to endure in his life, as he had hoped I would be a well-known Islamic scholar. He told me that when I was a little boy he had a sense of what I would become, and he wanted that to be rooted in Islam. The problem I had was that he saw nothing wrong in the constant abuse I had to endure in learning Islam. He believed it was part of the process. Today, my father still thinks that.

It wasn't only my father who was mad: stopping Quranic School also meant stopping my Islamic Religious class and, god help me, that did not go down well either. I want you to note that this was happening to me at age ten – the level of will I had at that time was so strong that many times when I look back I get really scared of that ten-year-old boy – and this singular act brought upon me one of the most dreadful abuses I have ever experienced.

When my Islamic teacher heard about my decision to leave his class he was not going to stand for any of that. I will remind you again; at this time I was ten. A ten-year-old in Nigeria has no voice: he should be seen, if he is lucky, but never heard. And here I was at ten, not only demanding to be seen and heard, but also making decisions.

My teacher, Mr Balogun, was furious. During morning assembly he asked me to come to the front. He wanted to know why I had stopped coming to his class, and if what he has been hearing about me attending Christian religious studies is true.

I answered yes. That was all he needed. He asked that I be lifted up and stretched out by four boys. Two hold each of my hands and two hold each of my legs.

I was turned face down. He looked for what I would then consider as the fattest cane in the school. There I was, at the morning assembly, about to be tortured and dehumanised for leaving one religion for the other.

The beating I endured lasted for almost five minutes. By the time he was done I was bleeding through my blue khaki. I could hardly walk or sit down. I hated school but I didn't want to go home: I knew my mum wouldn't mind what had happened to me; and the thought of seeing the happy face of my father was just dreadful.

I wanted my parents to go and complain to the school, to demand why I had been treated this way for just changing religion, but they did absolutely nothing.

This particular incident ranks as one of the worst among the many horrible experiences I have been through in life. This was the first time as a child I was seriously violated and abused with no-one standing up for me.

I got used to the pain, the rejection and the bullying, but as I grow older I realise that, though I pretended to be strong, I actually did not have the surviving skills. All I have done in my life is sweep everything under the rug whilst the reality still stares at me.

It is important to also state that this particular event does not reflect the overall reality of my primary school education. While it was not a stand-alone event, it was not an everyday occurrence either. Many times, I was very happy to be in school rather than to be at home.

The end of the year prize-giving day was one of the many times I loved my primary school experience. I was a brilliant kid, and I studied really hard. One, as a means of escape from the lack of love and attention from home, and two, it was all I had with which to gain the attention of my mother. I was always aware that though neither my bother nor sisters came home with anything, they still received the same if not a better amount of love than I did. The love and attention my brother got from our parents was all I could dream of. Thirty-eight years later I still strive for the same thing I have longed for ever since I knew my name.

I had very troubled teenage years: my childhood up to my late teens was spent trying to gain the attention of my parents and siblings. As much as I knew it was a lost battle, I tried never to give in to the neglect I was experiencing from everyone.

I look on as my brother Bamidele gets all the attention, the love, the care and even the hope, while I have to find my own space.

There were many times as I kid when the only way to actually get attention would be to fight my way through. I became a very angry person, upset at everything and suspicious of everyone around me. Love was never a word I could understand, and giving love to me was more of a way of making friends than something genuine. Since my brother had all the attention, I tried to bribe my way through life and bargain for the little that remained by sacrificing myself.

I did not really talk to my brother until his wedding in 1999, and this was because my late sister-in-law wanted me to be the best man, something my mother most especially saw as a face-saving process rather than something she would have endorsed. Deciding not to talk to was based on a particular incident that happened when I was nineteen.

I had just left secondary school. I did not do very well in my GCSEs, and had to retake all my papers. It was a Saturday, early afternoon. I was in the living-room watching my favourite television show. Halfway into the programme my brother walked in, picked up the remote control and switched the station. Considering the never-ending tension between us, and knowing that the smallest friction would erupt into a fight, and being conscious that earlier that day I had already been punished for something I had not done, I snatched the remote from his hand, stood up and told him that, as he can see, I am watching a programme on television.

He slapped me across the face, kicked me and punched me in the head, and that led to one of the longest fights I ever had, not just with my brother, but with everyone in my family all at once. Immediately my mother heard the commotion she rushed through from the kitchen, where she had been making lunch. It was pretty obvious that if there was going to be a fight, it would be between Bamidele and Ademola: no-one else fights in the family. Worse, if there was ever going to be a fight, it was very certain that Ademola would be involved in that fight.

Such was the reality of my childhood that I became a very aggressive and angry person: I shout instead of talk; I am always on the defensive. I am never relaxed, and in all of this I spent most of my time alone. I was extremely lonely, and when I discovered my sexuality I was scared. I was never ashamed of being gay. I think whatever feelings I had about it were based on the religious foundations my parents had given me: the damnation to hell and the glorious promise of heaven.

So, back to my story: my mother rushed in and immediately joined my brother in the assault, as also did my sisters. There I was, fighting my whole family, trapped under the elbow of my brother while I got kicked, slapped and punched. My teeth were close enough to my brother's elbow to land him a long, deep bite. With that I was able to free myself. His hand bleeding, the attention turned away from me to him, and in that split-second I was able to find a stick, which I broke into two and stabbed him with.

I saw my brother falling, my mother's eyes widen in shock. I was in shock too, but I was also proud of myself. All my life, seeing my brother falling to the ground based on my actions was something I had dreamed of. Up till then I had always been the one falling.

However, this was not the kind of falling I had envisaged, with everyone rushing to his side. I turned and fled. Sensing my cousin was coming after me, I ran as fast as I could, but he caught up with me, pinned me to the ground and dragged me home.

It was a long battle between us. Living in Mushin, I had learnt the street-skills to survive. Not only that, I really was a street kid: I lived on the street, ate on the street, played on the street. Many people today would not believe that Ademola would turn out the way I have. Though I would be considered too soft for it, I have come to learn that my survival and love is right there: in the street. I was never wanted at home, and I was never at home. If I wasn't being kicked out of the house by my mother for the smallest offence in the world, I would willingly just walk out of the house for days.

I remember being stripped naked by my mum and horse-tail-whipped for smoking at the age of ten. The smoking hadn't been my idea. My elder sister had found a pack of cigarettes while we were out playing. She opened it and showed it to me. I pulled one out, and out of curiosity went into the house and came back with a matchbox. My sister lit the cigarette and we passed it round. My mother came out just then and saw us smoking. She went up in anger and immediately ordered us inside and told us to strip naked.

311

She landed the first blow of the whip on me. I have to say that as part of my relationship with my mother, if she wanted to punish me I never begged her not to: I hated to let her see me subdued. On the other hand she won't stop beating until we cry out and beg her. So between her and me, it is always a battle. She will beat me over and over again, while most times I just crouch in a corner, my head between my legs as I don't want her to see me cry, and there I will be, crying, while she swears, curses and beats me.

I won many times, as she would normally give up after she started feeling the effect on the beating on her hands. At some other times I did get subdued, begged her, and then she left me alone.

On this occasion I was determined not to beg because, instead of punishing my sister and me equally, although she had ordered both of us to 'stood down' (a very harsh punishment where the offender is asked to rest all his/her body on a finger on the ground with one leg up), after thirty minutes, and with the sweat running down our naked bodies, my sister was allowed to leave while I was further punished.

My mother whipped me endlessly, the sweat making it easy for me to have scars, while at the same time the salty water was getting into the wounds. It was a never-forgettable experience, and I knew there and then that I would never forgive my mother. I will say forever till I die: I love my mother. But I find it really hard to forgive her for my battered childhood.

So my cousin dragged me back home, and right at that moment I knew I was in for the most painful punishment of my life. I was like a hardened criminal. I knew I wouldn't escape this and I was even contemplating killing myself.

By the time I got back home my brother had been rushed to the hospital, my father had rushed to the police station to report the incident, and my godfather, a police inspector, was waiting for me. I was handed over to over to him and on the spot I got a blinding slap across my face.

I have had to endure beatings from every member of the Alimi family. I have had to run for my life. I have had to endure being dragged along on the street like a criminal in broad daylight, and then, to top it up, here was a blinding slap that drew blood from my mouth and nostril.

At seventeen I was boiling with anger but overwhelmed by resignation. Nothing about my sexuality was obvious at this stage. Though, as it turned out, my mother was already very suspicious of me.

A conversation I had with my mother few months before the incident with my brother happened:

I had just got back from school, and I came back with my second boyfriend, Seyi. We went into the room I shared with my grandmother, the only room in the house where I could have at least some form of privacy.

My family lived in a room plus a living-room. We had a master bed, a double-decker bed, a big wardrobe and many other things. My mother and father shared the master bed while my sister slept on the upper deck and my elder brother slept on the lower deck of the bunk-bed. I had the luxury of a mat and blanket to share with my two other sisters. The living-room served as the place for reception, with sofas, a television, refrigerator and other pieces of furniture. This was the reality of my growing up till I was twenty-five years old, but compared to many of my friends in Mushin, my family was actually living in luxury.

So on this afternoon in 1992 I had just got back from school with my boyfriend and we headed through to my grandmother's room. Closing the door behind us, we went for each other's mouths. Though Seyi was not my first boyfriend, up until the time we started dated he was the only one who was comfortable enough to understand what it meant to have a relationship. We had no real idea what we were doing but we were both young, innocent and in love.

The first time Seyi asked me out I had just been appointed as a prefect in my school. I was having a celebratory drink with my friends when he walked up to us. I remember very vividly his shyness and honesty. He was very tall, very handsome, had low-cut hair, was always well-dressed, and his school uniform would be as white in the afternoon as it was in the morning.

Unlike me! The only things I had going were, as my friends would say, my brain and my long, beautiful legs. Even my teachers would comment on how my legs were too straight and beautiful for a guy.

Seyi, on that day in school, asked if I would like to spend my lunch-break with him. Teased by my friends, I agreed, and I went to have a bottle of Coke with him.

Over the drink he told me with sincerity and honesty how long he had liked me and had been too scared to tell me. He said he had discussed his feelings with his best friend, who told him to come and discuss them with me.

I think it was easy for many boys in my school to at least verbally express their same-sex feelings because it was an all boys' school. We didn't have the distraction of girls, and furthermore there was a common understanding of things that happen that no-one wants to talk about.

So Seyi told me his best friend told him to ask me, and who am I to say no to this stud? He stood six feet four, he was one of the lucky boys in my school who had grown beards, and he was one of the best footballers in the school. Handsome would be an understatement to describe him. If we had been co-educational, he would have been the boy every girl would want to date.

And there I was, talking to one of the coolest guys in my school.

And not just talking to him. He was actually asking me out.

After we sat down with our bottles of Coke he said shyly, 'I want you to know I mean what I am about to say.'

I am not a stranger to this kind of conversation. I had been beaten and otherwise punished many times by my teachers for my homosexual tendencies, and this was no secret in Eko Boys' High School. So when boys approached me they were not guessing, they knew very well about my sexuality.

I remember that afternoon, smiling so sheepishly as I told him, 'Do you think I don't know why guys want to have a bottle of Coke with me?'

He told me he wanted us to be friends, very close friends.

Seyi had to say little. I already counted myself lucky to have him for the lunch-break; having him as a boyfriend was even more exciting.

The love that we shared was so strong that whenever we had a little time to ourselves it was always spent cuddling up, kissing, getting to know each and admiring the true feelings we shared. But this afternoon after school, while in my grand-mother's room, we got so carried away that we were doing

314

more than that. Naked, and in a very compromising position, I looked up and there at the open window was the face of my little sister staring at me. She ran away when our eyes met and I knew I was in trouble. I informed Seyi what had happened and he dressed and I walked him home.

When I got back, my mother called me to the room and had this conversation with me:

Mum: 'I am not interested in what happened. However, whatever it is you are doing that the Lord Jesus Christ is against, you had better stop it or you will face the wrath of God.'

That monologue has plagued me for the rest of my life, even up till the moment I am writing this.

So that weekend, while I was being led away by my godfather to be locked up in a police cell like a criminal for standing up for myself, I was happy that my sexuality was not the issue for which I was being punished.

While I was behind bars my godfather, as a sign of his love for me, told me my brother wasn't seriously wounded and had been discharged from the hospital. After six hours of being locked up, with access to water and food a privilege, my godfather warned me seriously and told me to go home. My wounds unattended to, shirt stained with my blood, I headed home.

My grandmother, who had by then started developing dementia, was waiting for me. She took me in, gave me food and put me to bed. She was all the true love I would get in my family.

This particular incident remains the bedrock of my relationship with my parents even twenty years later.

And also played the part in my very first attempt to kill myself.

My grandmother continued to degenerate. I was turning more and more to religion to find love and compassion, and I was getting more confused about my relationship with Seyi.

As much as me, Seyi too was confused. We had no idea what we were doing. He got really heartbroken after the incident that led to my first suicide attempt.

I need to point out here that all the while I was dating guys, I was also a Christian. Though the enticements that came with childhood Sunday School had rapidly evaporated, attending Foursquare Gospel Church meant I belonged to a crop of cool Christians. The church was one of the most respected emerging evangelical churches in Nigeria, and I also had the privilege of having my aunt as a pastor in the establishment. However, as I went deeper, I realised that my sexuality was gradually becoming a core part of my life.

At that age, I was very vulnerable. I was facing rejection at home and looking for love and acceptance. Though I found that with Seyi, I was still not happy. So I got deeper into religion.

Two weeks before my first suicide attempt I was walking home with Seyi when we were approached by student from the Scripture Union offering leaflets for an end-of-term Christmas event. He told me they would be having many exciting events, including a showing of the film *Burning Hell*. As a moderate evangelical attending Foursquare, my lot believed that Scripture Union people had taken Christianity to the extreme – this was in the early '90s. I wasn't sure, but thought I wanted to go; Seyi, however, was sure it was not a good idea. Without telling Seyi, I went. The film was gory and scary. It showed the reward for evil was eternal damnation. It was so terrifying that I wept all through the screening.

For the very first time in my life I got really scared of what would become of me if and when I die like this. I remember going up to the altar, my eyes red with tears, asking God to forgive me. I was so scared of dying and going to hell. I went to the pastor, fell to my knees and begged God to forgive me. I called on Seyi next day and told him I had given my life to Christ and that I couldn't date him anymore.

His eyes still haunt me today.

He held my hand and asked me why. I told him I had found Christ. That homosexuality is evil, and that he too had to give his life to Christ.

I spent most my holiday period hunting him and trying to convince him to give his life to Christ. I also got on buses to preach. I was going mad. I hated the one who had shown me my true self. In my quest for the love that was denied me at home I turned away real, honest love.

I need to say that this fear of love has led me to develop a protective system where I tend to scare people who love me away.

Seyi saw me changing from the intelligent, charming boy he had fallen in love with, gradually becoming an introvert and a judgemental person. Despite this, a few weeks after the incident involving my brother he was back in my life again to offer me his comfort. He would come round to my house in the evening and we would hang out together with my friends. Or sometimes I would go to his house to sleep by pretending to be passing the night with my grandmother. We would run away from school just so we could be together.

As this was going on, I was at the same time having the graphic image of 'the burning hell' at the back of my head.

One day I came back from Seyi's house all teary and scared because I had met someone from the SU on my way home, and he had told me there was news making the rounds that I am homosexual. He prayed with me and told me to fast and ask God for His healing hands. After that I went home, went into my room, picked up a towel and headed for the bathroom with a plastic bucket with one aim: I was going to kill myself before I allowed homosexuality to consume me. My argument was, if I die now I will at least go to heaven instead of dying as a homosexual and going to hell. I stood on the plastic bucket and, with the door closed against the sun shining outside, tied the towel to the iron hook in the ceiling of the bathroom.

I could hear the laughter of my siblings outside. I heard my mother calling for my brother. There was someone in the other bathroom. It was a few weeks before Christmas. The house was alive and fulfilled.

I tied the towel firmly, creating a noose to twist around my neck. I then tried putting my head through the noose before kicking the bucket away with my feet so I could dangle and die. However, just as I was trying to put my head through, the bucket gave way under my feet. I came crumbling down with a thump, leaving the towel hanging but without my neck in it. The sound drew the attention of the person in the other bathroom. I quickly jumped up and removed the towel.

I was accused of trying to spy on the person in the next bathroom with the help of the bucket.

If any member of my family is reading this, it will be the first time they will know of my first attempt at suicide.

Twenty-one years later I have overdosed, cut myself, taken rat poison, and once attempted to jump in front of a train.

I have never seen anything worthwhile in my life. The reason being that I was conditioned to believe I was not wanted, I was worthless, and that I would never be loved. And even when many people have shown me love, I have not been emotionally intelligent enough to appreciate it.

I never discussed with anyone my first attempt at suicide, or the three stages of exorcism I subsequently went through, until January 2009, while I was tied to a bed in a psychiatric home after another failed attempt to kill myself due to the death of my boyfriend.

I have had my fair share of pain in life, but I will gladly say that I have had my own fair share of happiness as well. This is not a sob story. Writing this is my way of healing, finding answers, and showing to the lonely, terrified others out there that you are not alone.

To Be Young, Gay and African

By Diriye Osman

When I first came out to my family, most of them stopped talking to me. My father, who I was very close to, stopped speaking to me for two years before picking up the phone late one night to let me know that my being gay was not only an amoral form of psychic and sexual corruption but also an act of perverse Western mimicry. I was not only going against my Islamic upbringing but my African heritage as well.

I was born in Somalia, and I spent my formative years living in Nairobi, Kenya, before moving to London. Somalia and Kenya may have many sociological and cultural divisions but both states stand firm on one soil when it comes to the issue of homosexuality. Any form of sexual difference is considered not only repugnant but also devious, precisely because sexual difference in Somalia and Kenya, like most African states, is a narrative best kept to oneself. If you want to spin this story publically and share your experiences as an LGBT person, you had best buckle up and brace yourself for physical abuse, ceaseless harassment, imprisonment or death. Things are considerably more lenient in Kenya than Somalia amongst the cultural elite, but both nations still have a long way to go when it comes to ensuring basic rights for their respective LGBT communities.

When I came out to my family I did not flinch. I spoke my truth and stood my ground knowing that I would be punished in some way for having the audacity to assert my identity. What upset my family the most was the fact that I was proud of being gay. They could not configure the possibility that after years of silence, timidity and self-doubt I had finally cultivated courage and the kind of confidence that comes with a hard-won sense of comfort in one's own skin.

I come from a community that has been emotionally and psychologically traumatised by decades of civil war, mass migration and dislocation; a community that has through sheer collective willpower and survivalist instinct managed to rally together to form the tightest, most close-knit networks, with family life as the nucleus. In order to fully belong you must live up to absurd standards of virtue, honour and piety. The reality is no-one manages this, but the trick is to try – or act like you're trying. There are multiple degrees of scorn poured on any form of transgression: a girl without a headscarf is a harlot-in-training, and a teenager with a rebellious streak is ripe for daqan celis – a return to a grim part of Somalia for some much-needed 're-education'. All these taboos become miniscule in comparison to homosexuality. The fact that I wanted to write about my experiences as a young gay Somali did more than grate on my family's nerves. They were incensed enough to threaten me with violence, but I was smart enough to know that as a citizen of the UK there are laws that protect my rights as a gay man. This is a position of privilege, but it's only a position of privilege because I fully understand and exercise these hard-won rights.

I arrived at this point of self-acceptance by doing what came best to me, what generations of the Somali community have always done in order to sustain themselves when crisis kicked off: I told stories. I told stories of what it meant to be young and endure struggle. I told stories of what it meant to fall in love with another man and for that love to be reciprocated in the face of rejection and familial disapproval. I told these stories repeatedly and I wrote them down, drawing on the gorgeous history and culture of the Somali people. It's a natural human impulse to denounce the traditions of those who have rejected you, but I refused to do that. I wrote these stories down and compiled them into a collection of short fiction called *Fairytales For Lost Children*. These stories follow young gay and lesbian Somalis on the cultural and social periphery of both their adopted homelands of Nairobi and London as well as their motherland, Somalia. These characters experience a wide spectrum of dilemmas. Whether it is mental illness, civil war, immigration or complicated family histories, they still hold on to their sense of humanity and optimism without the need for apology or victimhood.

When I published this book last year I received emails from

young LGBT men and women from Somalia, Kenya, Nigeria and Uganda telling me how much the stories meant to them, and how they felt a sense of solace knowing that I was telling these narratives without shame or fear. Shame and fear are the most potent weapons in the homophobe's arsenal. If one rejects the notion that one has to be ashamed of being gay or lesbian, then half the battle is won.

With each email that I received I would not only encourage and motivate these young men and women as best as I could, but I would also tell them to go out into the world and form meaningful friendships and support networks where they could be themselves without fear of judgement. At a time when LGBT youth across the world are losing their lives to homophobic stigma it's important to remind them that they are worthy and their lives have value.

As for me, I'm wise enough to know that struggle will always happen. That's just the general texture of a life's pattern. But I keep moving forward in the knowledge that I'm simply a voice in a chorus of voices united in the belief that equality on all fronts is not a privilege but a basic human right that we must continuously fight for and defend.

As for my young fellow LGBT Africans, I will say this again and again because it bears repeating:

It's a beautiful thing to be young, gay and African.

The Brotherhood Dilemma

By Dr. Rob Berkeley

Without community there is certainly no liberation, no future, only the most vulnerable and temporary armistice between me and my oppression.
– Audre Lorde, The Cancer Journals *(1980)*

'Look, I'm not interested in black men, okay!' He spun away from me and walked to the other end of the bar. The look of horror and disgust on his face made me wonder if I'd developed scrofula or some other horrifying disfigurement on entry to the club. I checked in the mirror over the bar. No, still me. Okay, I'm not Denzel, and hardly challenging Idris for pin-up status, but now I felt like Lil B was wrong – this Black person is ugly. I ordered another pint of Stella and didn't leave the 30p change on the little black tray – if I'm not having a good time, why should I help the barman to?

The uninterested one walked past me towards the dancefloor and I hurriedly avoided eye contact. What had I done and why did he respond so badly to what I thought was a friendly, 'Hi, how you doing?' I didn't really fancy him anyway, I told myself, assessing the acerbity of those particular grapes. I'm used to rejection: it's just a part of the numbers game. I recalled the jokes I'd been sharing with a few friends earlier – ask at ten to two, or ask ten to get two; I get it, my self-esteem is not based on the approval or otherwise of strangers, and if a shag is what I wanted, as a young gay man in London, the gay capital of Europe, it was not that much of a challenge. I checked him out again: tall, with that verging-on-gawky air that I'd fallen for before, nice chest, snapback, box-fresh Air Max II's on, and from behind he was filling out those jeans very nicely. I looked at his skin – the skin that had first made me notice him; a blue-black complexion that I could happily get lost in.

I'd been here before – in fact a couple of years earlier his reaction might have been mine. I'd discussed it with friends ad nauseam. In my more coherent moments I'd argued that if our struggle was for freedom to be who we want to be, and have sex with who we want to have sex with, then we are well within our rights to express a preference, aren't we? He wasn't to know that only half an hour earlier the bouncer had thought it best to check with me that I was 'really gay' because, 'You know, we get a lot guys dealing in here, so we have to be careful', or that the only other conversation I'd had in the club that night began with, 'Is it true what they say?' and had ended very quickly afterwards with some choice expletives from me. I wondered whether the uninterested one had had a similar experience – guess I'll never know.

It would be too easy (and massively arrogant) to dismiss the uninterested one as engaged in a spiral of self-hate – though how healthy can it be to want to distance yourself completely from those who look like you? Maybe I am the one who is too race-conscious and have unrealistic expectations of solidarity from those who are also black. Maybe I was reading too much into a club conversation where surface is all and depth of thinking discouraged. But I couldn't stop myself reflecting on what this exchange meant to me, to him, and for the prospects of black gay men in a society in which, despite recent legislative progress, racism and homophobia remain rife. I wanted to understand: *tout comprendre, c'est tout pardonner* as our French cousins say.

When I came out I lived in a small provincial city; liberal enough, but with only one gay pub and a weekly club-night. On that scene, if that's not too big a word for it, there were, including me, three black men – and the occasional black visitor passing through. I would regularly be called by the other black guys' names as if we were interchangeable despite what to me were obvious differences in height, weight, complexion and personalities. After nine months of avoidance, surreptitious glances, and fear of what the white people around us might think, I'd made a point of speaking to the other two black guys. It turns out that I am really interested in other black gay men and their experiences; those we have in common and those that we don't. I'm interested, not always sexually; in that regard I consider myself an equal opportunities employer, but I'm definitely interested. It turned out that my (white) ex had been out with all three of us (me first, I hasten to add!) – it was merely his preference after all, like preferring chocolate to vanilla ice-cream, and once you go black... I was pleased to move to London.

London, in Disraeli's words a 'roost for every bird', is now my home, as it is to half of the Black people in the UK and probably a larger proportion of Black British gay men. There are not many clubs you can go to which do not have a few black faces in the crowd, and a few where there are only a few white faces. While I understand why it took me nine months to find out that I am interested in other black gay men in the provinces, I'm not sure that the metropolis affords the same excuses. In the provinces I experienced extreme isolation; used to being visibly different, used to being the object of white men's 'chocolate' fantasies, used to being misunderstood. Other black men were competition for sexual attention, given we were interchangeable to those with a 'preference'. Other black men embodied my dislocation from black communities, the awkward silences about my sexuality extended to include those who also identified as gay. Other black men were a drain on my new-found and fragile freedom – coming out proffered a whole set of new identity possibilities, while at the same time my black experience remained one of feeling constrained to only 'what black people do' in order to cling to some form of black authenticity. At that time, a popular valediction was, 'Stay Black'. While I wanted to live up to this, I often wondered if staying black meant staying the same, when I was intent on developing into something wonderful and new.

Part of my newly-found wonderfulness was to try and be a cool kid on London's gay scene. Looking back, I failed miserably. I tried too hard and that doesn't go well with being 'cool'. In this London nightclub the words of a stranger who claimed not to be interested in me because of my skin-colour, heritage, position in society, not interested ultimately because of my blackness; the words of a person who shares these characteristics hit me hard. After all, I recognised and in part empathised with his position, but this was supposed to be a new me: why couldn't he, of all people, see that? 'I'm not that black guy,' I thought, and then realised the nature of the trap. His obvious disgust at being found attractive by another black man took me aback. As did his willingness to embarrass me in front of the other barflies in order to make his point. But on reflection I realised that his reaction was not a new one but the manifestation of a dilemma we are constantly faced with. In the 1950s Frantz Fanon captured the dilemma of acknowledging racial affinity for those marginalised by racialisation:

> As I begin to recognise that the Negro is the symbol of sin, I catch myself hating the Negro. But then I recognise that I am a Negro. There are two ways out of this conflict. Either I ask others to pay no attention to my skin, or else I want them to be aware of it.
>
> Frantz Fanon – *Black Skins White Masks* (1952)

Fanon suggests that the sensible response is to 'rise above this absurd drama that others have staged around me . . . to reach out for the universal'. However this is far easier said than done. This timeworn dilemma plays out on the dancefloor, in the bar, sauna, on Grindr, or on the street – indeed, wherever desire collides with 'race'. I don't want you to make any decisions on the basis of the colour of my skin; that would be racist. Yet there are occasions when I do want you to make decisions on this basis. It is not unusual to see each other caught on the horns of this dilemma. The Grindr profile entitled 'Hung Black 28' that states either 'No Blacks, Asians or Femmes – just my preference ☺' or 'Black guys to the front of the queue' highlights our willingness to engage in race talk to get sex. While publicly rejecting the fantasy porn image of the hypersexual Mandingo black man, how many of us are prepared to use it sometimes in those private moments to get our oats?

Perhaps we should relax about it. As comedian Dave Chapelle notes,

> Sometimes racism works in Black people's favour; it doesn't happen often, it happens very rarely, but when it happens it is fucking sweet.

Perhaps this is one instance. But in those moments of desire there appears to be little room for nuance, and certainly no leap to Fanon's universal. Instead, we put aside our more noble aspirations, those encapsulated by Baldwin's dictum, 'I don't like people who like me because I'm a Negro; neither do I like people who find in the same accident grounds for contempt.' (James Baldwin, *Notes of a Native Son*, 1955) – in order to get down and get real.

Perhaps this dilemma is at the heart of what drives another phenomenon among black gay men in the UK – namely, our failure to get organised. The struggle for freedom, and the struggle for fairness in terms of both race and sexuality have long had a presence of black gay men. I ran the UK's largest racial justice think-tank until earlier this year, and was not breaking the mould in being an out black gay man. Ted Brown walked at the front of the first Gay Pride March in the UK, Dennis Carney, Dirg Aab-Richards, Simon Nelson, Rikki Beadle-Blair, Cecil Belfield-Clark and many others have been inspirational for me, and have been active in changing the ways this country deals with difference – challenging both racism and homophobia. There have been both successes and setbacks on the way, but it is clear we have had – and have – the talent and the drive to make change. While the focus has understandably been on ensuring liberty and equality, it would appear that along the way we forgot, prevaricated over, or put in the 'too difficult' file the third leg of the stool – solidarity.

The French (again) capture it well in their aspiration for *Liberté, Égalité et Fraternité* – Freedom, Equality and Brotherhood. We seem to be making some progress on being free to love who we want to. We also appear to be approaching equality before the law, with progress on marriage, anti-discrimination and access to justice. As we have learned from the struggles against racism, these hard-fought-for gains can be lost without our vigilance, but at least we appear to be moving in the right direction. What happened to brotherhood? What happened to solidarity?

Efforts to bring people together and find common cause in the UK have tended to emphasise cross-cultural understandings. We work hard on building solidarity in the alphabet soup of sexual identities; between the G and L, B, Q, T and I. We work hard on faith institutions' relationships with their LGBTQI co-religionists. We work hard on linking the class, feminist and antiracist struggles. Long may this continue. In the jargon, we work more on bridging than bonding social capital. It remains assumed that we bond as black gay men naturally and without any effort – after all, looking from outside in, we have so much in common. This assumption fails to recognise our persistent dilemma over whether to talk 'race' or not talk 'race', to seek community with other black gay men or not. It underestimates our willingness to not be 'interested' in each other. It also underestimates the effects of extant racism and homophobia in our lives and in our relationships with other black gay men.

Yet it is clear that until we find a means of addressing this brotherhood dilemma we will struggle to lead the fulfilling lives that we all deserve. If Audre Lorde is right that 'without community, there is no liberation' then the gains of recent years could amount to less than we had hoped. Rampant individualism is fine as a driver of the economy; it is less effective in pursuance of social justice. Our past experiences may have burned many of us who have sought to build community among black gay men; our histories are littered with the detritus. Whether we've been burnt by the essentialism that requires only one kind of black gay identity and judgement of those who do not live up to that archetype. Whether we have become jaded because another draughty community centre on a Wednesday evening after work is so far from the image of the fabulous life we had imagined for ourselves. Whether we have found ourselves co-opted by others to support their agenda and abandoned when we assert our needs. The struggle for community remains an important one because it is in the sharing of our experiences, and in collective action for collective change, that we begin to recognise our full capacity as humans rather than merely as consumers.

It is for this reason that we are beginning to see a much greater emphasis on community-building from activists. UK Black Pride, Zambarau and others have launched initiatives recently that are seeking to build community across minority ethnic LGBTQI identities. This is why the now defunct BGMAG hosted the Black LGBT Community Awards three times, why events such as the LGBT Splash, Social Sistas and ColourfulPink are seeking to get people out of the nightclub and into black-LGBT-led spaces where they can set their own agenda. This is why I am working with a small group of black gay men to establish a new website by us for us, Blackout UK, a place where we can share our dilemmas and our solutions.

The final word in the groundbreaking Marlon Riggs film *Tongues Untied* (1991) is part of a quote from Joseph Beam:

> I dream of Black men loving and supporting other Black men . . . I dare us to dream that we are worth wanting each other. Black men loving Black men is the revolutionary act of the eighties.

Thirty years on these words seem to be truer than ever. How we respond to our brotherhood dilemma in 2014 may well be the marker of our success or failure.

Black and Gay in the UK and…

By Cyril Nri

L abi Siffre wrote and sang a song called 'Why Isn't Love Enough?' Good question.
I have a first name, gifted to me with love by my parents. All of my experience, knowledge and instinct to date has filled that name with whatever current meaning and significance (if any) that it may have. I also have a family name to go with it. It was not a gift, it was more of a legacy. My family name gives me a place, context and history. Neither name has a race or sexuality. Race and sexuality are just a part of what I bring to my name. Together, my given names encompass me.

Yesterday morning, and not for the first or last time, I fell in lust with a man on the northbound Northern line platform. A dark black, midnight blue-black, black man. An inch taller than me. I looked at the tiny ripple of skin just below the hairline at the back of his neck, then the strong, gym-worked shoulder-blades, and on down to the biceps that scared his T-shirt sleeves, forcing them to double back on themselves. I wondered how safe and protected I would feel held in his 'all-man' embrace. I didn't talk, despite his warm inviting smile as I came to a stop beside him. Instead I tried to look as though I was reading the information board behind: *Edgware via Bank 3 mins*. Enough time to truly imagine our life together. If only I could find the courage to casually say, 'Hi' – if? and if? and if? – a thousand other little imponderables would fall into place. I don't say 'Hi'. It's as if our headphones somehow separate our worlds, as if he's in dancehall and I in disco. I long for that Queer Nation club moment when the DJ spins a fifteen-minute Latin section and we salsa or rumba together with wild Brazilian abandon, as I had done once upon a long-ago night amongst the ladyboys of Bahia and the sweltering torsos of Carnival in Salvador. I simply smile back, but something in my smile betrays my longing as I see him mentally move on.

Perhaps it's just the change of the song on his headphones? Either way, he has left me in my world and retreated to the day ahead. I play out this longing for Mr Right daily, with one dream or other, all over London. I know it now as 'lust with hope' and not 'love'. It is fleeting. It has passed by the time one changes lines at Stockwell, and begins anew with a dancer who has probably done the short one stop hop from Brixton and is heading to the centre of this town that can hold so many different dancing styles.

I recall, a long time ago, thinking that when I look in the morning mirror to shave, I just shave. I look, and I shave a section of my face. It is a unique face. Not a special face, just different in the way that no two faces are exactly alike.

My face, before it meets the outside world, has no race and no sexuality, it just is. I don't linger on it long. I concentrate on the areas that grow unwanted hair, around my chin and above my (slightly too large) lips. I take in only parts of the face. It is uncomfortable to take in the whole thing. I'm not sure I like it that much, as faces go. It's not like the faces of men others flock around in hope of an approving look. It doesn't make one stop when passed in some inappropriate late-night dance-club. It is not the face of a Carli, Delano or Denver. It is the face of someone who watches and 'wonders as I wander' when or if 'he who completes me' will come?

Being of my race and my late-admitted sexuality, I have spent my life questioning my place in the world. There has never seemed to be a place where all of me, all the many parts of me, could sit comfortably in one body. Neither in my own eyes, nor in the eyes of those who leave no room for the miracle of rainbows or duck-billed platypuses.

Constant questioning, brought on by a world which, (like Nina Simone pointed out in 'Turning Point'), is open, innocent and loving right up to the moment that adult fear, hate and negativity sew their corroding threads. This striving to see the validity of my equality and humanity (just as it is) means I can invalidate the agendas and doctrines of ignorance, of bigotry, of priests who would make my penis and not my love the limited vision of all that I see in a morning mirror. Can I be summed up by sex and race alone?

There is a lack of love and logic in the answers given to my questions, whether answered by government, church or even those local ministers: like the woman who regaled my bus journey from Clapham Junction to Chelsea Bridge with the word of The Lord, taking hostage her fellow travellers with her bible proclamations of abomination, and bringing anything but 'peace to all men'. They have left me a healthy mistrust of answers received or given, and therefore I keep searching for personal understanding and meaning, and a love that is whole and that encompasses all that I can be. Maybe love is too large a thing for any confinement in a word or type?

As I shave this particular morning I think about those three Israeli children, Gilad Shaer, Naftali Fraenkel, and Eyal Yifrah, who were kidnapped and killed, sparking the retaliatory kidnapping, burning and killing of sixteen-year-old Moham-med Abu Khdeir.

I think of the ensuing carnage that men of faith and politics have unleashed since those acts, and wonder whether any of the individual names of these children have been registered by anyone but their parents. I think, as the shower steams the mirror in front of me, how each of those lives were more than just symbols of a conflict. I wish they'd cut out the official on the news giving some number to the weapons fired and just spend the whole of the *Today* programme reading out each and every one of the names of the two-thousand-odd people on both sides lost so far. I wonder if through such personalisation we might actually hear that people are more than the sum of their parts. The news moves on and it takes us to a town called Ferguson in the USA. A young black Michael Brown is dead and civil riots (finally) are taking place. We don't know the com-plete facts of the incident that sparked the conflict, but in this report the rioting on the streets over another black boy dead at the hands of a white cop tells me someone, or perhaps both parties, in the moment of conflict, were defined by their outer descriptions and the false belief that the colours 'black' or 'blue' meant someone was going to have to get beaten or killed that day.

I think of my childhood, interrupted by a long-forgotten Biafran war. My mind flits to my own children, now both out of university and facing the world. Black, gay. And a dad. How will they fit me into such a confined definition? I think of W. B. Yeats, I think of Langston Hughes, James – *Fire Next Time* – Baldwin. I hear Marvin Gaye singing 'I Heard It Through The Grapevine'. I think how lucky I am to live in London: not Gaza or Ferguson, but London, where yesterday I fell in lustful hope of love on the Northern line, but before I leave the house I don't think, I don't ever think, I'm Black or Gay. Black and Gay are a given, they just are.

U.K.? I'm still working that one out.

Contributors

Ade Adeniji is a Coach, Group Facilitator and Storyteller. He is co-founder of The Quest for Gay Men, a UK based social enterprise that delivers personal development and transformation workshops for gay men. Ade is co-author and contributor to the anthology *Love Me As I Am: gay men reflect on their lives*. An explorer at heart, Ade spent many years searching for himself, only to discover that he was never lost, he had simply been hiding from himself. He divides his time between London and Amsterdam, where he lives with his partner.

Bisi Alimi is an international-award-winning LGBT/HIV activist. Born in Lagos, Nigeria on January 17 1975, he made history in 2004 when he came out on national television, making him the first gay man in the history of Nigeria to openly declare his sexuality on television.

In 2007, due to great threat to his life, he moved to the United Kingdom, where he was granted political asylum. Bisi presently lives in London, from where he travels the world sharing the story of equality, respect, love and humanity.

He has won many awards and been nominated for many more. In 2014 he was listed on the Guardian/Square Peg Media World Pride Power List at number 77. He has also featured on *the Independent on Sunday* Pink List of the most powerful LGBT people in Britain, as well as listed number three on the UK atheist/Humanist power list.

He has written for many magazines, journals and newspapers including *the Guardian, Huffpost, Gay Star News* and *Project Syndicate*. His most recent article, 'The Economic Cost of Homophobia', was translated into seven languages.

As a social commentator, he has been a regular guest on the BBC, CNN and Al Jazeera. He also lectures at Freie University, Berlin. As a motivational speaker he has spoken in schools and universities around the world.

Travis Alabanza is what he describes as a beautiful messy mix of African American, Filipino, Hawaiian, English and French. A 19-year-old student at King's College London, Travis studies theology whilst doing as much writing and community projects as he can manage. In his hometown of Bristol he created a theatre in education piece talking about homophobic language that toured around Bristol with the charity EACH and was recognised with a Diana Award. Travis is also fond of all types of jazz, funk and Black Power Kitty Cats.

Dean Atta is a writer and performance poet. He has been commissioned to write poems for the Damilola Taylor Trust, Keats House Museum, National Portrait Gallery, Tate Britain and Tate Modern. Atta won the 2012 London Poetry Award and was named as one of the most influential LGBT people by the *Independent on Sunday* Pink List 2012. His debut poetry collection *I Am Nobody's Nigger* was published in 2013 by The Westbourne Press. Atta lives in London and performs internationally.

Rikki Beadle-Blair. Born and raised in South London, Rikki Beadle-Blair is a writer, director, performer, choreographer, composer, designer, producer, activist and passionate mentor. He works in film, theatre, television, radio, music and publishing. Rikki founded Team Angelica to create 'Entertainment with Soul' to help provide opportunities for creatives and performers of all backgrounds, identities and disciplines. Rikki is a passionate mentor. If you want to work with Rikki, please contact rikki@teamangelica.com.

Dr. Rob Berkeley is a writer and equality activist. He was Director of the Runnymede Trust, the UK's leading race equality think tank, from 2009 to 2014. He was Deputy Director of Runnymede between 2005 and 2009. His doctoral studies at the University of Oxford focused on exclusion from school.

He has previously been chair of governors at a South London primary school, chair of Naz Project London, a trustee of Stonewall and the Equality and Diversity Forum, and a member of the Commission on 2020 Public Services. He was executive chair of the Black Gay Men's Advisory Group and is currently managing editor of a new website, *Blackout UK*. He is currently a trustee of the Baring Foundation.

Topher Campbell is an award-winning writer, theatre and film director and social commentator. He has directed plays throughout the UK. He established the BBC Norman Beaton Fellowship. Co-founded rukus! Federation Ltd, creating the rukus! Black LGBT Archive. As Artistic Director of The Red Room Theatre and Film Company he created The Jellyfish Theatre. His work about contemporary Black Gay life and culture has appeared in *The Guardian*, *The Independent on Sunday*, *Boyz*, *Qx* magazine, *Gay Times*, *Attitude* magazine and the US Black Gay anthology *For Coloured Boys...*

'Danse Macabre' is an artist and painter. He lives and works in London, England.

Daniel Fry is an aspiring writer originally from North London. In 2007 Daniel graduated from Journalism at the London College of Communications and went on to write for *Out in the City* before becoming editor of *Men Of Colour,* the UK's first magazine aimed at black gay men. Last year he left his role as Sexual Health Coordinator at the Naz Project London, (www.naz.org.uk), and is currently teaching English as a foreign language in Brazil.

John R Gordon is a multi-award-winning author, screenwriter and playwright, and is a mentor to in particular young and queer writers of colour. He worked on the groundbreaking black gay television series *Noah's Arc* and co-wrote the award-winning spin-off feature film *Jumping the Broom*. His six novels include *Faggamuffin* and, most recently, *Souljah*.

Keith Jarrett. Londoner Keith Jarrett writes poetry and short fiction. A former London and UK poetry slam champion, and World Cup semi-finalist in 2010, he has hosted English and Spanish poetry showcases and co-ordinated festivals in schools. In 2013, his five-star-reviewed poetry show *Identity Mix-Up* debuted at the Edinburgh Fringe festival.

Keith's short fiction has appeared in anthologies and magazines, including *Attitude* and *Tell Tales IV*. He currently teaches in a secondary school as part of a pioneering Spoken Word Educator programme, which includes an MA at Goldsmiths. He is writing his first novel.

Leee John – born in Hackney, London, of St Lucian descent and educated in New York City, he later studied drama at the Anna Scher Theatre School. His soul-funk supergroup Imagination had chart hits in twenty-eight countries, earning four platinum discs, nine gold discs and more than a dozen silver discs around the world between 1981 and 1983. In the late 90s and early 2000s Leee released a number of dance singles, and in 2005 a jazz album, *Feel My Soul*, featuring a mixture of standards and original compositions. Leee now tours the UK and Europe with his jazz quartet as well as performing with Imagination.

Leee is an ambassador for SOS Children's Villages, an international charity providing homes and mothers for orphaned and abandoned children.

Adam Lowe is a writer, publisher and performer from Leeds, although he now lives in Manchester. He was LGBT History Month Poet Laureate and Manchester Pride Writer in Residence. His solo show, *Ecstasies*, is currently touring.

Reverend Rowland Jide Macaulay is the founding Pastor of House Of Rainbow Fellowship. Jide is Anglican, British-Nigerian born in London, a Christian minister since 1998, a dynamic and inspirational speaker, author, poet, pastor and preacher, holds a degree in law, masters degree in theology and post-graduate certificate in Pastoral Theology. Jide focuses his ministry on inclusion and reconciliation of sexuality, spirituality and human rights. He writes for various Christian and secular journals. He has authored two books, *Poetry Inspired* (2001) and *Pocket Devotional for LGBT Christians* (2005), he has won several awards including the 2003 and 2007 Black LGBT Community Award for 'Man of the Year' for his work helping people of faith. He served from 2007 to 2013 as executive board member and co-chair of Pan Africa International Lesbians and Gay Association. He is currently vice chair on the steering committee of Global Interfaith Network.

Contact: Revjide@houseofrainbow.org
Website: www.houseofrainbow.org, www.rjmm.co.uk
Twitter: @revjide, @houseofrainbow

David McAlmont is a singer and art historian living in Brixton Hill, London. Of his legendary soaring falsetto *Melody Maker* commented, 'One day he will open his mouth and a cathedral will fall out.' He first came to notice in the band Thieves; in 1995 he was approached by ex-Suede guitarist Bernard Butler, and *The Sound of McAlmont and Butler* yielded two chart singles. David covered 'Diamonds Are Forever' for producer David Arnold and released two further solo albums, reuniting with Bernard in 2001 for *Bring It Back*. In 2005 he released the jazz album *Set One: You Go to My Head*; in 2009 *The Glare*, a critically-acclaimed collaboration with leading classical composer Michael Nyman.

His current project, with long-time collaborator Guy Davies, is Fingersnap. Their debut EP was *Smokehouse*; their most recent release the haunting 'Blackbirds'.

Paul J. Medford – Television appearances include *East Enders*, *This Life* and *Story Makers*. Theatre appearances include *Five Guys Named Moe* – Laurence Olivier nomination, 'Best Actor in a Musical '; *Sweet Charity* – Whatsonstage nomination, 'Best Supporting Actor in a Musical'; *The Lion King*, *Hair* and *Charlie and The Chocolate Factory*. Choreography credits include *Simply Heavenly* by Langston Hughes – Whatsonstage nomination, 'Best Choreographer'.

Television production credits include *Americas Next Top Model*, *Project Runway* and *The Face*. His company Myriad Model Casting is one of the most successful casting agencies in America. Contact: pjmedford@mac.com.

'Merlin' is a black gay British man resident in London, England.

Donovan 'Baz' Morris: 'I like to consider myself a renaissance man: four years hanging with art reprobates in bars around Central Sᵗ Martins somehow gained me a Fashion & Textile BA. Soon bored with moving pockets around for the likes of Top Shop I diversified. I've painted murals (Uphall School), coordinated events (Chinese New Year – Leicester Square), installed dead dresses (BT headquarters), informed on sexual health (GMFA), plus danced and performed in various museums, galleries and crypts (including Science, Tate and Deptford). In my various endeavours a primary interest has always been 'The Unseen Norm'. My writing follows this tradition, looking at undercurrent trends that often run unnoticed by the mainstream.'

Tonderai Munyevu is a prominent Afro-British performer. He was critically acclaimed for his performances as Styles and Buntu in the Young Vic production of *Sizwe Banzi is Dead*, and as the MAN in *ZHE [NOUN] UNDEFINED* at London's Soho Theatre, as well as various other characters in Two Gents Productions' version of *Two Gentlemen of Verona* at Shakespeare's Globe. In addition to his theatre credits he has made several appearances on BBC Radio Four and World Service. His film appearances have been in *The Day of the Triffids* (BBC/HBO) and *Something Nice from London* (Latimer). He recently completed his debut play, *Kanjani*.

Edd Muruako was born in the East End of London, into a family of three brothers and one sister. He is the middle child, and his parents are of Nigerian origin. Growing up in predominately white areas in the mid-eighties, the family came upon racial hatred on numerous occasions. It was there that Edd discovered his creative side, which he learnt to utilise in an effort to gain acceptance from his peers and become popular. As an actor Edd has worked in TV, film and theatre. Recently he has begun his journey as a writer, and has seen his work hit prolific stages such as the Bush Theatre and Theatre Royal Stratford East.

Cyril Nri is an award-winning actor with over thirty years'

professional experience (at the time of writing).
Latest stage role, 2012-13: Cassius in *Julius Caesar* for the Royal Shakespeare Co' in Stratford-Upon-Avon, London, New York and Moscow.
Latest film role: Cassius in *Julius Caesar* for BBC/illuminations Films.
Latest TV role 2014: Lance in Channel 4's latest Russell T. Davies series *Cucumber*.
Latest radio: BBC Radio 4's *Something Understood*.
He is also an occasional writer and director.

Leo Ofori is a 34 year old black, gay man from Wandsworth, South London, who writes poetry and stories for leisure. His efforts at practicing poetry started from the young age of 8, when it was clear to his schoolteachers that he had an aptitude for English language and literature. From that point Leo has continued increasing his knowledge and understanding of how to write insightful and emotive literature by reading the works of Poe, Keats and Baudelaire, as well as the more contemporary publishings of Sylvia Plath, Maya Angelou and Benjamin Zephaniah.

Salawu Olajide is a graduate of English and literary studies, Obafemi Awolowo University, Nigeria. He is a poet whose poem has been published in *Stony Thursday*, an Ireland-based annual poetry journal. He is interested in New Writing and Experimental Poetry. He writes short stories and he is a regular contributor to *Litcaf Supplement*.

Anu Olu is born and raised in London and is of Nigerian descent. As an anthropology graduate from Goldsmiths his work is concerned with the human experience, African Diaspora and social injustice. Anu Olu works with Visual Ideation. V I is a response to society and contemporary culture, and is dedicated to the creation and dissemination of socially driven thought, content and experiences.

Diriye Osman is a Somali-British short-story writer and visual artist. His writing has appeared in *Time Out*, *The*

Huffington Post, Attitude, Prospect, Poetry Review, Kwani?, Jungle Jim, Under the Influence and *SCARF* magazine. His critically-acclaimed debut collection, *Fairytales for Lost Children*, is published by Team Angelica.

PJ Samuels is a poet, storyteller and LGBT activist. Originally from Jamaica, she is passionately vocal about human rights, mental wellness, stigmatisation and inequalities. A rural soul, she now calls London home. She does outreach for Metropolitan Community Church North London, an LBGTI-affirming faith charity. 'People mystify me. Words help me frame slices of life and corral the inexplicable, making it less menacing. I sometimes wish I could write the world right. If only things were that simple. I reconcile that with a compromise - being a cartographer of life's dichotomies as I navigate the complexities of my existence.'

Rogue 'Marbie' Scott, born and resident in London, was raised by his single Black-Dominican mother and four half-siblings. He went to drama school in the late '90s, and has dabbled in modelling and club-singing. He started a blog expressing himself and his thoughts on many subjects, and went on to build his own Youtube Channel to give a face to the words. He is the crazy mind behind the hilarious and provocative *Drunk Diallers (Group Therapy)* webseries on Youtube, (now in its second series), which he not only writes and directs, but in which he plays every character, straight, gay, male, female. His first play, *Give Me Your Heart*, debuted at the Bush Theatre as part of Team Angelica's *Boom!* festival in 2014. 'I write because I love to. I write because you listen.' – Rogue Scott.

Mickel Smithen: Performance Artist Mickel Smithen has always had a passion for the arts. In 2000 he followed that passion at college, where he studied performing arts and majored in music and dance at the Royal National College for the Blind Hereford in summer 2003, and then went on to study dance at Winchester University. In September 2004 Mickel joined the CandoCo Contemporary Dance Foundation course for disabled dancers.

Mickel's training continued as he went onto become a dance practitioner, leading and co-leading inclusive dance workshops for Amici Dance Theatre Company, Entelechy Arts, Salamanda Tandem and The Joy Of Sound music group. Mickel continues to develop his authentic approach to dance through attending Ballet, 5rhythms, Skinner Releasing Technique, African/Caribbean, Salsa and Tango dance classes.

Mickel has performed nationally and internationally, and in 2012 gained three stars and two reviews for the biographical performance of *Hard Core Pawn* with Mick, Lewis and Shaun at The Edinburgh Festival. Mickel regularly performs his new works *Shapes* (solo) and *Fusion* (duet). In February 2013 Mickel's Ultra Ego Ebony Rose Dark performed at London's Tate Modern in a piece titled *GENDER TALENT: A SPECIAL ADDRESS*, choreographed by Matthias Sperling and Carlos Motto.

Robert Taylor explores and celebrates people through photographic portraiture and nudes. His work has been exhibited, published and collected widely, and is part of several permanent collections including the National Portrait Gallery, the Victoria & Albert Museum and the Royal Society.

Recent major projects include the promotion of women of outstanding achievement in science, engineering and technology, rehabilitation through the arts in UK prisons, positive perspectives on bereavement, and sustainable development in Africa.

Many of Robert's major photographic projects have featured his own short texts, as well as contributions from his subjects.

Giles Terera trained as an actor and musician. He acts in, directs and writes for both film and theatre. As a writer his work includes his National Theatre production *Walk in the Light - a Celebration of Black Artists in British Theatre* and his BBC documentary *Muse of Fire: a Shakespearean Road Movie*. He has written for both Whatsonstage.com and *The Arts Desk*. His major influences are Zora Neale Hurston, Norman Mailer, James Baldwin and Hunter S Thompson.

Dr Cheikh Traore is a public health worker currently based in Lagos, Nigeria. He moved to London in 1996, where he lived for fourteen years, during which time he became actively involved in public health work with various vulnerable communities and social justice movements, working for a number of organisations including the Greater London Authority and Terrence Higgins Trust.

With leaders such as Reverend Jide Macaulay, he was one of the organizers of TUMAINI, the first UK African gay men's conference in 2004.

Z. Jai Walsh is a conflicted misanthrope with a stubborn streak of optimism; an aspiring alcoholic, and the last working-class boy left alive. He has lived in Ireland, Australia (against his will), New York City (where he was a toy boy), and for the past twelve years, London. His first work appeared in *The Gay Times Book of Short Stories: The Next Wave*. He is working on a novel, and is responsible for the occasionally pornographic gay news and pop culture blog *kaos*. He wishes the '90s could happen all over again.

D'relle Wickham (Khan) lives in East London and is a performer, writer and a coordinator for a sexual health organisation. He has performed for some of the biggest names in the industry, from Chris Brown, Madonna and Jessie J to dancing in front of the late and great Michael Jackson. His writing is therapy for him as he often talks of subjects he has been through. His piece for the anthology was his memory of growing up in a homophobic community. The only difference was one day he decided not to be beaten down any more, and to help people going through similar situations as himself. Giving himself the nickname Mr Clark Kent (after Superman), his performance work can be found online at:

www.youtube.com/MrClarkKentUK
www.twitter.com/MrClarkKentUK
instagram: MrClarkKentUK

Geoffrey Williams is a graduate of the BRIT school for

performing arts and technology. After a career in the entertainment industry as a manager he currently holds the position of Diversity and Inclusion specialist in a global media company. His writing is fictionalised experiences and tales he has heard throughout the years. He aims to spark debate and education by giving a voice to underrepresented groups, through this medium as well as in the work he does as a D&I specialist. Geoffrey hopes to complete and publish a novel in the near future.

Rhys Wright: 'I fell in love with poetry after my mother died and the break-up of my relationship with my partner. It was a stressful time with a compounding sense of loss. During this time last year I felt victimised and fell into a hole of self-pity and self-neglect. During my grief I turned to sex, spending money I could not afford to spend, comfort eating, and none of these could fix my pain, my torment. The poems that I wrote are primarily about acceptance. Accepting the nature of one's circumstances is the pinnacle of how I began to understand that I was not a 'victim' of circumstances but I was a participant. And I could spend the next few months blaming others, God, family, society, myself. Or I could live 'existentially' through poetry and find meaning in life's hardships again. I hope the poems I write speak to you on a personal level. I believe poetry is the combination of visual art, music and literature, and thus it has the arduous task of speaking to you, and about you. Poetry should be understood by a ten-year-old and a hundred-year-old, and I tried to use language which is easily understood.'

Lightning Source UK Ltd.
Milton Keynes UK
UKOW04f1008141114

241602UK00002B/9/P